Principles and Applications of Resonance Ionisation Spectroscopy

Principles and Applications of Resonance Ionisation Spectroscopy

G S Hurst

Institute of Resonance Ionisation Spectroscopy, Department of Physics, University of Tennessee, and Consultant to the Oak Ridge National Laboratory

and

M G Payne

Oak Ridge National Laboratory

Adam Hilger, Bristol and Philadelphia

British Library Cataloguing in Publication Data

Hurst, G. S.
    Principles and applications of resonance
    ionisation spectroscopy.
    1. Resonance ionization spectroscopy
    I. Title   II. Payne, M. G. (Marvin Gay)
    535.8′4   QC454.R47

    ISBN 0-85274-460-9

Library of Congress Cataloging-in-Publication Data

Hurst, G. S. (George Samuel), 1927–
    Principles and applications of resonance ionisation spectroscopy.
    Bibliography: p.
    Includes index.
    1. Resonance ionization spectroscopy
I. Payne, M. G. (Marvin Gay), 1936–   II. Title
QC454.R47H87   1988   535.8′4   87-35642

    ISBN 0-85274-460-9

Consultant Editor: Professor C Grey Morgan

Published under the Adam Hilger imprint by IOP Publishing Ltd
Techno House, Redcliffe Way, Bristol BS1 6NX, England
242 Cherry Street, Philadelphia, PA 19106, USA

Typeset by KEYTEC, Bridport, Dorset
Printed in Great Britain by
Butler & Tanner Ltd, Frome and London

This book is dedicated to Keith Boyer who directed the early laser programs at Los Alamos National Laboratory. His support of our basic work at ORNL and especially his confidence that the RIS technique would be used to count atoms were vital to the success of the endeavour.

Contents

Preface

Discoveries in radioactivity and subsequent studies on the interaction of energetic particles with matter represent an enormously important part of the physical sciences. Throughout the history of this field, we became accustomed to thinking that all ionisation events were impartial to the type of matter and nearly independent of the type of radiation. Thus, non-selective ions such as electrons or α-particles ionise all types of atoms or molecules with essentially the same low probability. When the group at the Oak Ridge National Laboratory (ORNL) conceived of the idea of using tunable lasers to selectively (and efficiently) ionise a given type of atom, we called the photo-ionisation process resonance ionisation spectroscopy (RIS) to distinguish the new ionisation process from non-selective ionisation.

Independently, lasers were being used for isotope separation where even greater wavelength resolution is required. The ORNL group, however, was interested in the use of lasers for absolute measurement of the population of specific quantum states in irradiated gases and for the counting of atoms in their ground states. For these reasons the stress was on the saturation of the RIS process and the use of sensitive ionisation detectors to make it possible to count atoms. In isotope separation work, neither of these features is important. The well-known work on isotope separation is summarised in a recent book by Radziemski et al (1987) (see Chapter 8). Another recent book (Letokhov (1987), see Chapter 8) describes some uses of the technique for sensitive analyses. Isotope separation and sensitive detection are now recognised as special cases of the remarkably selective ionisation process that can be carried out with modern lasers.

The present book describes the origin of RIS, explores the physics of the process, and then treats a spectrum of applications. The fact that this spectrum ranges from the use of RIS in elementary particle physics to environmental and human health concerns is a consequence of the versatility of the fundamentally new measurement principle.

The authors wish to recognise their colleagues at ORNL (S D Kramer, C H Chen, J P Judish, J P Young, S L Allman and R C Phillips) who, as a team, performed the experiments demonstrating the potential of RIS. At ORNL we were greatly assisted by visiting scientists on appointments. M H Nayfeh was a postdoctorate from Stanford University, while B E Lehmann (University of Bern) and R D Willis (Scripps Institute of Oceanography) helped develop techniques for earth sciences applications. William M Fairbank Jr (Colorado State University) was associated with the group to develop elementary particle applications. The sustained effort to bring RIS to fruition would not have been possible without the financial support and personal interests of Robert W Wood and Gerald Goldstein from the Office of Health and Environmental Research of the US Department of Energy.

Investigators worldwide are finding the technique useful and are responsible for the growth of the field. Credit is due to Professor C Grey Morgan at University College, Swansea, and Jim Revill of Adam Hilger for making our symposia on RIS truly international.

Finally, we wish to thank the many supporting personnel who helped in the preparation of this book and our families who developed a tolerance for our enthusiasm for RIS.

The research was sponsored in part by the US Department of Energy under contract DE-AC05-840R21400 with Martin Marietta Energy Systems Inc., in part by the Nationale Genossenschaft für die Lagerung Radioaktiver Abfalle (Switzerland), in part by the Scripps Institution of Oceanography, and in part by The Science Alliance Program of the University of Tennessee.

G S Hurst
M G Payne
September 1987

1

The origin of resonance ionisation spectroscopy

1.1 Introduction

Resonance ionisation spectroscopy (RIS) is a new method, developed almost entirely in the last decade, for the ionisation of matter. However, the process itself is very simple and is based on well established principles in quantum physics. In its most elementary form, the RIS process can be carried out by using a single laser tuned such that an electron is excited from its ground state in an atom to a bound excited state by the absorption of a photon, and another photon of exactly the same wavelength causes photo-ionisation to occur from the excited state of the atom. Clearly, such a process is Z-selective, i.e. atoms of only one type will be ionised efficiently, depending on the photon wavelength. Moreover, the process can be so efficient that nearly all of the atoms of the selected Z are ionised. This combination of high selectivity and an efficiency approaching unity makes the RIS process a very useful one. In this book we show how this selective and efficient ionisation process can be generalised to nearly all of the elements, and we discuss how RIS has been combined with sensitive means for detecting single electrons or single ions to make atom counting a reality. Numerous applications of RIS and one-atom detection will be described with no attempt at completeness—but rather as illustrations of this remarkable process.

This chapter deals with the origin of RIS, which, curiously, emerged from work with non-selective ionisation. Following the discovery of x-rays by Roentgen in 1895, Thomson and Rutherford discovered the ability of these penetrating rays to ionise gases. The discovery of radioactivity by Becquerel in 1896 and the development in the early 1900s of the charged particle accelerators made a wider variety of radiation types available for experimentation. Studies of these non-selective ionisation processes have helped us to understand the ionisation process and the structure of matter as well. The authors originated the concept of RIS to resolve a very detailed aspect of the ionisation of helium gas by charged particles.

A review of work on the ionisation of gases by charged particles will serve not only to describe the need for and the origin of RIS, but, more importantly, will summarise some useful methods for the measurement of ionisation and will describe important processes which occur at pressures where atomic and molecular collisions play dominant roles. Finally, we believe that the laser method for selective ionisation of matter is best appreciated by comparing it with methods of non-selective ionisation. The first two chapters of this book deal with the measurement of excited state populations which are created by charged particles that also produce direct ionisation. The remainder of the book deals with the measurement of atoms in their ground state. Curiously, little has been done with the original application of RIS due to the need for elemental analysis at the one-atom level.

1.2 Excitation and ionisation of gases with charged particles, W values

When charged particles of a wide variety (e.g. electrons, protons, α-particles or heavy ions) interact with matter, numerous types of processes occur that account for the energy losses of the charged particle. Yet some simple conclusions can be made that are quite common to all types of particles and even the type of matter has a surprisingly small effect. Take as an example the case where an α-particle loses all of its energy in a gas (see figure 1.1). Rutherford, in 1905, made the first absolute measurement of the 'energy required to produce a pair of ions', and thus originated the concept of a W value. If an α-particle loses all of its energy in a gas (i.e. the gas pressure is high enough to stop all of the particles), $W = E_\alpha/N_I$ where E_α is the energy of the α-particle and N_I is the number of ion pairs made. We reserve for later discussions the proper measurement of N_I, since first we wish to state some general conclusions about W and what they imply concerning the interaction of charged particles with matter. Because of the importance of W values to radiation dosimetry, the subject is periodically reviewed by the International Commission on Radiation Units and Measurements. For a recent report, see ICRU-31 (1979).

Essentially, the experiment of figure 1.1 has been carried out for electrons, β-rays, protons, α-particles, and heavy ions in many kinds of gases. The astounding conclusions are: (a) to a good approximation, W values are independent of the charge, mass, or energy of the particle,

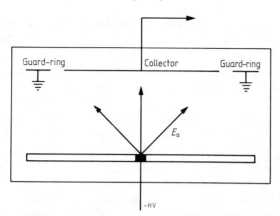

Figure 1.1 Simple experiments on the ionisation of gases with charged particles, illustrated with α-particles which lose their entire energy in the sensitive region of the detector.

and (b) W values lie within the range of 20–50 eV per ion pair for nearly all gases. These simple conclusions have some interesting implications and have attracted theoretical interpretation (Bethe 1930, Fano 1946, Platzman 1961, Inokuti 1975). Platzman (1961) points out that for the noble gases, the W value is about twice the ionisation potential of the atom and this implies that the charged particle loses about the same amount of energy in producing excited states of the atom as it does in just bringing electrons out of the atom. In fact, the simplest kind of treatment of the interaction, known as the optical approximation (Platzman 1961), is in agreement. In this theory, the charged particle interaction is treated classically in terms of the coulomb forces on a fixed atom (see figure 1.2). As the charged particle moves by the atom with velocity v, the time-dependent field, $E(t)$, can be resolved into $E_H(t)$ (horizontal component) and $E_T(t)$ (transverse component), but only the transverse component has a net effect on the atom. In the

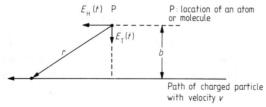

Figure 1.2 Schematic representation of the interaction of a charged particle with impact parameter b for an atom located at point P. Fourier components of $E_T(t)$ represent a frequency spectrum of virtual photons.

optical approximation it is assumed that the spectrum of virtual photons, derived from the Fourier components of $E_T(t)$, interact with the atom like real photons. Thus, the distribution of the energy lost to excitation and to ionisation depends only on the distribution of oscillator strengths in the atom. If the charged particles are fast enough so that virtual photons are produced over a wide frequency spectrum, very similar effects will be produced on the atom regardless of the type of charged particle or its energy. This view is consistent with the observed independence of W on particle type or energy. To a first approximation, the magnitudes of W values for the noble gases are understandable in terms of the distribution of known oscillator strengths (Platzman 1961). However, accurate calculations of W values must take into account a number of other factors such as excitation and ionisation by secondary electrons. In the case of helium, very detailed calculations have been made which start with energetic charged particles and follow all of the energy losses until all primary and secondary particles have become thermal. Alkhazov and Voreb'ev (1969) found a W value for pure helium of 46.6 eV, in good agreement with a value of 46 eV measured by Bortner and Hurst (1953). See also a later calculation by Alkhazov (1971) who obtained 46 eV for pure helium.

Even though the earlier calculations of Platzman (1961) gave a somewhat low W, 42.3 eV, it is instructive to follow his method of calculation to appreciate the magnitude of the various components of W. If an incident particle of energy E is completely stopped in a gas, one may write for the energy balance:

$$E = NE_I + N_{ex}E_{ex} + N\varepsilon$$

where N is the total number of electrons produced, N_{ex} is the number of discrete excited states produced, E_I is an average energy expended in the production of an ion, E_{ex} is an average energy of discrete excited states, and ε is an average kinetic energy of those electrons (subexcitation electrons) which are too slow to excite or ionise an atom in the gas. By definition, the W value is the ratio E/N. Hence, the ratio of W to the (first) ionisation energy, I, is written as

$$W/I = E_I/I + (E_{ex}/I) \times (N_{ex}/N) + \varepsilon/I.$$

Each of the three terms on the right-hand side depends on the particle energy E, and so does the W value. But the E-dependence is negligible for $E \gg I$. For helium, the value of each term at high E was estimated by Platzman (1961) as

$$1.72 \approx 1.06 + (0.85)(0.40) + 0.31.$$

Thus, one has a general understanding of the energy balance.

Accurate values for W are important for calibration of nuclear instrumentation—for example, in the use of ionisation chambers or proportional counters to measure the energies of nuclear decay. Some values for several noble gases are compiled in table 1.1. As we will see, these W values can also be used to calibrate the number of ion pairs produced by lasers using the RIS process, and thus indirectly to determine the number of atoms in a given population. Table 1.2 lists some gases and gas mixtures selected especially for this purpose. The small difference between W_α for α-particles and W_p for protons can be noted. Even for β-rays or electrons, W values differ little from those of table 1.2.

Table 1.1 W values for α-particles in some of the rare gases†.

Gas	W value (eV)	Ionisation potential, I(volts)	W/I
He	46	24.6	1.9
Ne	36.8	21.6	1.7
Ar	26.4	15.8	1.7
Kr	24.1	14.0	1.7
Xe	21.9	12.1	1.8

†See ICRU (1979) for extensive data on W values for pure gases and mixtures of gases.

Table 1.2 W values for α-particles and protons in some molecular gases and mixtures†.

Gas	W_α (eV)	W_p (eV)
N_2	36.4	36.68
CO_2	34.2	34.37
Air	35.1	35.18
CH_4	29.2§	
P-10‡	26.2§	

†See ICRU (1979) for extensive data on W values for pure gases and mixtures of gases.
‡90% Ar + 10% CH_4.
§Melton *et al* 1954.

1.3 The Hornbeck–Molnar reactions

The significance of a reaction of the type

$$He^* + He \rightarrow He_2^+ + e^-$$

to total ionisation in a gas at pressures where W values are normally measured has been reviewed by Hurst and Klots (1976). These Hornbeck–Molnar reactions contribute to the total ionisation, hence they decrease W due to the collision of high Rydberg state with ground state atoms to make molecular ions and W values can decrease by several electron-volts.

In Chapter 2 we show how these reactions can be very useful in saturating the RIS process; thus, a brief discussion is given. Hornbeck and Molnar (1951) were the first to study the kinetics of molecular ion formation from purely neutral precursors and to show that an excited state somewhat below the ionisation potential of an atom (high Rydberg state) could induce these effects. These reactions occur only because the noble gas molecular ions are stable, as shown by Mulliken (1970). Calculated dissociation energies, along with experimental energies (Huffman and Katayama 1966), are shown in table 1.3. Evidently, there is an energy barrier $B = E_{Th} - I + D(Ar_2^+)$ associated with the process.

Table 1.3 Energy parameters, in eV, associated with the Hornbeck–Molnar reaction $A^* + A \rightarrow A_2^+ + e$.

Gas	Ionisation potential, I	Threshold energy, E_{Th}	$D(A_2^+)$	B
He	24.6	23.01	2.47	0.9
Ne	21.6	20.9	1.1	0.4
Ar	15.8	14.71	1.25	0.2
Kr	14.0	13.00	1.2	0.2
Xe	12.1	11.16	0.97	0.03

Cross sections for these reactions are quite large; hence, above a few torr all of the excited species will be converted to molecular ions in fractions of a microsecond. In Chapter 2 we make specific use of this fact when the RIS experiment with $He(2^1S)$ is discussed.

1.4 Jesse effects

As a practical precaution, we must stress that the values in table 1.1 apply only to very pure gases. For instance, if pure helium were used to fill a detector and if only the usual care were taken to prevent contamination by other gases, a W value near 30 eV per ion pair (instead of 46 eV per ion pair) would apply. This effect, in which the W value in helium decreases due to even small concentrations of impuri-

ties, is known as the Jesse effect, in honour of W P Jesse who carefully
pursued the problem (Jesse and Saduskis 1952), see figure 1.3. Small
effects have been found in other noble gases and have been studied in
detail in the case of argon (Hurst *et al* 1965). While ionisation
measurements due to the passage of charged particles are simple to
make, they are difficult to interpret, due in part to the fact that the
process of excitation and ionisation is non-selective. We saw from the
brief theory of the optical approximation that many excited states are
created, depending on the oscillator strengths for the transitions, and
these are competing with the ionisation continuum. Furthermore,
measurements are nearly always made at pressures ranging from a few
torr to a thousand torr; thus, collision processes can alter the outcome.
In fact, collisions involving the impurities must be connected with Jesse
effects, as recognised by Niels Bohr (1915) who stated, 'For helium, *W*
is nearly twice as great as for hydrogen. From (31) and (34) we should
therefore expect a value for the ionisation only half of that in hydrogen.
Taylor, however, found the same ionisation in hydrogen as in helium.
Since in this case the value observed is greater than that calculated from
(34), the disagreement is difficult to explain, unless the high value
observed by Taylor possibly may be due to the presence of a small
amount of impurities in the helium used.' This problem had not been
solved in the early 1950s when Jesse conjectured that the effects could

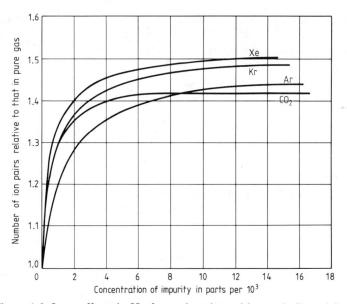

Figure 1.3 Jesse effects in He for various impurities, as indicated for
a total pressure of 875 Torr.

be due to energy transfer from metastable states of helium, either He(2^1S) or He(2^3S), to the impurity. In fact, the process

$$He^* + X \rightarrow X^+ + e^- + He$$

had already been suggested to explain the dramatic effect of impurities on the breakdown potential in helium discharges and was well known as Penning ionisation.

Jesse effects in argon were explored by Melton *et al* (1954). It was shown that when small amounts of impurities are added to argon, extra ionisation is produced by α-particles moving through the gas. These effects were studied as a function of the ionisation potential of the added impurity, and it was found that the ionisation increased even when the ionisation potential was much higher than the well known metastable states of argon. In subsequent work (Hurst *et al* 1965) the suggestion was made that the states responsible for the Jesse effect were not metastable states, but essentially their opposite, i.e. very favourable, allowed resonance levels. From figure 1.4 we note a strong correlation of the magnitude of the Jesse effects with well known resonance levels in argon. Thus, the suggested picture is

$$Ar + h\nu \rightleftarrows Ar^* + X \rightarrow X^+ + e^- + Ar$$

where the Ar* owes its long lifetime to the imprisonment of resonance radiation (Mitchell and Zemansky 1934). Such a mechanism is consistent with the optical approximation since a transition must have large values of oscillator strength to be abundantly excited by charged particles. On the other hand, metastable states have small oscillator strength and their abundant production by charged particles must involve some intermediate step which provides a strong channel to the ground state of the atom. The search for this channel led to a broader programme of study on energy pathways.

1.5 Energy pathways rsearch

These open questions on thenature of th long-lived excited states that could be responsible for the Jesse effects motivated a series of energy pathways experiments in which a wide variety f ionisation and spectroscopic methods were employed to investigate the nature and the abundance of excited species in the noble gases. The objectives of a comprehensive programme on energy pathways research (see figure 1.5) were to obtain: (a) information on the spectrum of excited states produced by a charged particle in a noble gas; (b) the rate of decay of the various states through each possible decay channel; and (c) the modification of the decay channels due to impurities capable of causing the Jesse

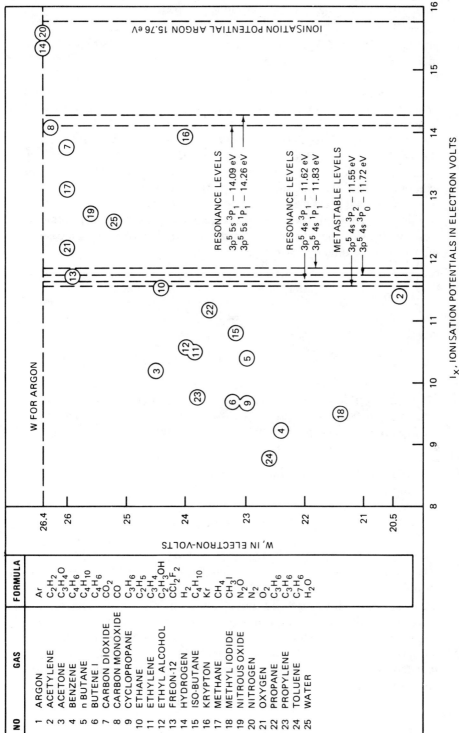

Figure 1.4 A Melton-type plot of Jesse effects in Ar due to impurities with various ionisation potentials, showing strong correlation of Jesse effects with some resonance levels in argon. The minimum W value is plotted as a function of ionisation potential of the impurity gas.

effects. In figure 1.5 we show schematically a list of some of the individual tasks which were initiated to meet these objectives. Use was made of a 6 MV Van de Graaff accelerator to provide proton beams which penetrated a gas cell filled to various pressures with noble gases or mixtures of gases in an arrangement for simultaneous studies of total ionisation and emission of light in the vacuum ultraviolet (vuv) region (see figure 1.6). Thus, Parks *et al* (1972) measured W values for all of the noble gases of table 1.1 for protons at a nearly constant energy equal to 3.6 MeV. The most important feature of the Parks *et al* experiment was the measurement of W values in gas mixtures as a function of total pressure for mixtures involving helium (see figure 1.7). In this way, Jesse effects could be studied while emission measurements were made with the vuv monochromator, so that these two measurements could be directly correlated.

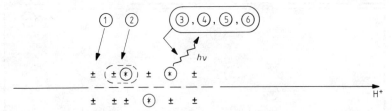

Figure 1.5 List of individual tasks for the study of energy pathways in the noble gases in a programme established at the University of Kentucky in 1966 and continued at ORNL after 1970. (1) $W(P)$: W values. (2) $W(P,P_x)$: Jesse effects. (3) $N(P,\lambda)$: intensity of vuv radiation. (4) $d\varepsilon/d_x$: absolute measurement of vuv energy. (5) $N(P,\lambda,t)$: time-dependent vuv emission. (6) Radiation transport and atomic collision theory.

Investigation of the vuv emission to obtain information on excited states that could be precursors to the Jesse effects (Hurst *et al* 1968, 1969) revealed continuous emission spectra that gave good results as a function of gas pressure. Some problems associated with interpretation of similar spectra measured with gas discharges were resolved through these studies. However, the basic question remained. Were these emissions really associated with the same excited states that were responsible for the enhanced ionisation? To answer this question, Stewart *et al* (1970) developed a method for measuring the total radiated energy per cm of proton track length, $d\varepsilon/dx$, to compare with the known stopping power, dE/dx, in order to use the principle of energy conservation to help answer this question. Here

$$d\varepsilon/dx \equiv \int \varepsilon(\lambda)\phi(P,\lambda)\,d\lambda$$

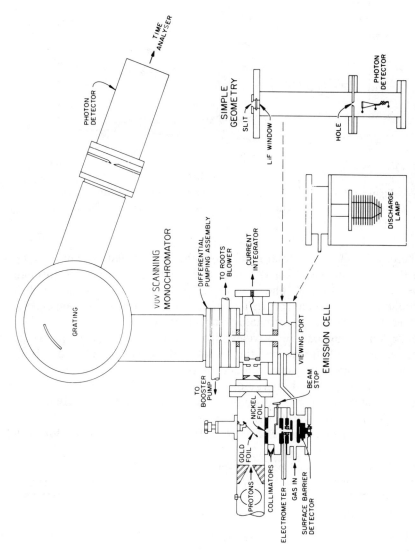

Figure 1.6 Diagram of experimental apparatus for VUV emission measurements.

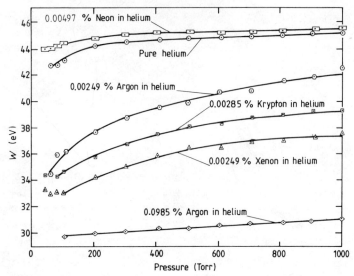

Figure 1.7 Plot of W values in mixtures of He with specified concentrations of certain of the other noble gases as a function of the total pressure.

where $\phi(P,\lambda)\mathrm{d}\lambda$ is the total number of photons emitted per cm of track in the region between λ and $\lambda + \mathrm{d}\lambda$ due to one proton passing through the gas at pressure P, and $\varepsilon(\lambda)$ is the photon energy. To accomplish absolute measurement of $\mathrm{d}\varepsilon/\mathrm{d}x$, the simple geometry arrangement, along with the monochromator shown in figure 1.6, was carefully calibrated throughout the wavelength region of 50.0 to 200.0 nm. Thus, Stewart *et al* (1970) reported the values of $\mathrm{d}\varepsilon/\mathrm{d}x$ compared to $\mathrm{d}E/\mathrm{d}x$ in table 1.4. From these measurements, arguments were made (Hurst *et al* 1970) that the radiated energy $\mathrm{d}\varepsilon/\mathrm{d}x$ must be associated with the same excited states that were responsible for the Jesse effects. This conclusion is made for two self-consistent reasons. First, the energy fraction associated with the Jesse effects, $E_J\,(\mathrm{d}E/\mathrm{d}x)^{-1}$, was estimated for each

Table 1.4 Energy radiated per cm of proton track, $\mathrm{d}\varepsilon/\mathrm{d}x$ (in the vuv region), compared to the stopping power, $\mathrm{d}E/\mathrm{d}x$, for 4 MeV protons in the noble gases.

Gas	Pressure (Torr)	$\mathrm{d}\varepsilon/\mathrm{d}x$ (keV cm^{-1})	$\mathrm{d}E/\mathrm{d}x$ (keV cm^{-1})	$\dfrac{(\mathrm{d}\varepsilon/\mathrm{d}x)}{(\mathrm{d}E/\mathrm{d}x)}$	$\dfrac{E_J}{(\mathrm{d}E/\mathrm{d}x)}$
He	400	2.2	9.1	0.24	0.24
Ne	200	4.7	17.2	0.27	0.24
Ar	400	16.0	55.4	0.29	0.13
Kr	400	10.5	84.4	0.12	0.04
Xe	300	8.1	87.1	0.09	—

of the gases and found to be equal to or less than the radiant energy fraction $(\mathrm{d}\varepsilon/\mathrm{d}x)\,(\mathrm{d}E/\mathrm{d}x)^{-1}$; thus, there is more than enough energy associated with the excited species to account for the Jesse effects. Second, if the last two columns of table 1.4 were added independently to other fractional energy losses known to be associated with the direct ionisation of helium, neon, or argon, they would sum to a number greater than unity; thus, the principle of energy conservation requires that the Jesse effects and the radiant energy arise from common excited states.

The above conclusions do not reveal the nature of the excited states since both the Jesse effects and the vuv emission could originate from metastable states or from highly allowed states that derive their lifetimes from imprisonment of resonance photons. Other aspects of the program outlined in figure 1.5 were designed to shed light on the nature of these states. A major tool for this understanding was developed by N Thonnard who originated time-resolved spectroscopic studies of the interaction of charged particles with the noble gases (Thonnard and Hurst 1972). That work utilised a 250 keV accelerator to pulse electrons into an emission cell so that time-resolved studies could be made at any desired wavelength (see figure 1.8). This method was used to study both line emission and continuum radiation from argon at various pressures,

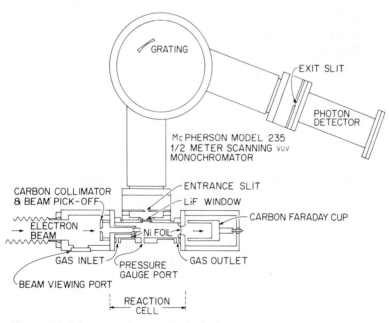

Figure 1.8 Diagram of a method for time-resolved studies of vuv emission due to the interaction of charged particles with noble gases.

and these studies helped to clarify the complex energy pathways followed as the several types of excited states decay.

1.6 Energy pathways in helium

The interaction of swift charged particles, such as protons, with helium gas should be one of nature's simplest examples of the interaction of radiation with matter. For this reason, this problem has attracted extra attention. It was the desire to understand energy pathways in helium and the failure of available experimental methods to provide as much detail as was needed on the population of metastable states that led to the development of RIS. In this section, we review the application of the energy pathways programme (outlined in figure 1.5) to helium and take up the RIS concept itself in the final section of this chapter.

Figure 1.9 is a Grotian diagram for He(I) (neutral helium), showing energy levels relevant to our discussion. Some of the allowed transitions, as well as a metastable transition (dashed line), are also shown. In the singlet system, two levels, $He(2^1S)$ and $He(2^1P)$, are of special interest to us. Of course, $He(2^1S)$ is a metastable state having a long lifetime in the isolated atom, while transitions from $He(2^1P)$ to the ground state are highly allowed with a lifetime of *about* 0.5 ns and an oscillator strength of 0.28. (For convenient tabulations of energy levels, see Moore (1949); and for transition strengths, see Weise *et al* (1966).) It will also be immediately clear from the diagram that the radiation from $He(2^1P) \rightarrow He(1^1S)$ at 58.4 nm is resonance radiation, which can readily be absorbed by another ground state atom. Therefore, if the pressure of helium is greater than about 10^{-3} Torr, photons can be absorbed and re-emitted many times before escaping from a container with dimensions of the order of 1 cm. As we remarked in connection with Jesse effects in argon, resonance states can play key roles in the sense that they can be excited with the passage of charged particles, because they are connected to the ground state with considerable oscillator strength; yet they can have long system lifetimes (like metastable states) so that collision processes are significant. A recent theory dealing with the transport of resonance radiation and a detailed comparison with experiments on the 104.8 nm resonance radiation in argon was developed by Payne *et al* (1974).

Emission studies in the vuv region from helium following excitation with protons were carried out by Stewart *et al* (1971). At the resonance line (58.4 nm), the total intensity was measured at pressures between 0.01 and 100 Torr. Broad continuous spectra were observed around 60.0, 67.5, and 80.0 nm up to a pressure of 800 Torr for which the measured radiant energy $d\varepsilon/dx$ was significant compared to the proton stopping power (see table 1.5). From these experiments it was suggested that these continua arise from Franck–Condon transitions in the He$_2$ molecular system, as shown in figure 1.10. Specifically, the continuum near 67.5 nm was assumed to be due to $D^1\Sigma_u^+ \to X^1\Sigma_g^+$, i.e. from the

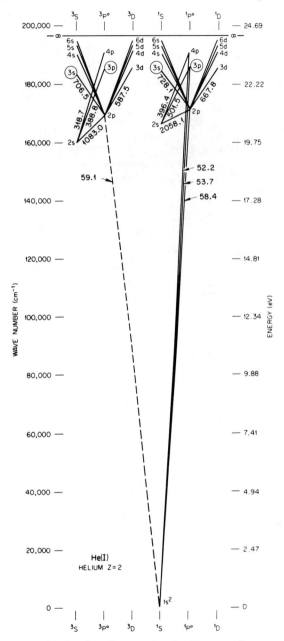

Figure 1.9 Partial Grotian diagram for the He atom for some of the excited states relevant to the Jesse effect in He.

Table 1.5 Values of $d\varepsilon/dx$ (keV cm^{-1}) for continuous emissions when 4 MeV protons excite helium gas at 400 Torr, and the ratio of $d\varepsilon/dx$ to dE/dx. (For the 4 MeV protons, dE/dx is 9 keV cm^{-1}.)

Emission continuum (nm)	$d\varepsilon/dx$	$(d\varepsilon/dx)(dE/dx)^{-1}$
60	0.33	0.036
67.5	1.05	0.115
80	0.65	0.71

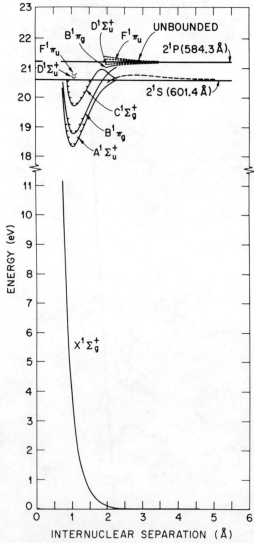

Figure 1.10 Potential energy curves for selected states of He$_2$.

bound molecule D to the unbound molecule X. The continuum near 80.0 nm, as well as the 60.0 nm continuum, was assigned to transitions from $A^1\Sigma_u^+$ to $X^1\Sigma_g^+$. Bound states in excited molecules which have repulsive ground states are called excimers. In fact, energy pathways studies of exactly the type described here have also been used to study kinetics for excimer laser applications.

The importance of the method introduced by Thonnard is again evident from time-resolved studies in helium. Thus, Bartell *et al* (1973) studied the time dependence of the 58.4 nm resonance line and the broad VUV continuum region extending from 60.0 to 90.0 nm. The decay rate of this continuum was proportional to $A + BP + CP^2$. Further, the so-called 67.5 and 80.0 nm continua had almost identical time dependence with a fast and a slow component, the latter being the same as the decay of the 60.0 nm continuum. Thus, it turned out that the continua were more distinguishable on the basis of decay time—rather than wavelength. Following these observations, Bartell *et al* were able to construct the first realistic energy pathways model. However, the explanation of the Jesse effect in which the metastable B state is the precursor did not survive a theoretical development by Payne *et al* (1975).

According to Bartell *et al*, the time dependence of the 58.4 nm resonance line can be represented by a single exponential with decay constant $\beta = 2.8 \times 10^6 + 6.0 \times 10^4 P + 90P^2$, where β is in s^{-1} and P is in Torr (see figure 1.11). The constant term is the sum of an allowed

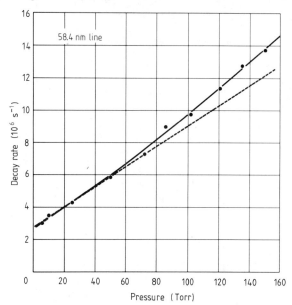

Figure 1.11 Pressure dependence of the 58.4 nm decay rate. The dotted curve is a straight line through the low-pressure data points.

rate of transition $(1.9 \times 10^6 \text{ s}^{-1})$ to the 2^1S state plus a rate of escape of resonance radiation to the cell walls and is about $0.9 \times 10^6 \text{ s}^{-1}$ (using the theory of Holstein (1951)). This sum agrees with extrapolation of the measured β to $P = 0$. The term $90P^2$ represents three-body conversion of $\text{He}(2^1\text{P})$ to the molecular D state at a rate of $30P^2$ and to the B state at a rate of $60P^2$, shown in figure 1.12. The above is written

$$\text{He}(2^1\text{P}) + \text{He}(1^1\text{S}) + \text{He}(1^1\text{S}) \rightarrow (\text{He})_2 \, \text{D}^1\Sigma_u^+ + \text{He}(1^1\text{S})$$

with $\beta = 30P^2$, and

$$\text{He}(2^1\text{P}) + \text{He}(1^1\text{S}) + \text{He}(1^1\text{S}) \rightarrow (\text{He})_2 \, \text{B}^1\Pi_g + \text{He}(1^1\text{S})$$

with $\beta = 60P^2$. Rapid decay of the D molecule to the X molecule accounts for the observed fast continuum extending from 64.0 to 95.0 nm. The theory of Payne *et al* (1975) described in a compact way the fate of the metastable B molecule of helium and the large $6 \times 10^4 \, P$

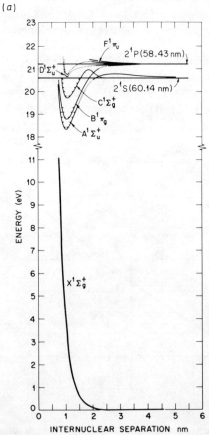

Figure 1.12(a) Some molecular states for $(\text{He})_2$.

term as having a common origin. Normally, one does not expect large two-body rates for conversion of one excited species to another. However, the process

$$He(2^1P) + He(1^1S) \rightarrow He(2^1S) + He(1^1S)$$

may occur rapidly due to a curve crossing, as illustrated in figure 1.12(*a*). The curves $B^1\Pi_g(1^1S + 2^1P)$ and $C^1\Sigma_g^+(1^1S + 2^1S)$ cross at 0.204 nm, and, according to the calculations of Payne *et al*, a rotational coupling of these states leads to a rate for the two-body process which agrees closely with the $6 \times 10^4 P$ observed rate. Furthermore, this same coupling mechanism is responsible for the rapid predissociation process shown (figure 1.12(*b*)) by the dashed line leading from the $(He)_2B$ to $He(2^1S)$ which occurs before vibrational relaxation can stabilise the molecule into its lower levels. After the state $He(2^1S)$ is produced from either of the three mechanisms, it is converted to a

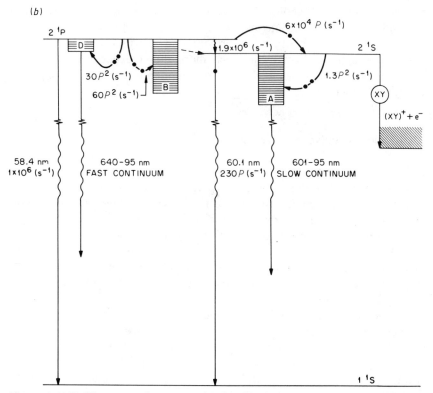

Figure 1.12(b) Energy pathways model for He based largely on the work of Bartell *et al* (1973) and Payne *et al* (1975), including the processes leading to the Jesse effect.

molecule via

$$He(2^1S) + He(1^1S) + He(1^1S) \rightarrow (He)_2\ A^1\Sigma_u^+ + He(1^1S)$$

at the slow rate of 1.3 P^2 (s^{-1}), and the decay of this molecular species accounts for the slow continuum observed to extend from 60.1 to 95.0 nm.

With the modified energy pathways model of figure 1.12, the Jesse effect involving another atom A is

$$He(2^1S) + A \rightarrow A^+ + e^- + He(1^1S)$$

or if the impurity is a molecule XY,

$$He(2^1S) + XY \rightarrow (XY)^+ + e^- + He(1^1S)$$

which has competitive non-ionisation processes leading to dissociation of XY, that is

$$He(2^1S) + XY \rightarrow X + Y + He(1^1S)$$

Thus, we have arrived at precisely the suggestion initially made by Jesse for the enhanced ionisation. But the energy pathways research resolved a paradox—namely, the inconsistency of abundant production of metastable states with the optical approximation. Furthermore, it was the strong desire to confirm by a much more direct experimental method that the $He(2^1S)$ metastable state is abundantly created by charged particles that led to RIS.

1.7 Resonance ionisation spectroscopy

As discussed above, much effort has been directed to unravelling the various energy transfer processes (pathways) as irradiated noble gas systems return to equilibrium. These pathways are complex and include the redistribution of energy amongst resonance and metastable atomic states, three-body conversion of excited states to noble gas excimers, Franck–Condon emission from excimers, the transport of resonance photons, and the diffusion of excited species to the walls. Ionisation can even occur due to collisions of highly excited states via the Hornbeck–Molnar mechanism.

Information on resonance states had traditionally been obtained from time-dependent studies on the escape of resonance radiation from gas cells (Holstein 1947, 1951). On the other hand, information on metastable states was obtained using a rather different method, i.e. absorption spectroscopy (Phelps and Molnar 1953). It is, in fact, difficult to determine even the relative number of resonance and metastable states using these methods (Payne *et al* 1974). Clearly, what was needed was a new experimental method for determining the actual number of excited states of each type as a function of time following irradiation of a system.

It is clear from the energy pathways diagram of figure 1.12(b) that a direct measurement of the population of He(2^1S) would be a significant test of the entire model. All of the emission processes are indirect since He(2^1S) is metastable; thus, we conceived of the idea of a method of photo-ionising the metastable states so that electrical measurement could be made of the atomic population (Hurst 1974), first reported at a conference on small accelerators (Hurst *et al* 1975). The measurement of electrical charge is one of the most accurate and most sensitive of all physical measurements; thus, it was felt from the beginning that ionisation measurements of atomic states would have advantages over fluorescence measurements. As seen in figure 1.13, the idea was to use a laser to convert metastable states to ionisation. It was quickly realised that the real significance of photo-ionisation methods would come from the quantum state selectivity of the process if a tunable pulse laser were used to first raise the excited state to another bound state and then obtain photo-ionisation from the absorption of a second photon from the same laser pulse. The use of an intermediate state ensures that the ionisation process will have a resonance at a unique wavelength (known from atomic spectroscopy); thus, the process was called resonance ionisation spectroscopy. In Chapter 2 we show that the resonance ionisation process could be saturated and thus used to make absolute measurements of the He(2^1S) population following proton excitation of

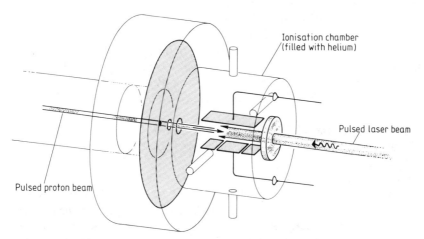

Ionisation chamber
(filled with helium)

Pulsed laser beam

Pulsed proton beam

Figure 1.13 Schematic representation of the first RIS experiment to measure the absolute population of a selected excited state. For details of this experiment to measure the absolute population of He(2^1S), see Chapter 2.

helium. A known transition shown on the Grotian diagram for helium in figure 1.9, i.e. from 2s to 3p in the singlet system at a wavelength of 501.5 nm, was used for the bound–bound step and another photon at 501.5 nm completed the two-step process. In this way (discussed in detail in Chapter 2) nearly all of the He(2^1S) states were converted to ionisation, yet no other quantum state of the excited helium system was perturbed.

Those with an interest in radioactivity or the interaction of accelerated particles with matter will recognise the remarkable simplicity of resonance ionisation compared with the complexities of non-resonance ionisation processes. With charged particles, a small amount of ionisation occurs from each species present, i.e. the process is non-selective and inefficient. By contrast, resonance ionisation is a quantum-state-selective process and can be made to have nearly 100% efficiency for the desired species.

References

Alkhazov G D 1971 *Zh.Tekh. Fiz.* **41** 2513 (Engl. transl. 1972 *Sov. Phys.–Tech. Phys.* **16** 1995)

Alkhazov G D and Voreb'ev A A 1969 *Phys. Lett.* **29A** 25

Bartell D M, Hurst G S and Wagner E B 1973 *Phys. Rev.* A **7** 1068–78

Bethe H 1930 *Ann. Phys., Lpz.* **5** 325

Bohr N 1915 *Phil. Mag.* **30** 581

Bortner T E and Hurst G S 1953 *Phys. Rev.* **90** 160

Fano U 1946 *Phys. Rev.* **70** 44

Holstein T 1947 *Phys. Rev.* **72** 1212

—— 1951 *Phys. Rev.* **83** 1159

Hornbeck J A and Molnar J P 1951 *Phys. Rev.* **84**, 621

Huffman R E and Katayama D H 1966 *J. Chem. Phys.* **45**, 138

Hurst G S 1974 Health Physics Division Progress Report for Period Ending July 31, 1974. *Oak Ridge National Laboratory Report ORNL-4979* pp 230–3

Hurst G S, Bortner T E and Glick R E 1965 *J. Chem. Phys.* **42**, 713–19

Hurst G S, Bortner T E and Strickler T D 1968 *J. Chem. Phys.* **49** 2460–1

Hurst G S, Bortner T E and Strickler T D 1969 *Phys. Rev.* **178**, 4–10

Hurst G S, Judish J P, Nayfeh M H, Parks J E, Payne M G and Wagner E B 1975 in *Proc. 3rd Conf. on Application of Small Accelerators (North Texas, State University) 1974* CONF 741040-P1 vol. I pp 97–119 (Springfield, Virginia: National Technical Information Service)

Hurst G S and Klots C E 1976 Elementary Processes in Irradiated Noble Gases in *Advances in Radiation Chemistry* vol. 5 ed M Burton and J L Magee (New York: Wiley) pp 1–96

Hurst G S, Stewart T E and Parks J E 1970 *Phys. Rev.* A **2**, 1717–20

International Commission on Radiation Units and Measurements 1979 Average Energy Required to Produce an Ion Pair *ICRU Report 31* (Washington, DC: ICRU)

Inokuti M 1975 *Radiat. Res.* **64** 6

Jesse W P and Sadauskis J 1952 *Phys. Rev.* **88**, 417

Melton C E, Hurst G S and Bortner T E 1954 *Phys. Rev.* **96** 643–5

Mitchell A C G and Zemansky M W 1934 *Resonance Radiation and Excited Atoms* (London: Cambridge University Press)

Moore C E 1949 Atomic Energy Levels *National Bureau of Standards Circular 467* (Washington, DC: US Government Printing Office)

Mulliken R S 1970 *J. Chem. Phys.* **52** 5170

Parks J E, Hurst G S, Stewart T E and Weidner H L 1972 *J. Chem. Phys.* **57** 5467–74

Payne M G, Klots C E and Hurst G S 1975 *J. Chem. Phys.* **63** 1422–8

Payne M G, Talmage J E, Hurst G S and Wagner E B 1974 *Phys. Rev.* A **9** 1050–69

Phelps A V and Molnar J P 1953 *Phys. Rev.* **89** 1202

Platzman R L 1961 *Int. J. Radiat. Isot.* **10** 116

Stewart T E, Hurst G S, Bartell D M and Parks J E 1971 *Phys. Rev.* A **3**, 1991–7

Stewart T E, Hurst G S, Bortner T E, Parks J E, Martin F W and Weidner H L 1970 *J. Opt. Soc. Am.* **60** 1290–7

Taylor T S 1913 *Phil. Mag.* **26** 402

Thonnard N and Hurst G S 1972 *Phys. Rev.* A **5** 1110–21

Wiese W L, Smith M W and Glennon B M 1966 *Atomic Transition Probabilities* vol. I *National Bureau of Standards NSRDS-NBS 4* (Washington, DC: US Government Printing Office)

2

RIS studies on He(2^{1}S)

2.1 Introduction

The first RIS experiments were made to measure the absolute population of He(2^{1}S) and its time decay following proton excitation of helium gas. The RIS technique is an efficient and selective method of ionising isolated atoms and can, therefore, be a powerful technique when combined with methods for measurement of ionisation both in gases and *in vacuo*. These are very familiar to experimenters in radioactivity, x-rays, nuclear physics and radiation protection. At appropriate places in this book, those ionisation measurement techniques will be briefly discussed to show their applicability to laser ionisation phenomena. Here, we take up the problem of the transport of electrical charge in gases before describing the He(2^{1}S) experiments.

2.2 Gaseous electronics

The history of the interaction of radiation with matter is traceable to the discovery of x-rays by Roentgen and of radioactivity by Becquerel. Even before the discovery of these penetrating radiations, J J Thomson and his students at the Cavendish Laboratory had extensively investigated the passage of electricity through gases. Thus, it is not surprising that the phenomenon of ionisation of gases with penetrating radiation was quickly recognised and employed for practical measurements. Becquerel used an electroscope to investigate uranium. The conduction of gases due to x-rays was investigated by Thomson and Rutherford. They obtained the saturation curve for air and demonstrated that the current was proportional to the number of 'conducting molecules', one year ahead of the discovery of the electron. A modern continuation of these studies occurs in aspects of gaseous electronics which deal with the transport of charged species through gases, due to the application of electric or magnetic fields. At present, very active work is underway at a number of laboratories worldwide. Several excellent books keep us informed of the status of the field (Healey and Reed 1941, Huxley and Crompton 1974, McDaniel 1964, Christophorou 1971).

When electrical charges of two signs are created in a gas, many processes combine to determine the fate of the charge carriers. Essentially all of these phenomena apply whether the initial ionisation is created by x-rays, α-particles, fast electrons, or a laser beam. In weak electrical fields most of the ionisation will eventually recombine or reach the chamber wall. The time-scale for ion recombination depends on the initial spatial distribution, properties of the gas, and the applied fields. Various carriers of the electrical charge are free electrons, negative atomic or molecular ions and positive atomic or molecular ions. If, for instance, free electrons are created in air, O^- and O_2^- will be found as principal carriers, and recombination of these with various positive ions will rapidly occur to neutralise the system. For free electrons, diffusion plays a more significant role than it does for the heavier negative and positive ions.

The applied electrical fields are characterised in an interesting way by a quantity written as E/P and this is appropriate for the description of electron motion described by 'electron swarms'. When an electron is accelerated by the field, it can gain energy as if it were in a vacuum between collisions with an atom or molecule of the gas. Collisions result in either elastic scattering or inelastic losses to rotational and vibrational states in molecules or to electron excitation in both atoms and molecules. In moving a given distance (say 1 cm) in the field direction, electrons will make a number of collisions proportional to the number density N of the gaseous atoms or molecules. While the energy gained by the electrons is proportional to E, collisions account for electron energy losses, thus an equilibrium energy (called agitational energy) is established after many collisions and is characterised by E/N, rather than by E alone. Unfortunately, all of the older literature uses E/P where the pressure is measured in torr—an E/P of $1 \, \text{V cm}^{-1} \text{Torr}^{-1}$ is typical in gaseous electronics. The newer quantity, E/N, has a special unit, the Townsend (T_d) where $1 \, T_d = 10^{-17} \, \text{V cm}^{-2}$. Thus, E/N in T_d units equals $2.828 \times E/P_0$, where P_0 is the temperature-normalised or temperature-reduced pressure, i.e. $P_0 = (273.26/T)P$ and T is the absolute temperature.

Under the influence of a constant electric field, electrons drift with a terminal velocity w which is a function of E/N alone for a given type of gas. This drift velocity must not be confused with the random (agitation) velocity which is usually much larger than w. Drift velocity measures the motion of the centre of gravity of the electrons as they swarm around an imaginary plane. Agitation energies are widely distributed (as in a Maxwell–Boltzmann distribution) and have a characteristic spectrum for a fixed E/N. The mean agitation energy can be many times the value $3/2(kT)$, reflecting a disequilibrium of electrons with gas atoms. Hence, a Maxwell–Boltzmann distribution is not assured. Further, as the swarm plane is transported (at a typical drift velocity $w = 10^6 \, \text{cm s}^{-1}$ and individual electron velocities exceeding $10^8 \, \text{cm s}^{-1}$ or more), significant spreading occurs due to electron diffusion. Finally, some of the electrons may leave the free electron swarm due to the formation of heavier negative ions which drift much more slowly. Electron diffusion is characterised by the diffusion coefficient D while electron attrition is described by the attachment coefficient α. Thus, $w(E/N)$, $D(E/N)$, and $\alpha(E/N)$ are all macroscopic parameters which accurately express the behaviour of swarm electrons in a gas, and each of these is a function of E/N. At very high electric fields, some of the electrons in the swarm may acquire enough energy between collisions to exceed the ionisation potential of the gas—thus, ionisation by electron impact can occur. This process can lead to ionisation cascades and is responsible for the gas amplification process used in proportional counters or Geiger–Müller detectors. It is a most remarkable fact that in spite of the many microscopic processes taking place in electron swarms, simple macroscopic parameters are quite adequate for describing the motion of charged species in a gas. The book references given above on gaseous electronics can be consulted for extensive tabulations of these macroscopic parameters.

For the present discussion, we stress that for most gases there is a range of E/N in which electron swarms are very well behaved. In this region all of the electrons (and positive ions) can be collected without recombination, without electron capture, and without gas multiplication; thus, accurate measurements of the total amount of ionisation can be made. In this chapter we give some quantitative details on how these measurements are made with pulsed ionisation chambers, and in Chapter 3 we illustrate the use of proportional counters to increase the sensitivity of the measurement of ion pairs.

A word of caution is required at this point. Above, it was stated that there is a useful range of E/P in which accurate ionisation measurements are made. The lower limit of E/P is determined by ion recombination and the time for diffusion to the chamber walls, while the upper limit is determined by gas multiplication. Strictly speaking, these concepts apply only when the total amount of electrical charge is so small that the electric field is not perturbed. If the ionisation is too large—a region referred to as space charge—drastic effects can occur on the motion of the electrical charge.

We will now make an estimate of charge density required to produce some non-linear effect on electron collection. Suppose that a pulsed laser produces a high density of ion pairs in a small volume of space at $t = 0$. At some density N of these charges it is clear that the electrons, which normally escape rapidly by diffusion through the gas, will be attracted by the less mobile positive ions. Let $|Q_+| = |Q_-| = [(4\pi R^3)/3]Ne$, where R is the radius of a small sphere with uniform charge density. To estimate N for a given R where the effects of space charge will be important, imagine first that the electrons have escaped; then the potential (assumed to be zero at infinity) is given by

$$V = Q_+/4\pi\varepsilon_0 R = (9 \times 10^9 \; Q_+)/R$$

$$V = 12\pi \times 10^9 \; Ne \; R^2 = 6.0 \times 10^{-9} \; NR^2$$

where R is in metres.

Since V is a potential due to the positive charge alone, free electrons could be attracted back into the positive cloud. For $V = 1$ and $R = 10^{-3}$ m, $N = 1.7 \times 10^{14}$ m^{-3}, or 1.7×10^8 cm^{-3}. Therefore, we expect space charge to be a factor whenever more than 10^8 ion pairs per cm^3 are made in a laser beam of 1 mm radius. Even a potential of 1 V prevents electrons from escaping the positive charge and tends to make the region neutral. If only a modest electrical field (e.g. 10 V cm^{-1}) is applied, there will be a polarisation of the charge distribution until the field inside adds to zero; thus, electrons and positive ions stay near each other until the positive ions can diffuse into a larger volume. This process is known as ambipolar diffusion. These diffusion rates are low at pressures of the order of 1 atmosphere since typical diffusion coefficients for positive ions are only about 50 cm^2 s^{-1}, even at a pressure of 1 Torr (McDaniel and Mason 1972).

At electron and ion densities of the order of 10^8 cm^{-3}, recombination times are of the order of 1 s. Thus, for most instances where large numbers of ion pairs are made in a laser pulse, space charge effects determine the time behaviour of the electrons rather than ion pair recombination. It is interesting to note that an α-particle, by contrast, produces a very high density of ions in a small track; and ion pair recombination, rather than space charge, limits the collection of the ionisation. The product NR^2 can be much larger with a laser than with an α-particle.

To conclude this brief discussion of gaseous electronics, we will discuss a time-of-flight method (Hurst *et al* 1963) for the measurement of D, w and α, and give some results for D and w for a few gases, including helium. This will give the reader a brief look at typical data, and will show the importance of the helium case to the first RIS experiments. Prior to 1963, nearly all investigations of electron diffusion in gases were based on the original method of Townsend and Bailey (1922) (see also Townsend (1948)). Electrons from a steady state point source were allowed to diffuse in a gas subject to a uniform electrical field of known strength. Lateral diffusion was measured by using a planar geometry in which the receiving electrode was divided into two concentric regions. The ratio of currents gave the ratio of w/D, based on interpretations of various time-independent solutions to the diffusion equation in three dimensions. The time-of-flight method is based on solutions of a time-dependent transport equation in one space dimension, which gives D and w independently (not just w/D). Further, the method can be extended to measure the electron attachment coefficient α, i.e. the probability of capture per cm of drift in the field direction per torr of the attaching gas. We point out here that electrons only attach to a limited number of common substances, and these are usually avoided in precise ionisation measurements. For example, with O_2, O_2^- is formed near thermal energy by direct capture and O^- is formed by dissociative capture for electron energy greater than approximately 5 eV. Similarly, negative ions can be formed in H_2O and a number of more complex substances. For all of the noble gases, plus H_2, N_2, CH_4, CO_2, etc, we can assume that $\alpha = 0$ for nearly all E/N values of interest to us. Thus, we discuss only D and w below.

Consider a swarm of electrons which at time $t = 0$ is spread uniformly over the plane $x = 0$ (figure 2.1). This type of electron swarm could be initiated by using a pulsed light source, such as a flashlamp or a pulsed laser, to release photoelectrons from a metal plate at negative potential. We are interested in the time of arrival of electrons at the point P on the detector plane due to the liberation of a uniform layer released from a source plane at distance L and at time $t = 0$. The intervening space is filled with a gas for which the electron diffusion coefficient is D and the drift velocity is w. If the gas had impurities at partial pressure f_1P that would capture electrons, then the rate of capture would be $wf_1P\alpha = \beta$. Thus,

$$\partial n(x,t)/\partial t = D(\partial^2 n(x,t)/\partial x^2) - w(\partial n(x,t)/\partial x) - \beta n(x,t)$$

is the appropriate transport equation, where $n(x,t)$ is the volume density of electrons. A solution of this equation is

$$n(x,t) = At^{-1/2} \exp\{-[(x - wt)^2/4Dt] - \beta t\}$$

where $A = N(4\pi D)^{-1/2}$ and N is the area density of electrons at $x = 0$ and $t = 0$. The number of electrons arriving at a small aperture at P

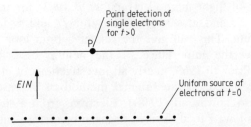

Figure 2.1 Geometry for time-dependent studies of electron transport in one dimension.

between t and $t + \Delta t$ is

$$E(t) = (aNw\Delta t)/[(4\pi Dt)^{1/2}] \times \exp\{-[(L - wt)^2/4Dt] - \beta t\}.$$

If t_m is the time for a maximum in $E(t)$ and t_1 is the time when $E(t_1) = e^{-1} E(t_m)$, it is seen that

$$w \approx L/t_m$$

$$D \approx L^2(\delta t)^2/4t_m^3$$

where $\delta t = |t_m - t_1|$. Further, if C is the total number of electrons arriving at P, that is

$$C = \int_0^\infty (E(t)/\Delta t)dt$$

then

$$C/C_0 \approx \exp(-f_1 P\alpha L)$$

where C_0 is the total number of counts for a pure gas that does not capture electrons. Figure 2.2 is a plot in which the solution $E(t)$ is compared with experimental data for C_2H_4 gas (ethylene) at

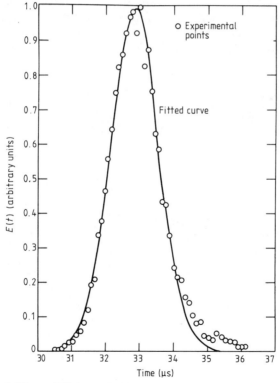

Figure 2.2 Time-of-flight distribution in ethylene at E/P = 0.1 V cm⁻¹Torr⁻¹ with $P = 50$ Torr and $T = 300$ K for a flight length of 27 cm.

$E/P = 0.1 \, \mathrm{V \, cm^{-1} \, Torr^{-1}}$ at a pressure of 50 Torr and at 300 K. The good agreement between theory and experiment is typical and gives some confidence in the macroscopic parameters. For the data in figure 2.2, $L = 27$ cm, $t_m = 33 \times 10^{-6}$ s, and $\delta t = 1.1 \times 10^{-6}$ s. Hence $D = 6.13 \times 10^3 \, \mathrm{cm^2 \, s^{-1}}$ or D_1 at a pressure of 1 Torr would be $3.1 \times 10^5 \, \mathrm{cm^2 \, s^{-1}}$. From the plot of figure 2.2, one sees the relative importance of electron diffusion at a glance. After drifting 27 cm through C_2H_4, $\delta t / t_m$ is about 3%. Similarly, a snap-shot at a given time would reveal a mean spatial spread about the swarm plane of 3%. Electron diffusion plays a major role only at low pressures (say below 20 Torr) for most gases.

To obtain the experimental results in figure 2.2, electrons were released from a planar metallic surface by using a UV light pulse from a flashlamp. Time of arrival of single electrons was measured by a Geiger–Müller detector (Hurst *et al* 1963, Hurst and Parks 1966). A more refined experiment using time-of-flight methods but with differentially pumped electron multipliers was carried out by Wagner *et al* (1967). Some results for w in Ar, H_2, N_2, and He are shown in figure 2.3, and results for DP are shown for several gases, including helium, in figure 2.4. Since P-10 (10% CH_4 and 90% Ar) is a common counting gas, we show w as a function of E/P in figure 2.5 based on an older method (Bortner *et al* 1957).

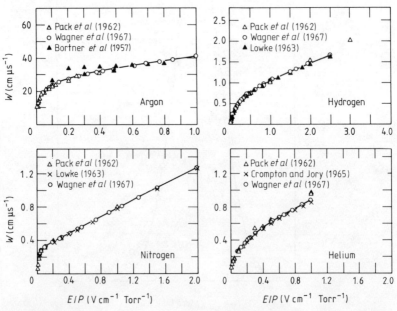

Figure 2.3 Drift velocity, w, as a function of E/P for He, Ar, H_2 and N_2 as determined by the time-of-flight method (Wagner *et al* 1967) compared with other methods.

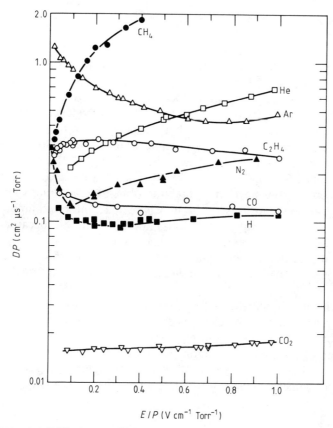

Figure 2.4 Diffusion coefficient, normalised to a pressure of 1 Torr, as a function of E/P for several gases (from Wagner *et al* 1967).

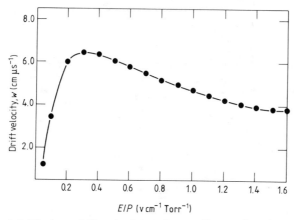

Figure 2.5 Electron drift velocity w (cm$\,\mu$s^{-1}) as a function of E/P for P-10 gas (from Bortner *et al* 1957).

2.3 Pulsed ionisation measurements

Much of the early work with x-rays, β-rays, α-particles and accelerated charged particles to create ionisation utilised steady state sources. Total ionisation was studied by measuring the direct current with electrometers or with DC amplifiers, and the current was plotted against E/P to obtain saturation. A wide plateau was taken as evidence that all of the ions were being detected. As we have seen from the brief discussion on gaseous electronics, this is only possible when recombination is avoided at low E/P, gas amplification is avoided at high E/P, and when the total current produced is so small that space charge is not a factor. All of these precautions have to be taken to obtain the accurate values of W (energy per ion pair) discussed in Chapter 1. Information on pulsed ionisation measurement is of great importance to RIS because of the common use of pulsed lasers for these purposes. The use of pulsed lasers can provide valuable time resolution. It also turns out that the RIS process is saturable over a much wider range of wavelengths with pulsed lasers.

The classical treatment of the pulse shape in ionisation detectors was given by Corson and Wilson (1948). Their treatment, using α-particle sources for ionisation, requires no substantial modification for our discussion of resonance ionisation. In figure 2.6 we illustrate the simplest form of ionisation detector, but with a well collimated laser beam of negligible diameter replacing the α-particle source considered by Corson

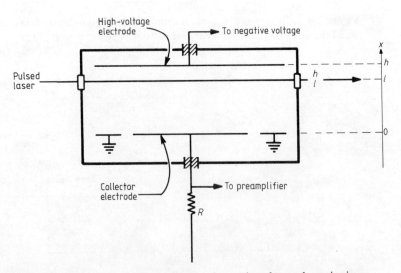

Figure 2.6 Schematic diagram of pulse formation due to laser ionisation of gases in a uniform electric field.

and Wilson. We begin by assuming that the laser beam produces ionisation along every element of its path in the gaseous atmosphere of the detector. However, only that part of the ionisation above the collector will be important since the concentric guard electrode assures uniform field lines and eliminates all edge effects. In RIS experiments, guard electrodes serve another important function; namely, they eliminate backgrounds due to non-resonance ionisation when a laser beam is directed through window materials.

Following Corson and Wilson, assume that the resistor R is so large that the system is nearly isolated. Thus, the energy of the isolated system is $CV_0^2/2$, where C is the capacity of the collector electrode with respect to the high voltage electrode. Conservation of energy is applicable at all times; therefore, as the electric field E does work on n ions of charge e, the voltage V_0 must decrease a small amount to V (i.e., $V_0 = V + \delta V$). If the ions are moved from x_0 to x,

$$CV^2/2 = CV_0^2/2 - \int_{x_0}^{x} neE \, dx$$

which can be rewritten as

$$\delta V = 1/V_0 C \int_{l}^{x} neE \, dx$$

to emphasise that the signal δV is generated as ions are displaced by the field E. For a uniform field,

$$\delta V = (ne/C)[(x - l)/h]$$

where l and h are, respectively, the separation of the laser beam and the high voltage electrode from the collection electrode. From the discussion above on gaseous electronics, we saw that all types of ions reach a terminal, or drift, velocity w due to gas collisions; thus $x = l - wt$, and, neglecting the minus sign

$$\delta V(t) = (new/Ch)t$$

showing that the signal is changing as long as charges are in motion. Note that we have tacitly assumed that all ions move with the same drift velocity w which, in effect, neglects ion diffusion. As seen in the section on gaseous electronics, this would rarely be a serious error, even for electrons. The rate of rise $(d/dt)(\delta V) = new/Ch$ can be evaluated for ions of any velocity w. Suppose we assume that all electrons remain free, i.e. not captured to form negative ions, and that the positive ions are of one species. Then, $w_- \gg w_+$ since the drift velocity of electrons is of the order of 10^6 cm s^{-1}, while w_+ for positive ions is only about 10^3 cm s^{-1} for the same E/P.

Figure 2.7 is a highly schematic representation of the pulse shape, applicable to the detector of figure 2.6. A fast component of the pulse

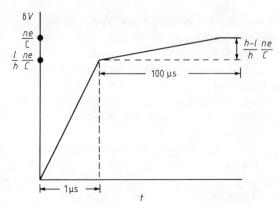

Figure 2.7 Pulse shape due to motion of free electrons (on $1\,\mu s$ time-scale) and positive ions (on $100\,\mu s$ time-scale) induced by laser ionisation in a gas-filled ionisation chamber with uniform electric field.

$(l/h) \times (ne/C)$ is added to a much slower component $[(h - l)/h] \times (ne/C)$; thus, at $t \to \infty$, the total δV is ne/C, the familiar result. In practice, pulse amplifiers are used to make δV easy to measure, and these have time constants which are comparable to the collection time of free electrons. The net effect is that only the fast component of the pulse in figure 2.7 is measured. For this reason, the pulse height δV is proportional to $(l/h) \times (ne/C)$ and thus depends on the position of the laser beam. These very elementary considerations apply whether the pulse amplifier is 'voltage sensitive' or 'charge sensitive'. It is misleading to speak of the signals due to the collection of charge on the plate of a capacitor, since it suggests that nothing happens until the charge arrives. The principle of conservation of energy applies at all times; hence, voltage pulses arise as long as charges are in motion. Measurement of δV for a known distance of the laser beam, the plate separation, and the system capacity can lead to accurate determination of the number, n, of ion pairs created by the laser. However, this requires controlled gaseous electronics conditions in which there is no ion pair recombination, no electron capture, no gas amplification, and no space charge. In practice, by using low-noise amplifiers, values of n as small as 10^3 can be measured. The next chapter contains examples of the use of proportional counters, with gas amplification, to measure individual electrons.

We conclude this section with a quantitative discussion of the effect of the amplifier on the pulse shape of figure 2.7 to see how the actual number of electrons generated by laser ionisation can be extracted from the measured pulse height. As already stated, it is best to use gases in which electron capture is not a factor. However, we include electron capture in the analysis to show how important its effects can be and, thus, the care needed to exclude attaching gases. From the definition of the attachment coefficient, it is easily shown that the number, N, of electrons surviving after drifting a distance x is

$$N(x) = N_0 \exp(-\alpha f_1 P x)$$

where N_0 is the number of electrons at $x = 0$ (Bortner and Hurst 1958). Thus, the voltage induced by the free-electron component is decreased due to capture and is given by

$$\delta V(t) = (A/f) [1 - \exp(-ft/\tau_0)]$$

where $A = (N_0 el)/Ch$, $f = \alpha f_1 Pl$, and τ_0 is the electron collection time (i.e. the time for electrons to drift the distance l from the laser beam to the collector plate) and is given by $\tau_0 = l/w$. The effect of the pulsed amplifier can be expressed in terms of the convolution integral

$$\delta V(\tau) = \int_0^{\tau_0} (\mathrm{d}/\mathrm{d}t)\delta V(t)V'(\tau-t)\mathrm{d}t$$

where $V'(t)$ is the amplifier response to a step function. In many cases $V'(t)$ can be described by a single time constant, t_1, as

$$V'(t) = V_0(t/t_1)\exp(-t/t_1)$$

where t_1 is both the 'integration' and 'differentiation' time constant of the pulse amplifier. The maximum pulse height, $\delta V'(\tau)$, was obtained analytically as a function of the ratio τ_0/t_1 and is plotted in figure 2.8.

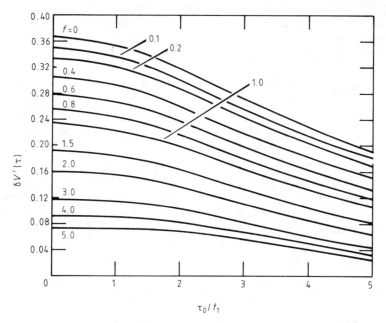

Figure 2.8 Calculated dependence of pulse height on τ_0/t_1 for various values of the attachment parameter f (see text).

The curve for $f = 0$, corresponding to no electron attachment, is useful for calibrating the output of a pulse amplifier to obtain the number of electrons created in a pulsed laser beam for any measured electron collection time τ_0, and for a particular amplifier response time. Calculation of the number of electrons generated in a pulsed laser beam, N_l, can be made by using the formula

$$N_l = [0.363/(\delta V'(\tau)](C/e)(h/l)V_p$$

where V_p is the reading in volts of a fast rise time pulser injected into the preamplifier to give the same output pulse height produced by the laser.

2.4 Concept of the RIS experiment on He(2^1S)

We describe (Hurst 1974, Hurst *et al* 1975a, 1975b) a means by which a beam from a pulsed dye laser converts all members of a selected excited species to ion pairs, and hence allows the direct measurement of the number of the species present at the time in question; see figure 1.13 for the basic experimental idea. To selectively ionise a given species, a resonant two-step process is used in which an atom of the selected species is first promoted to an excited state lying more than half-way to the continuum and then photo-ionised by the same laser pulse (see figure 2.9). The technique of producing almost 100% ionisation of a given state by making use of the two-step excitation–ionisation process is an example of resonance ionisation spectroscopy (RIS).

A single laser beam can be tuned to promote transitions between an excited state and an intermediate state, and a second photon from the same laser pulse can photo-ionise the intermediate state. Such a process involving two photons in discrete steps to produce ionisation has been utilised by Dunning and Stebbings (1974) to obtain cross sections for photo-ionisation of the intermediate state. We are not discussing here what are usually referred to as multiphoton ionisation processes which require very high peak power (see Chapter 4). It is possible to observe true resonances in the ionisation current at several wavelengths for each excited state. Any one of the states can be removed while the other states will not be disturbed, because a resonance wavelength for one excited state is not a resonance for another state.

We will now give a quantitative discussion of RIS. It will be helpful to discuss first the process in a rather definite context. Thus, we consider the situation illustrated in figure 2.9. Suppose that a noble gas has been excited by a pulse of protons which is short in duration and occurred at time $t = 0$. After a time delay t, a broad beam of photons is fired antiparallel to the proton beam. Assume the laser beam is tuned to a

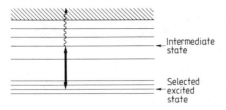

Figure 2.9 Illustration of the photo-ionisation of an excited state in a two-step process. In the first step a photon of the required frequency promotes a selected excited state to an intermediate state. The intermediate state is promoted to the ionisation continuum by another photon in the same laser pulse of width τ_0.

transition from a selected excited state (level 1) to an intermediate state (level 2), i.e. it contains photons of frequency $h\nu_{12}$. If $2h\nu_{12}$ is greater than or equal to $h\nu_{1c}$, where ν_{1c} is the frequency of a photon which will ionise just level 1, some photo-ionisation will be produced as a consequence of the two-step process.

Assuming rapid collisional redistribution among magnetic substates, rate equations for levels 1 and 2, having populations of N_1 and N_2 respectively, are

$$dN_1/dt = -(\lambda_0^2/8\pi)\gamma_{21}(g_2/g_1)F(\nu_{12})g(t)N_1$$
$$+ (\lambda_0^2/8\pi)\gamma_{21}F(\nu_{12})g(t)N_2 - \beta_1 N_1 + \gamma_{21}N_2$$
$$dN_2/dt = (\lambda_0^2/8\pi)\gamma_{21}(g_2/g_1)F(\nu_{12})g(t)N_1$$
$$- (\lambda_0^2/8\pi)\gamma_{21}F(\nu_{12})g(t)N_2 - \sigma_{2c}(\nu_{12})g(t)N_2 - \beta_2 N_2.$$

In these equations, the term λ_0 is the photon wavelength corresponding to frequency ν_{12}; γ_{21} is the rate of spontaneous decay from state 2 to state 1; β_1 and β_2 denote the total rate of decay of state 1 or 2 due to all processes occurring when the system is returning to thermodynamic equilibrium without interference from the laser beam; $F(\nu)d\nu$ is the fraction of laser photons in the frequency interval between ν and $\nu + d\nu$

(assigned to be nearly constant over the spectral line). The term $g(t)$ is the frequency-integrated number of laser photons crossing a unit area per unit time, i.e. the photon flux, and $\sigma_{2c}(\nu)$ is the cross section for photo-ionisation of state 2 by a photon of frequency ν. We have not allowed for the extra source term due to cascade or collisional transfer from other states to state 2, which is assumed to be initially unpopulated. These assumptions put some minor restrictions on the times after excitation where the method is applicable. At pressures greater than approximately 50 Torr, the above equations hold for either polarised or unpolarised light for any time greater than approximately 10^{-10} s. Energy transfer collisions between excited atoms and ground state atoms can change the magnetic quantum number from $m = 0$ to $m = \pm 1$, and this is rapid enough to keep an equilibrium population between all magnetic substates in times which are short compared with the natural lifetime. Information on energy transfer collisions can be found in Byron and Foley (1965) and in Watanabe (1967). Energy transfer collisions with cross sections greater than 10^{-12} cm^2 are typical (Berman and Lamb 1969) and bring about equal populations of magnetic sub-levels in about 10^{-10} s, even at modest pressures. For this reason, σ_{2c} values are averaged over magnetic quantum number and are correspondingly smaller than those measured by Stebbings *et al* (1973) where collisions are absent and where the light is polarised. The quantity σ_{2c} is estimated for He(1s,3p) states by using the theory for σ_{2c} in H(3p). Stebbings *et al* (1973) have also measured σ_{2c} for the 2^1S and 2^3S states near the threshold.

We are interested in the number, N_c, of the selected excited states which are promoted to the continuum; this is obtained from

$$N_c = \sigma_{2c}(\nu_{12}) \int_t^\infty g(t')N_2(t')\mathrm{d}t' + Nk_A \int_t^\infty N_2(t')\mathrm{d}t'.$$

We shall also be comparing it with $N_1(t)$, the number of the He(2^1S) states as a function of time following excitation by the proton beam. Specifically, if $N_2 = 0$ when the laser pulse is fired, the number N_c represents some fraction of the states, $N_1(t)$, that we wish to measure. In the above, N is the number of ground state atoms and k_A is the rate constant for associative ionisation, i.e. the Hornbeck–Molnar process discussed in Chapter 1. In some cases it is necessary to allow for collisional transfer from level 2 to another state (or states) and for associative ionisation or transfer back from that state. However, we shall not explicitly include such effects here.

For the pulsed laser source under consideration, $g(t)$ is of the order of 10^{24} photons per cm^2 per s; therefore, the first two terms in the above rate equations dominate the other terms. Quasi-equilibrium (i.e. $g_2 N_1(t) \approx g_1 N_2(t)$) is reached very early, in which the number of photons in the stimulated emission process is almost equal to the rate of absorption. Define $f_c(t) \equiv N_c(t + \tau)/N_1(t)$. Then, at quasi-equilibrium,

$$f_c(t) = \sigma_{2c}(v_{12})[1 + (g_1/g_2)]^{-1} \int_0^{\tau} (dF/d\tau')(\tau')d\tau' \exp{-[q(\tau')]}$$

$$+ Nk_A[1 - (g_1/g_2)]^{-1} \int_0^{\tau} d\tau' \exp{-[q(\tau')]}$$

where

$$F(\tau') = \int_t^{t+\tau} g(t')dt'$$

and

$$q(\tau) = [1 + (g_1/g_2)]^{-1} [(\beta_2 - \gamma_{21})\tau + (g_1/g_2)\beta_1\tau + \sigma_{2c}(v_{12})F(\tau)].$$

Consider as an example the 2^1S state of helium, which is excited to the 3^1P state by tuning the laser to 501.5 nm. To evaluate the fraction $N_c(t + \tau_0)/N_1(t) = f_c(\tau_0)$ for He(2^1S), we make use of the diagram of figure 2.10. When the photon flux is applied, the 2^1S and 3^1P states come into quasi-equilibrium. The 3^1P state radiates to the ground state (53.7 nm) at a rate of $5.66 \times 10^8 \text{ s}^{-1}$ and to the 3^1S state at a rate of $2.5 \times 10^5 \text{ s}^{-1}$. The 53.7 nm radiation is trapped at moderate pressure. According to the Holstein (1947, 1951) theory, the lowest eigenmode estimate of the rate of escape from a cylinder of 1 cm radius is $2.6 \times 10^5 \text{ s}^{-1}$. Thus, the effective value of $(\beta_2 - \gamma_{21})$ is just $5.1 \times 10^5 \text{ s}^{-1}$. Up to pressures of a few hundred torr, β_1 does not exceed 10^6 s^{-1}. Assuming a laser pulse of 2.5 J at 501.5 nm with $\tau_0 = 0.3 \times 10^{-6}$ s and $\sigma_{2c} = 4.3 \times 10^{-18} \text{ cm}^2$, we find $F(\tau_0)\sigma_{2c} = 35$ and $f_c(\tau_0) = 0.99$.

At higher pressure, other processes which must be considered are the

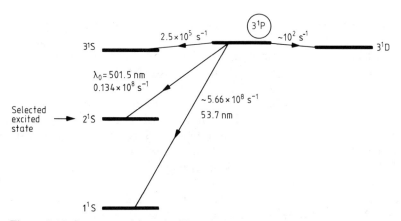

Figure 2.10 Some transitions in He relative to the consideration of resonance ionisation of the 2^1S metastable state via the absorption of 501.5 nm radiation to the 3^1P intermediate state.

interconversion of energy between the various $n = 3$ levels (Wellenstein and Robertson 1972a) and associative ionisation. The rate of associative ionisation from $n = 3$ levels is $10^7 P \, s^{-1}$, where P is the helium pressure in torr. However, starting with the intermediate state, 3^1P, the transfer to 3^1D is much more likely than the transfer to 3^1S. As a consequence of associative ionisation, most of the states promoted to 3^1P will be converted to ions (molecular) at pressures greater than 100 Torr without the assistance from the second photon from the laser. Under these conditions, there will be some loss of excited states through the $3^1S \rightarrow 2^1P$ radiation. We emphasise that these losses (about 20%) do not apply at low pressure. In some cases we believe it will be possible to choose an intermediate state from which associative ionisation is a fast process. This assures ion saturation from a single photon absorption by an excited state and eliminates the high-pressure restriction on absolute measurements.

Earlier, it was suggested (Hurst *et al* 1975a) that the analysis of a lower singlet state which emits resonance radiation proceeds in a similar way. For the $He(2^1P)$ state, which emits at a 58.4 nm resonance line to the ground state, we utilise 3^1S as an intermediate state by tuning the laser to 728.1 nm. Consideration of the low-lying triplet states shows that resonance ionisation measurements of the 2^3P state through the transition $2^3P \rightarrow 3^3S$ (706.5 nm) and of the 2^3S state through the transition $2^3S \rightarrow 3^3P$ (388.8 nm) are also feasible. We believe that the long-lived resonance and metastable states for each of the noble gases can be studied with the RIS technique. To our knowledge, these early suggestions have not been followed to extend the RIS experiments to excited states other than $He(2^1S)$ which is described below.

2.5 Results of the RIS experiment on $He(2^1S)$ involving photo-ionisation

Figure 2.11 is a schematic diagram of the RIS experiment used for the $He(2^1S)$ demonstration (Hurst *et al* 1975a,b). Narrow pulses (15 ns) of 2 MeV protons arrived at a beam deflector every 64 μs. One pulse of approximately 10^8 protons entered the ionisation chamber and triggered a dye laser after a variable delay time. Each encounter between the proton pulse and the delayed laser pulse was recorded on a transient recorder. The proton pulse created about 5×10^7 ion pairs at 0.6 Torr, and this caused a current to flow through a signal resistor of a few kilo-ohms. These pulses were amplified 100 times with a wide-band pulse amplifier and then recorded. Modifications of a commercial (Phase-R Corporation) laser yielded: (a) a beam of reasonable quality over a 10 mm diameter; (b) an energy per pulse of about 0.7 J at

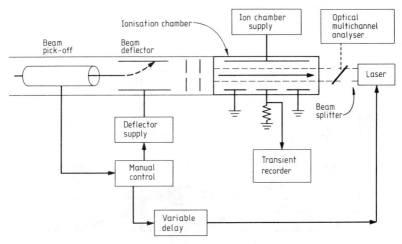

Figure 2.11 Schematic of resonance ionisation spectroscopy applied to excited states created by pulses of charged particles.

501.5 nm; (c) a photon spectrum of about 3 nm full width at half maximum (FWHM); and (d) a pulse width of about 300 ns.

Figure 2.12 shows a typical recording obtained when photons followed by the laser pulse were injected into helium at 0.6 Torr. With 50 V applied to the field plates spaced 2 cm apart, the positive ion signals were collected in about 8 μs, in agreement with ion mobility and diffusion data. The electron pulses were collected very quickly and are not resolved in the figure. It was shown that below 10^8 ion pairs, the pulse heights are linearly related to the number of ion pairs. A simple ratio of pulse heights gives the number of quantum-selected (metastable) atoms per ion pair of the non-selective ionisation due to the proton beam. The He(2^1S) state at 0.6 Torr should have a lifetime of the order of 10^{-3} s in the apparatus. The He(2^1S) population was measured at 20 and at 88 μs after proton excitation. There was little observable change between the two delay times.

In these first RIS experiments, several checks were made to ensure that ionisation of the He(2^1S) population was actually what was observed. First, the same procedure which yielded figure 2.12 was carried out except that a quartz beam-viewer was used to block the proton beam from the ionisation chamber. In the absence of direct ionisation and of the He(2^1S) population, only the radiofrequency transient (see the sharp time dependence near the beginning of the second ion peak in figure 2.12) was observed when a 0.7 J pulse tuned to 501.5 nm was fired into the 99.9998% pure helium. Second, the laser

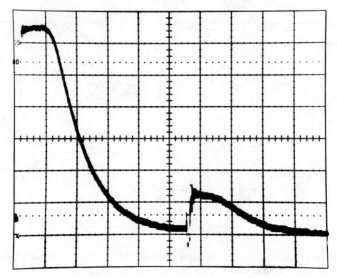

Figure 2.12 Reproduction of a pulse recorded in the first RIS experiment to measure the population of He(2¹S). An oscilloscope trace of the positive ionisation current as a function of time. The large pulse is direct ionisation created by protons; the smaller pulse is created by the laser tuned to 501.5 nm and delayed 22 μs.

was detuned to 506.0 nm (and to 497.0 nm) and both the protons and a laser pulse of 0.7 J were fired into the cell. In these cases the peaks due to laser-induced ionisation were absent. These observations, together with the pulse shapes (which indicate that the ions producing the signal are created nearly simultaneously near the cell centre), led to the conclusion that the second peak of figure 2.12 is due entirely to resonant two-photon ionisation of He(2¹S). Figure 2.13 shows the ratio of peak heights plotted against nergy per pulse at 501.5 nm, suggesting that the ionisation process is close to saturation.

The above experiment was carried out with a laser which produced long and slowly changing pulses (duration ≅ 0.3 μs). Also, the line width was very broad (i.e. FWHM ≅ 3 nm) compared with the 3¹P → 2¹S emission line of helium. Further, collisional broadening effects destroy quantum coherence in times of about 10^{-9} s at 0.6 Torr. For these reasons, rate equations can be used to estimate the percentage of the He(2¹S) population converted to ion pairs by the laser pulse. Calculations showed that a 0.7 J pulse (duration 0.3 μs and 3 nm spectral width centred at 501.5 nm) causes about 80% conversion of He(2¹S) to ion pairs at a pressure of 0.6 Torr. However, the yield of ion pairs may be higher than 80% since some photons are reflected back into the interaction region by a mirror at the end of the cell. About 92% of

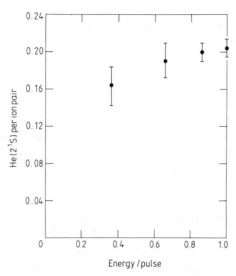

Figure 2.13 The number of He(2¹S) states ionised in the RIS process of non-selective ionisation (produced by the proton beam) per ion pair as a function of the laser energy per pulse (700 mJ = 1 on energy scale).

these ion pairs were created by two-photon resonance ionisation, while 8% were due to associative ionisation out of the 3¹P and 3¹D states. Recall that the 3¹D state comes into the picture because two-body collisions with ground state atoms convert 3¹P to both 3¹D and 3¹S (Wellenstein and Robertson 1972b).

Since calculation and data suggest that the ionisation is nearly saturated, the ratio at 0.7 J per pulse was compared with theory. From the work of Alkhazov (1968) on electron excitation, Bartell *et al* (1973) estimated that about 1 μs after proton excitation, the He(2¹S) population per direct ion pair is 0.27 at 0.6 Torr. This is in reasonable agreement with the measured ratio (0.20) in figure 2.13. At times greater than 1 μs the He(2¹S) population comprises directly excited states and much of the original populations of He(2¹P), He(3¹S), and He(3¹P) which eventually cascade to He(2¹S). These cascade effects were included, of course, in estimating the 27%.

In summary, complete conversion of excited state populations to ion pairs was accomplished (Hurst *et al* 1975b) with a photo-ionisation process involving the absorption of two photons, one of which was resonant with an intermediate state. Thus, the two-photon ionisation process, when saturated, can be used as a basis for absolute and very sensitive measurements of quantum-selected (including ground state) populations. For example, if He(2¹S) is excited at low presure (0.6 Torr) and irradiated with a pulsed dye laser tuned to 501.5 nm, He(2^1S) is promoted to He(3^1P) as the intermediate state. This intermediate state is photo-ionised with a cross section of approximately 4.4×10^{-18} cm^2 at 501.5 nm; thus, a laser pulse of 1 J cm^{-2} converts nearly all of the He(2^1S) to ionisation via the He(3^1P) state.

2.6 The RIS experiments on He(2^1S) using associative ionisation

Experiments on proton excitation of helium at higher pressures (10 to 100 Torr) were also carried out to show that the RIS technique could help to unravel a host of more complex phenomena. In this case, He(2^1S) can be produced as well as destroyed by collision processes. These high-pressure experiments could also be used to demonstrate (Payne *et al* 1975a) that saturated ionisation can be accomplished by single-photon absorption followed by collisions with ground state atoms. This technique requires less laser energy per pulse than does the two-photon method. This version of the RIS technique was applied to kinetic studies of He(2^1S) over a wide range of helium pressures.

For helium, the states lying above the 3^3P can be converted to ionisation by an associative process (the Hornbeck–Molnar reaction). Our RIS-intermediate state, He(3^1P), is converted to ionisation with a two-body cross section of about 3×10^{-16} cm^2 (Wellenstein and Robertson 1972a), and to He(3^1D) with a cross section of about 30×10^{-16} cm^2 (Wellenstein and Robertson 1972b); He(3^1D) is associatively ionised with a cross section of about 20×10^{-16} cm^2 (Wellenstein and Robertson 1972a). Effectively, the He(3^1P) is converted to (He)$_2^+$ at a rate of about $10^7 P$, where P is the helium pressure in torr and the rate is in inverse seconds. However, a competing process is a collisional conversion of 3^1P to 3^1S (with $\sigma = 4.5 \times 10^{-16}$ cm^2) (Wellenstein and Robertson 1972b) which is not associatively ionised but, instead, radiates 3×10^7 s^{-1} to 2^1P. Return of He(2^1P) to He(2^1S) occurs at the rate of $(1.9 \times 10^6 + 6.4 \times 10^4\ P)$s^{-1}, where the pressure is in torr (Bartell *et al* 1973, Payne *et al* 1975b). During the cycle there is a loss from the He(2^1P) state due to resonance radiation transport to the wall at a rate of 0.9×10^6 s^{-1} and due to excimer formation at a rate of $90P^2$. These losses are not important over a wide range of pressure since the chance that an atom promoted to the He(3^1P) intermediate state will enter the return part of the cycle (where the losses occur) is small. As the pressure increases, associative ionisation dominates over photo-ionisation; at 15 Torr, photo-ionisation contributes only a few per cent at an energy of about 1 J per pulse.

Pulses (15 ns) of 2 MeV protons were injected into a parallel plate ionisation chamber filled with rapidly flowing 99.9998% pure helium.

After a suitable delay, a laser tuned to 501.5 nm provided a photon flux which bathed the region of the chamber surrounding the proton path. Recordings were made of the electron currents due to: (a) the direct proton ionisation; and (b) laser-induced ionisation of the selected excited state.

Data were collected by using a transient recorder in order to store the signal, which was generated across a resistor of a few kilo-ohms following the passage of a pulse of protons through the ionisation chamber and the subsequent passage of a dye laser pulse. When the laser was tuned to 501.5 nm and delivered at least 0.1 J per pulse, signals like those in figure 2.14 were obtained. When the laser was detuned from 501.5 nm but delivered 0.7 J per pulse, the second peak was observed to disappear (i.e. there was little background). Since the number of ion pairs produced per centimetre of path by the proton pulse is less than 10^7, and almost all of the He(2^{1}S) population is ionised as a consequence of the passage of the laser pulse, the number of He(2^{1}S) states per ion pair is given by the ratio of the second peak height to the first. The production of more than 10^8 ion pairs per cm leads to space charge effects which were avoided by producing less than this.

Saturation of the ionisation of He(2^{1}S) as a consequence of the laser pulse (0.7 J at 501.5 nm) was checked by attenuating the beam by a factor of three and observing that $R(t)$ (the ratio of the second to the

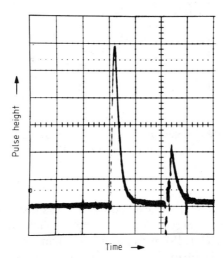

Figure 2.14 Electron signals due to direct proton interaction and resonance ionisation of the single metastable He(2^{1}S) with a dye laser tuned to 501.5 nm. Helium at a pressure of 15 Torr was excited with pulses of protons followed by laser pulses after 10 μs.

first peak height) was unchanged, within experimental error. The insertion of a lens system which increased the beam radius by a factor of 1.5 also gave no observable change in $R(t)$. Whenever associative ionisation occurs at a rapid rate (i.e. higher pressure), a very modest energy (i.e. 0.1 J) per pulse is required to saturate the ionisation, even when the spectrum is wide (3 nm FWHM). This experimental proof was confirmed with appropriate rate equation calculations, using the input data discussed above.

Measurements were carried out under saturation conditions for a large number of delay times at various pressures from 15 to 100 Torr; the decay curve for 100 Torr is shown in figure 2.15. At times greater than 2 μs following excitation, it was found that the He(2^1S) population decays exponentially with decay constant $\beta(2^1S)$ which is given by

$$\beta(2^1S) = 220\,P + 1.4\,P^2.$$

At low pressures this rate agrees well with Phelps (1955), and at pressures above 100 Torr it is nearly the same as that of the 60.1 nm, collision-induced emission of He(2^1S) (Bartell *et al* 1973).

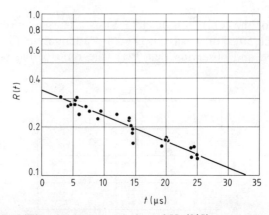

Figure 2.15 The absolute population of He(2^1S) states per direct ion pair as a function of time, $R(t)$, after 2 MeV proton excitation of He at 100 Torr.

The absolute number of excited states was used to verify a key process in a recent energy pathways model for helium (see figure 1.12). The population of He(2^1S) at times greater than 1 μs is due not only to the initial excitation of this state but also to excitation of higher states followed by radiative cascade and collisional conversion processes (Bartell *et al* 1973, Payne *et al* 1975b) which ultimately lead to He(2^1S).

Initially, the He(2¹P) population makes up about 50% of all the excited state population, and it is about a factor of five more than He(2¹S). However, it is observed (Payne *et al* 1975b) that He(2¹P) decays exponentially with time with a decay constant $\beta(2^1P) = 2.8 \times 10^6 + 6.4 \times 10^4 P + 90 P^2$. The $2.8 \times 10^6 \text{s}^{-1}$ term represents a rate of spontaneous emission to the 2^1S state ($1.9 \times 10^6 \text{ s}^{-1}$), plus a rate of escape of resonance photons to the cell wall ($9 \times 10^5 \text{ s}^{-1}$). A theoretical argument (Payne *et al* 1975b) suggests that the $6.4 \times 10^4 P$ term represents a rate for the process He(2¹P) + He(1¹S) $\rightarrow$ He(2¹S) + He(1¹S). The $90P^2$ term presumably represents the rate of formation of the $B^1\Pi_g$ and $D^1\Sigma_g^+$ dimers. If the linear term does represent collisional conversion of He(2¹P) to He(2¹S), then at $P \cong 100$ Torr about 89% of the initial He(2¹P) population is converted to He(2¹S); otherwise, only about 20% of the He(2¹P) population would become He(2¹S). Figure 2.16 shows the experimental $t = 0$ intercepts (R_m) of the curves $R(t)$ against t as a function of pressure. The upper solid curve is based on the assumption that the $6.4 \times 10^4 P$ term represents collisional conversion of He(2¹P) to He(2¹S), while the lower solid curve is based on the assumption that the only conversion of He(2¹P) to He(2¹S) is due to radiative transitions. Theoretical excited state populations per ion pair formed were taken from Bartell *et al* (1973) and Alkhazov and Voreb'ev (1969). Figure 2.16 strongly suggests that two-body conversion of 2¹P to 2¹S does indeed occur.

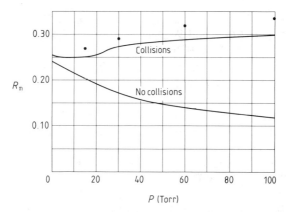

Figure 2.16 Estimated number of He(2¹S) states per direct ion pair (R_m) as a function of He pressure. Collisional conversion of He(2¹P) to He(2¹S) is assumed to obtain the upper curve. The lower curve is the calculated ratio assuming that collisional destruction of He(2¹P) does not lead to He(2¹S). Points represent RIS measurements.

Thus, it was shown (Payne *et al* 1975a) that the RIS technique can be extended to situations where the final step is collision induced. Associative ionisation is one collision mechanism; Penning ionisation of an impurity and charge transfer to electronegative impurities may provide other useful mechanisms. Utilisation of these collision processes in resonance ionisation spectroscopy is very important because it makes possible the use of lasers having rather modest energy per pulse.

Verification of a key step in a model for energy pathways in helium provided a means to ensure that the RIS process was understood, since the helium example was the simplest known case of the interaction of radiation with matter. We also believed that RIS would be very useful for the study of other excited species in irradiated gases. These studies in radiation physics have been slow to develop, due mainly to the more pressing need to detect atoms in their ground state. Therefore, essentially the rest of this book deals with the use of RIS for elemental analyses. Chapter 3 deals with its use for the detection of individual atoms in their ground state, as an illustration of the ultimate sensitivity of this selective ionisation process.

References

Alkhazov G D 1968 Ioffe Institute of Physics and Technology, Leningrad, *Report No FTI-108* (unpublished) (Engl. transl. Scientific Translation Service *STS Order No 7926*)

Alkhazov G D and Voreb'ev A A 1969 *Phys. Lett.* **29A** 25

Bartell D M, Hurst G S and Wagner E B 1973 *Phys. Rev.* A7 1068–78

Berman P R and Lamb W E Jr 1969 *Phys. Rev.* **187** 221

Bortner T E and Hurst G S 1958 *Health Phys.* 1 39–45

Bortner T E, Hurst G S and Stone W G 1957 *Rev. Sci. Instrum.* **28** 103–8

Byron F W and Foley H M 1965 *Phys. Rev.* **140** A 1044

Christophorou L G 1971 *Atomic and Molecular Radiation Physics* (New York: Wiley Interscience).

Corson D R and Wilson R R 1948 *Rev. Sci. Instrum.* **19** 207

Crompton R W and Jory R L 1965 *Proc. 4th Int. Conf. Phys. Electronic and Atomic Collisions* (New York: Science Bookcrafters) p 118

Dunning F B and Stebbings R F 1974 *Phys. Rev. Lett.* **32** 1286

Healey R H and Reed J W 1941 *The Behaviour of Slow Electrons in Gases* (Sydney: Amalgamated Wireless)

Holstein T 1947 *Phys. Rev.* **72** 1212

—— 1951 *Phys. Rev.* **83** 1159

Hurst G S 1974 Health Physics Division Progress Report for Period

Ending July 31 1974 *Oak Ridge National Laboratory Report ORNL-4979* pp 230–3

Hurst G S, Judish J P, Nayfeh M H, Parks J E, Payne M G and Wagner E B 1975a Use of a 3-MV Proton Accelerator for Study of Noble Gases, Including Laser Ionisation of Excited States in *Proc. Third Conf. on Application of Small Accelerators* CONF 741040-Pl vol I pp 97–119 (Springfield, Virginia: National Technical Information Service)

Hurst G S, O'Kelly L B, Wagner E B and Stockdale J A 1963 *J. Chem. Phys.* **39** 1341

Hurst G S, Payne M G, Nayfeh M H, Judish J P and Wagner E P 1975b *Phys. Rev. Lett.* **35** 82–5

Hurst G S and Parks J E 1966 *J. Chem. Phys.* **45** 281–95

Hurst G S, Wagner E B and Payne M G 1974 *J. Chem. Phys.* **61** 3680

Huxley L G H and Crompton R W 1974 *The Diffusion and Drift of Electrons in Gases* (New York: Wiley)

Lowke J J 1963 *Austral. J. Phys.* **16** 115

McDaniel E W 1964 *Collision Phenomena in Ionised Gases* (New York: Wiley)

McDaniel E W and Mason E A 1972 *The Mobility and Diffusion of Ions in Gases* (New York: Wiley)

Pack J L, Voshall R E and Phelps A V 1962 *Phys. Rev.* **127** 2084

Payne M G, Hurst G S, Nayfeh M H, Judish J P, Chen C E, Wagner E B and Young J P 1975a *Phys. Rev. Lett.* **35** 1154–6

Payne M G, Klots C E and Hurst G S 1975b *J. Chem. Phys.* **63** 1422–8

Phelps A V 1955 *Phys. Rev.* **99** 1307

Stebbings R F, Dunning F B, Tittel F K and Rundel R D 1973 *Phys. Rev. Lett.* **30** 815

Townsend J S 1948 *Electrons in Gases* (London: Hutchinson's Scientific and Technical Publications)

Townsend J S and Bailey V A 1922 *Phil. Mag.* **44** 1033

Wagner E B, Davis F J and Hurst G S 1967 *J. Chem. Phys.* **47** 3138–47

Watanabe T 1967 *J. Chem. Phys.* **46** 3741

Wellenstein H F and Robertson W W 1972a *J. Chem. Phys.* **56** 1077

—— 1972b *J. Chem. Phys.* **56** 1072

3

One-atom detection

3.1 RIS of atoms in their ground states

Immediately following the concept of RIS—as a means of measuring a population of excited states—it was recognised that application to atoms in their ground states could lead to one-atom detection. Pressing needs for analysis at the one-atom level diverted the RIS development into this new arena rather than for the purpose it was originally intended.

The first RIS experiments were done on $He(2^1S)$ at 20.5 eV, which is only 4.1 eV from the ionisation continuum. This was very favourable for a two-step process with photons of about 2.4 eV, since flashlamp-pumped dye lasers were available to provide these photons in large numbers. In the early stages of RIS it was by no means clear that the process could be carried out for atoms in their ground states other than a few species like the alkali atoms. For this reason, many of the early demonstrations on one-atom detection involved the caesium atom, since its ionisation potential is only 3.9 eV. Fortunately, RIS schemes have now been found in nearly all of the elements—as predicted in a review by Hurst *et al* (1979). The theory of RIS and its generalisation to nearly all of the elements are discussed in Chapter 5. Here we wish to review the various experiments done to demonstrate sensitivity of the RIS method to single atoms.

We have already discussed (Chapter 2) the essence of the RIS principle in connection with the $He(2^1S)$ experiment. Actually, when the detected species is in the ground state the process simplifies considerably, since the population of the state of interest is not time dependent (assuming the free atom is not reacting chemically). For atoms in their ground states, some of the key considerations can be emphasised by referring to the term diagram for caesium, as shown in figure 3.1. Suppose it is desired to saturate the RIS process using 455.5 nm radiation that promotes the ground state $(6^2S_{1/2})$ to $(7^2P_{3/2})$. Once the excited state $(7^2P_{3/2})$

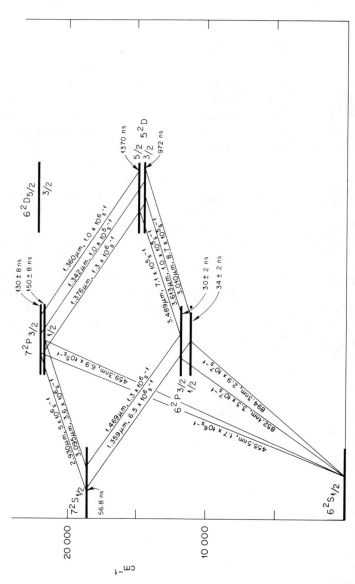

Figure 3.1 Partial term diagram for the Cs atom. Many of the early experiments on RIS were done with the Cs atom since resonance transititions at 455.5 and 459.3 nm are convenient wavelengths for pulsed dye lasers.

is formed, it would be desirable to complete the photo-ionisation step as quickly as possible so that all of the ground states ($6^2S_{1/2}$) will be converted to Cs^+ plus an electron in the two-step process. That is, it is desired that the process

$$Cs(6^2S_{1/2}) + \hbar\omega(455.5 \text{ nm}) \rightarrow Cs(7^2P_{3/2})$$

$$Cs(7^2P_{3/2}) + \hbar\omega(455.5 \text{ nm}) \rightarrow Cs^+ + e$$

be saturated. For a schematic representation of the process see figure 3.2. However, we note in figure 3.1 that the lifetime of the $7^2P_{3/2}$ state is only 130 ns due to the several radiative pathways back to the ground state. Individual transition rates are shown from which it can be seen that, in the absence of photo-ionisation, most decays occur through the $7^2S_{1/2}$ state. However, some transitions occur to the $5^2D_{5/2}$ state which lives for 1370 ns. Now suppose the laser field is such that the $6S \rightarrow 7P$ transition is quite rapid (greater than 10^7 s^{-1}) and the laser pulse width is about 1 μs. From a close inspection of figure 3.1, we learn that those decays through the $7^2S_{1/2}$ state will recycle several times during a laser pulse, while the small fraction of the decays to $5^2D_{5/2}$ will be held up for a time comparable to the laser pulse width. These circumstances could make it more difficult to saturate the RIS process; however, we note for caesium that photo-ionisation of the 5D states is also energetically possible with the 455.5 nm photons. Regardless of the complexity of the radiation decay modes, it will nearly always be possible to saturate the RIS process by using a high flux, F, of photons applied for a sufficient time to produce a large fluence, ϕ, of photons.

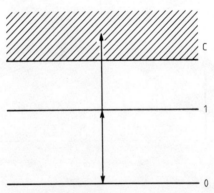

Figure 3.2 Schematic representation of a RIS process carried out for an atom in its ground state. Saturation of the RIS process occurs when each atom in the ground state, 0, is promoted to the ionisation continuum, C, in a two-step process which begins with resonance absorption to an eigenstate 1.

To find conditions on F (photons cm^{-2} s^{-1}) and ϕ (photons cm^{-2}), it will be convenient to make a simple calculation for a more schematic case; see figure 3.3 (Hurst *et al* 1977b). A laser of bandwidth Δv, centred about v_0 brings the ground state 0 and the intermediate state 1 into quasi-equilibrium as explained in Chapter 2. Here we assume that the rates of absorption and stimulated emission are both much larger than the sum of the rates due to photo-ionisation, radiation, and chemical reaction from the intermediate state. A laser produces a flux and a fluence $\phi = FT$ during its pulse width T. We let $\sigma(v)$ be the photo-ionisation cross section of state 1 at frequency v; A be the area of the uniform beam; L the length of the laser beam in an ionisation detector; n_0 the total number of atoms in the volume AL in the ground state before the laser is fired; and $n_{0,1}(t)$ is the number of atoms in the states 0 or 1 as a function of time t where $0 \le t \le T$. Also, let $g_{0,1}$ be the statistical weights; γ_{12} the rate of spontaneous decay from 1 to 2; and β, the rate of destruction of 1 due to all collisional processes.

If F is great enough to keep states 0 and 1 in equilibrium,

$$n_1(t) = (g_1/g_0)n_0(t)$$

and at $t = 0$,

$$n_0(0) + n_1(0) = n_0.$$

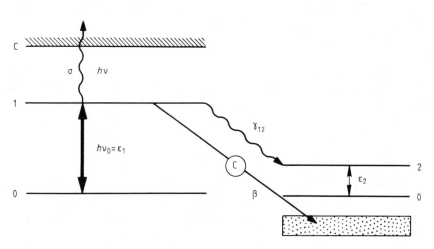

Figure 3.3 Schematic diagram of the RIS process utilising two photons of the same wavelength. Here γ_{12} represents the rate at which the intermediate state decays to a state 2, which cannot be ionised, and β is the rate at which the intermediate state reacts chemically to escape ionisation.

The rate of change of $(n_0(t) + n_1(t))$ is

$$(-d/dt)(n_0(t) + n_1(t)) = (\sigma F + \gamma_{12} + \beta)$$

$$= [g_1/(g_0 + g_1)](\sigma F + \gamma_{12} + \beta)(n_0(t) + n_1(t)).$$

The solution of this equation is

$$(n_0(t) + n_1(t)) = n_0 \exp(-\sigma F + \gamma_{12} + \beta)g't$$

with $g' = g_1/(g_0 + g_1)$. The number of atoms which have been ionised at the termination of the laser pulse is

$$n_1(T) = \int_0^T \sigma F n_1(t) dt$$

$$= [\sigma F n_0/(\sigma F + \gamma_{12} + \beta)]\{1 - \exp[-(\sigma F + \gamma_{12} + \beta)g'T]\}.$$

To saturate the RIS process, i.e. to have $n_1(T) = n_0$, requires a *flux condition* $\sigma F \gg \gamma_{12} + \beta$ and a *fluence condition* $g'\sigma FT = g'\sigma\phi \gg 1$. Even though these results were obtained for a highly schematic process, they illustrate requirements which must be considered to saturate any RIS process. Even if the fluence condition has been met, saturation will not occur unless the flux condition is also met.

The early work with caesium (Hurst *et al* 1977a,b) can be reviewed to see how these conditions were met. A flashlamp-pumped dye laser was used to produce pulses of a few mJ at the desired wavelength. The beam diameter was about 3 mm, the line width (FWHM) was 0.07 nm, and the pulse width (FWHM) was 1.2 μs. When focused, the laser produced 200 mJ cm^{-2}; thus, at 455 nm

$$F = (200 \times 10^{-3} \times 5 \times 10^{15}/1.2 \times 10^{-6}) \times 455 \text{ photons cm}^{-2}$$

since a convenient conversion is $1 \text{ J} = 5 \times 10^{15}\lambda$ (nm) photons. This large photon flux F (which equals 3.8×10^{23} photons cm^{-2} s^{-1}) combined with the cross section σ $(8.8 \times 10^{-18}$ cm$^2)$ gives for $F\sigma$, the rate of photo-ionisation, 3.3×10^6 s^{-1} (Zeman 1974). In general, one expects (Hurst and Klots 1976) the rate of collisional depopulation to be less than $10^4 P + 100 P^2$; or at 100 Torr to be less than 2×10^6 s^{-1}. We would expect β, the rate of an irreversible chemical reaction of caesium with some chemically inert buffer gas like argon, to be very much less than these values. Since the radiation process γ_{12} is of no consequence as noted above, the flux condition will be met in mixtures of caesium with argon at less than 200 mJ cm^{-2}. The fluence condition may be examined as follows. For excitation to $7^2P_{3/2}$, $g' = 2/3$, $\sigma = 10^{-17}$ cm^2, $\phi = 5 \times 10^{17}$ cm^{-2} (200 mJ cm^{-2}) and $g'\sigma\phi = 3.3$. Since both the flux and the fluence conditions appear to have been met, we expect that the RIS process in caesium (with an argon buffer gas) would be saturated with $200 \, \text{mJ cm}^{-2}$ at $455.5 \, \text{nm}$ in about a $1 \, \mu s$ pulse. However, the real test of saturation must be based on an experimental observation that $n_I(T)$ reaches an asymptotic limit as ϕ increases.

Experiments were carried out in a parallel plate cell, illustrated in figure 3.4. Standard guard plates (made of Ni) were used to define a collection length, but they also served to decouple the photoelectrons produced when a laser beam interacted with a window from the resonance ionisation signal observed on the collector plate. Caesium metal was contained in the small arm, and noble gases could be added at the desired pressure. Even at 300 K, the vapour pressure of caesium is $1.8 \times 10^{-6} \, \text{Torr}$ or 6.5×10^{10} atoms cm^{-3}. However, as we will show in more detail when we discuss one-atom detection, it is expected that there will be a strong concentration gradient due to the chemical

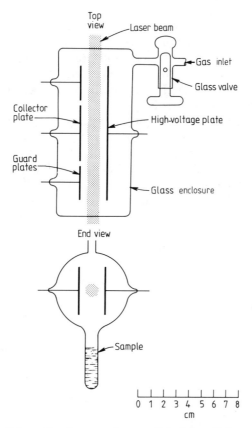

Figure 3.4 Schematic diagram of a parallel-plate cell for RIS studies of Cs in an Ar buffer gas. The laser beam was much narrower than shown.

reaction of caesium with impurity molecules, such as traces of O_2. Thus, it was possible to keep the concentration of caesium atoms so low that space charge effects were not important, even when the resonance ionisation process was saturated. Figure 3.5 shows the data acquisition system. A photodiode measured the relative energy per pulse and this signal, along with the ionisation signal, was kept correlated in a two-parameter analyser. A plot of $S(I)$ is shown in figure 3.6. The scale S was converted to the number of atoms detected, n_0, as follows. Let S_{in} be the signal level in volts measured at the input of a voltage sensitive preamplifier (e.g. ORTEC model 113); then

$$S_{in} = (1.6 \times 10^{-19} \, n_0/C)(l/h) \, G(w)$$

where C is the input capacitance in farads, l is the distance of the narrow laser beam from the collector plate, h is the plate separation, and $G(w)$ is a number less than unity (see §2.3) that corrects the gain of the amplifier for a pulse of finite rise time, which in turn depends on the drift velocity w (see Chapter 2). In the results of figure 3.6, approximately 1.2×10^7 atoms were found at saturation of the RIS process in a volume of approximately $1.5 \times 10^{-2} \, cm^3$. The validity of these results depended critically on careful attention to the gaseous electronics principles reviewed in Chapter 2.

In the course of these studies on the resonance ionisation of caesium atoms in the ground state it was noticed that RIS was a very sensitive way to measure the influence of collisional broadening on the line shape. Further studies of these effects were made by Nayfeh *et al* (1977, 1978). A plot of the resonance signals near the $Cs(7P_{1/2})$ and $Cs(7P_{3/2})$ fine structure levels is shown in figure 3.7. There are the expected

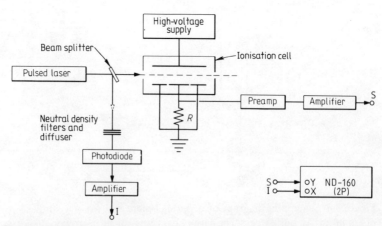

Figure 3.5 Data acquisition for RIS experiments on Cs with an Ar buffer gas. The ionisation signal, S, is correlated with the photodiode signal, I, in a two-parameter analyser, permitting the plot of $S(I)$.

strong resonances at the known wavelength. Saturation of the RIS process makes the line shapes much broader than expected from the usual collisional broadening. At lower photon fluence the curves are much narrower, as can be inferred from figure 3.8

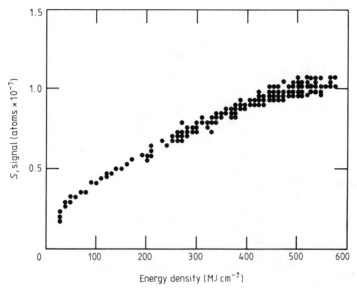

Figure 3.6 Number of Cs atoms detected as a function of laser energy per cm^2 delivered in one pulse for a low concentration of Cs atoms in 1 atm of Ar.

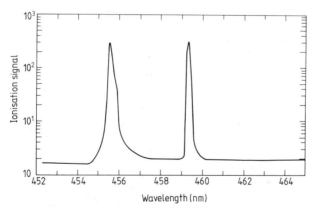

Figure 3.7 Tuning curve showing the RIS signal of Cs in 100 Torr of Ar. A photon at 455.5 nm drives the transition Cs($6^2S_{1/2} \rightarrow 7^2P_{3/2}$), or photons at 459.3 nm excite Cs($6^2S_{1/2} \rightarrow 7^2P_{1/2}$). In either case, a second photon ionises a 7P level.

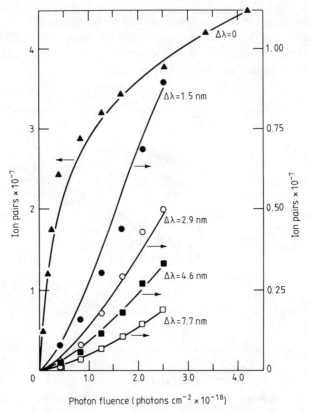

Figure 3.8 Ionisation signal as a function of photon fluence for the indicated detuning for Cs atoms in Ar gas at 760 Torr.

3.2 Sensitive ionisation measurements

The history of sensitive ionisation measurements is traceable to Rutherford and Geiger (1908) who developed an electrical method for counting individual α-particles. Their method employed high electrical fields to produce gas multiplication in which each electron gained enough energy between collisions with the gas to create secondary electrons. This utilisation of the Townsend mechanism to magnify 'the electrical effect due to single α-particles' led to the first proportional counter which replaced the tiresome 'spinthariscope' for the recording of individual α-particle events. It was much later that H Greinacher (1926) used radio tubes to make the first pulse amplifier so that single α-particles could even be recorded with parallel plate chambers where no gas amplification occurred (see Chapter 2).

Detection of individual electrons first became possible with the development of a detector by Geiger and Müller (1928). However, in this detector, space charge plays a dominant role and all pulses, whether initiated by many electrons or only one electron, are of the same size. This feature limits the use of Geiger–Müller tubes to digital counting and provides no analogue information. Thus, further development of the proportional counter was important for one-atom detection. Curran *et al* (1949) were the first to show that by using carefully designed proportional counters in combination with the electronic amplification available in 1949, a single thermal electron could be detected. Figure 3.9 summarises the evolution of pulsed ionisation measurement systems, along with a general perspective of their capabilities.

Proportional counters have played a major role in nuclear instrumentation, and many reviews show the evolution of the method which is still very important today, especially in particle physics (Charpak 1978, Nygren and Marx 1978). The classic article by Corson and Wilson (1948) is an excellent treatment, given just prior to one-electron detection. A review by Genz (1973) treats the subject of single-electron detection.

When detecting individual electrons with proportional counters, statistical fluctuation in the amplification process must be considered (Legler

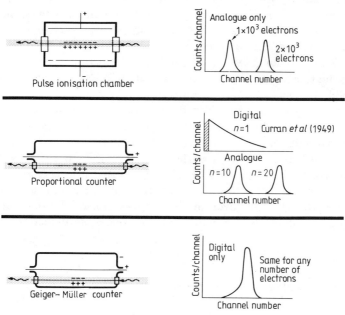

Figure 3.9 Summary of the evolution of gaseous ionisation detectors, showing the advent of one-electron sensitivity with Geiger–Müller counters (1928) and with proportional counters (1949).

1961, Byrne 1962, Gold and Bennett 1966, Genz 1973, Neumann 1980). The RIS technique has been used to study the statistical fluctuation of proportional counters and has provided a new method to obtain the so-called Fano factor associated with fluctuations due to ionisation by a charged particle of fixed energy (Hurst *et al* 1978).

Because of its relevance to one-atom detection based on RIS, we discuss in somewhat more detail the statistics associated with one-electron detection with proportional counters. A very useful treatment is given by Byrne (1962). Early theories of the statistics of gas multiplication were developed by Snyder (1947) and Frisch (1948, 1959). Both theories neglected photoelectric effects, recombination, electron attachment and space charge effects, and assumed that the probability of ionisation is a function only of the radial distance from the counter wire. These led to a distribution function (known as the Furry distribution) in which the probability of N electrons in the avalanche decreased monotonically with N. On the other hand, the first careful experiments (Curran *et al* 1949) on the pulse height spectrum due to one electron had a maximum. Byrne developed a new theory based on the fact that fluctuation of the number of electrons at a given point is accompanied by fluctuations in the average electron energy. The general type of distribution found was the so-called polya function (Jeffreys 1948) and could be made to agree with experiment. A convenient plot of the polya distribution (which applies to one initial electron and its convolutions) to generate pulse height spectra for $N = 1$ to $N = 10$ electrons was made by Neumann (1980) (see figure 3.10).

It is still an open question whether a one-electron spectrum can, in general, be represented by the polya distribution. But, in any event, it is reasonable to conclude that if a low-noise preamplifier is used, nearly all of the single electron events can be recorded, as shown experimentally as early as 1949. However, a proportional counter does not provide accurate analogue information for $N < 5$ electrons.

Further, it was shown even earlier (Bay 1938, Allen 1939, 1947) that single electrons or positive ions could be detected in evacuated electron multipliers (see Chapter 10). Thus, a variety of detectors is available for very sensitive detection, even at the one-electron or the one-ion level. When this capability is combined with RIS, one-atom detection is made possible.

3.3 A demonstration of one-atom detection

As stated, it has been known since 1949 that one electron could be detected if produced within a proportional counter. Following the realisation that one electron could be removed from each atom of a

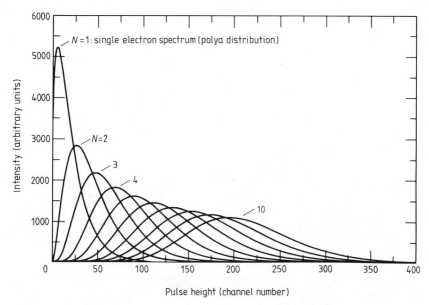

Intensity (arbitrary units)

Pulse height (channel number)

Figure 3.10 Single-electron spectrum for $N = 1$ can be represented as a polya distribution and convoluted to obtain pulse height spectra for $N > 1$ electrons. (After Neumann 1980.)

selected type by using a tuned laser for resonance ionisation, the concept of an experiment to demonstrate that a single atom could be detected was complete. This came within a few days after the concept of the He(2^1S) RIS experiment (Hurst *et al* 1975), yet the first demonstration of one-atom detection (Hurst *et al* 1977a) occurred more than a year later. The concept of this demonstration experiment is shown in figure 3.11 (Hurst *et al* 1977a). It was decided to do the first one-atom experiments with a proportional counter (rather than an evacuated electron multiplier) to demonstrate the selectivity of one type of atom in a background of a high concentration of the gas filling a typical proportional counter. Thus, in figure 3.11 the proportional counter was typical of those used in nuclear decay detection and filled with 100 to 200 Torr of P-10 gas (90% Ar, 10% CH_4), but it had windows which allowed a pulsed laser beam to be directed through it. The design included the use of field tubes normally used to define the active length of a detector, but with RIS this feature has a special advantage. Large signals that were produced by electrons ejected when the laser interacted with the quartz window can be decoupled from the RIS signal. Another unusual feature of the proportional counter was the use of a caesium metal source (which could be heated to somewhat above ambient temperature) to admit a controlled number of atoms into the path of the laser beam. The objective of the experiment was to pulse a

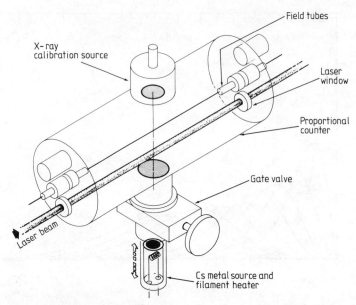

X-ray calibration source

Field tubes

Laser window

Proportional counter

Gate valve

Laser beam

Cs metal source and filament heater

Figure 3.11 Schematic diagram of the first experiment to demonstrate the detection of a single atom.

laser beam through a population of atoms, to selectively ionise each such atom, to attract the free electrons to the high-field region of the proportional counter wire, and to detect the number of atoms in the volume of space probed by the laser beam at the time the laser is pulsed on. Further, it was the objective to calibrate the pulse height recorded in the conventional data acquisition scheme of figure 3.12 by using a ^{57}Co x-ray source placed inside the detector.

For direct study of the fluctuation of a few atoms and, in particular, the detection of a single atom, it is necessary to understand how to control the population of the atoms to be detected as they diffuse through a gas containing a much larger number of inert atoms or molecules. Interesting questions arise as a consequence of the present technique in which a ground state population of atoms in a laser beam is totally removed during a short laser pulse. For instance, do atoms diffuse into the laser beam (radius r) during the pulse? We take D_1 (the diffusion coefficient at 1 atm) equal to $0.25 \text{ cm}^2 \text{ s}^{-1}$ as representative of an alkali atom in an inert gas. The mean spread, x, of atoms due to diffusion in an infinite space is given by

$$x^2 = 4D_1(760/P)t$$

where x is in cm, t is in seconds, and P is the pressure in torr. Let us put $x = r/20$ to get a small (10%) effect due to diffusion and take $r = 0.1$ cm. For a pulse duration of 10^{-6} s, we estimate that the pressure

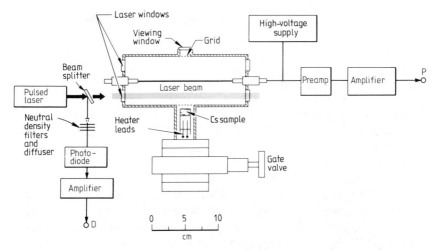

Figure 3.12 Schematic diagram of data acquisition system for experiments to study density fluctuation of a few atoms and for one-atom detection.

P is less than 20 Torr. Above this pressure, effects due to the diffusion of atoms back into the laser beam (of radius r) would be negligible. A related question is at what pressure would diffusion be too low to refill the laser volume between pulses? With t equal to the period between pulses (e.g. 10^{-1} s and $x = 2r$), $P = 1900$ Torr. So, to avoid this effect, the gas pressure should be kept below 1 atm. Thus, in this example, interesting experiments can be done on the absolute populations in a small volume in the pressure (of the buffer gas) range between about 20 and 500 Torr.

The slow rate of diffusion of an alkali atom in an inert gas can cause enormous ground state chemistry effects during the transport of the alkali atom from the source to a laser beam. Consider the transport of atoms evaporated from a small source at a rate of S_0 atoms per second and assume that these leak into an infinite hemisphere filled with an inert gas. At a distance R, much greater than the source dimensions, one finds for the concentration of atoms

$$\rho_0 = S_0/4R^2(\bar{v})$$

where $\bar{v}$ is the speed of the alkali atom. One can calculate (Dushman 1949) S_0 per unit source area (1 cm^2) from vapour pressure data; for caesium, we find 5×10^{14} atoms cm^{-2} s^{-1} at 300 K. When $R = 2$ cm, one finds $\rho_0 = 4 \times 10^8$ atoms cm^{-3} above a source 1 cm^2 in area. If caesium reacts chemically, the concentration is reduced to ρ which is given by

$$\rho = \rho_0 \exp(-\sigma_i \rho_i \bar{v} t)$$

where σ_i is the cross section for caesium to react chemically with an 'impurity' at concentration ρ_i, and t is the time for caesium to diffuse from the source to the laser beam. The time is of the order of 4 s for a distance of 2 cm when the inert gas pressure is 760 Torr. To ensure that the exponential argument is no more than one requires that ρ_i be less than 3×10^{11} cm^{-3} (for $\sigma_i = 5 \times 10^{-17}$ cm^2), which is an impurity level less than one part in 10^8 at 1 atm! At large concentrations, the above discussion points out the necessity for ultraclean systems. However, one can take advantage of the process as a means of preparing a very small concentration of atoms for one-atom demonstrations and for fluctuation studies (Hurst *et al* 1977a).

The proportional counter constructed for one-atom detection (figure 3.11) had gold-plated brass walls equipped with quartz windows to admit the laser beam. The counter wire had a 12 cm active length defined by field tubes at either end. The caesium source could be heated to increase the rate of evaporation of atoms, and it could be positioned at various distances from the laser beam. Thus, the concentration of atoms in the laser beam could be changed over a wide range. It is important in these studies to avoid electron capture in the counting gas. For this reason the gas, P-10, (i.e. 90% Ar + 10% CH$_4$), was pumped through the counter—a procedure which avoids the build-up of O$_2$, a highly electronegative gas.

Calibration of the proportional counter was done at the one-electron level by illuminating the walls with a mercury pen lamp, thus releasing single electrons from the walls at a very low rate. Calibration at the 250 electron level was achieved by placing a weak ^{57}Co source (giving Fe($k\alpha_1$) x-rays at 6.4 keV) just inside the window. The argon escape peak at 3.44 keV provides another calibration at the 130 electron level. The mean number of electrons produced in the x-ray peaks is found by using a W value (see Chapter 1) equal to 26 eV.

In the proportional counter experiments the laser beam was focused below the centre of the wire and directly above the caesium source with a lens of 25 cm focal length. With 1 mrad divergence, the beam was moderately focused (to achieve saturation of the RIS process) to a 0.025 cm diameter and was approximately 0.10 cm in diameter under both ends of the counter wire, creating an effective volume of about 5×10^{-2} cm^3.

Detuning the laser beam from the caesium wavelengths provides a definitive way to measure photoelectric backgrounds. With the field tube arrangement, these laser backgrounds were not detectable. At various concentrations of the caesium atoms the signals showed the narrow resonances characteristic of the caesium transitions at counting gas pressures of 100 to 200 Torr. By gating the analysers with a sync-out pulse from the laser, backgrounds due to external radiation (such as cosmic rays) were eliminated.

Two signals from the wire were coupled to the main amplifier with a charge-sensitive (ORTEC 109 PC) preamplifier. The main amplifier had about a 1 μs rise time and about a 1 μs decay time. In the proportional counter, the pulse height produced is proportional to the number of free electrons liberated by the primary ionisation event (in this case, the laser); it does not depend on where the electrons are produced, provided they are not captured.

A pulse height distribution for the case where the laser pulses always produced saturation is plotted in figure 3.13. The fluctuation about the mean is comparable to that which one expects in the case of the iron (6.4 keV) x-ray line. However, note the much more narrow distribution in the case of laser ionisation of the caesium atoms. At the peak, the x-ray source produces about 250 electrons per interaction. From this calibration we see that about 1.0×10^4 caesium atoms were ionised by each laser pulse, in agreement with the number obtained by using the 130 electron escape peak as a calibration.

To demonstrate one-atom detection, the distance of the caesium source from the laser beam was increased such that it was unlikely that a single atom would be in the path of the laser beam. Thus, figure 3.14

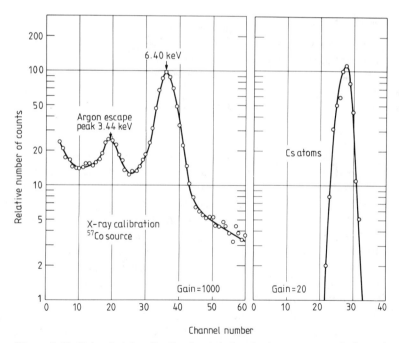

Figure 3.13 Pulse height distribution of signals due to a population of Cs atoms compared to a pulse height spectrum for a calibration source (^{57}Co with a 6.4 keV x-ray).

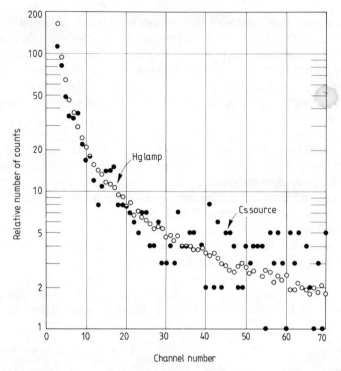

Figure 3.14 Pulse height distribution for the case where less than one Cs atom was counted per 20 laser pulses. Distribution is compared with that of one electron produced by an incoherent light source. This distribution is interpreted as that due to one atom in the laser beam. Fluctuations represent counting statistics.

shows the pulse height spectrum for the case where the laser would have to be pulsed an average of 20 times to detect one event. If Poisson statistics hold, it would be quite unlikely (one out of 800 laser pulses) that two atoms would be in the sensitive volume. The observed pulse height spectrum for the RIS process had the same shape (nearly exponential decay) as for the incoherent light source data. Both sets of data are more similar to the Furry distribution since the polya peak was not observed. It was found that at least 95% of all pulses were greater than the noise levels due to all sources; thus the proportional counter provided a good digital detector of one atom.

These demonstrations proved that a single atom could be detected if it were in the small sensitive volume (about 0.05 cm^3) at the time the laser was fired. The total volume probed by the laser in the 20 shots required to find one atom was about 1 cm^3, and at 200 Torr this is more than 5×10^{18} atoms of argon or more than 5×10^{17} molecules of CH$_4$. Since no backgrounds were observed without the caesium atoms or with a slightly detuned laser, the authors concluded that one caesium atom could be sorted out of more than 10^{19} atoms of Ar. However, it must be recalled that caesium in argon is a very favourable example. Because of the large value of the ionisation potential, non-resonant multiphoton ionisation events in argon would be very rare (see Chapter 5), under the conditions discussed above.

Hurst *et al* (1977b) also proved that the new method of counting atoms could be used to study density fluctuations of freely diffusing atoms. They reported the frequency distribution for the case in which the mean number of atoms in the sensitive volume was only 67. Such density fluctuations were previously not observable by direct measurements and had to be deduced from such indirect evidence as Rayleigh scattering of light and the study of Brownian motion. Density fluctuations will be discussed in Chapter 6, along with applications of RIS and one-atom detection to other statistical phenomena.

3.4 One-atom detection in time coincidence with nuclear decay

Detection of individual atoms in time coincidence with a nuclear event would give a new dimension to rare event analysis in nuclear physics. For example, daughter atom detection would resolve many problems in radioactivity where signatures derived from radiation detectors are not unique. As an example, consider the detection of ^{7}Be, whose electron capture decay leads only to an Auger electron of low energy which cannot be resolved from noise in a proportional counter. The 'noise' signals would be used to fire a laser at the daughter atom (^{7}Li) and an electron would be removed by the selective RIS process to produce a coincidence signal to indicate true decay of ^{7}Be. Such a desire motivated an experiment by Kramer *et al* (1978), using the binary fission decay of ^{252}Cf.

The concept of an experiment to demonstrate the detection of individual daughter atoms in time coincidence with the decay of the parent atom is the following. When spontaneous fission occurs in a heavy atom like ^{252}Cf, it begins as a binary process, and to conserve linear momentum the heavy fission fragment and the light fragment must recoil 180° apart. Thus, if a charged particle detector accepts recoil atoms in a small aperture, the detector signals when the complementary fragment is going in the forward direction. Choices of path length and gas pressure can be made to cause the heavy fragment (which contains the caesium atoms) to come to rest in the region to be swept with a pulsed laser. Of course, the very large number of electrons created by the non-selective ionisation must be cleared out of the detector before the laser is pulsed in to create just one electron in the resonance ionisation process. Clearly, this extra electron will not be created unless the caesium atom, which is highly ionised at its initial energy of nearly 100 MeV, comes to rest as a neutral atom. Since neither theory nor previous experiments provided a definite value for the charge state of the thermalised species, the answer to this question became another objective of the experiment.

The details of the experimental approach are shown schematically in figure 3.15. Energetic charged particles were produced by the spontaneous, binary, symmetric fission of ^{252}Cf, which had been implanted in a 1 μm thick nickel foil. The foil was mounted in front of an apertured surface-barrier detector, which sensed a fission fragment to signal that the complementary fragment had been injected into the chamber. About one fission fragment was emitted per second. It was possible to determine whether a fission fragment from either the light- or heavy-mass peak had entered the active region of the chamber by energy analysis of the complementary fragments striking the surface-barrier detector. It was estimated that about 14% of the fission products in the heavy-mass peak would be isotopes of caesium. The laser beam, which

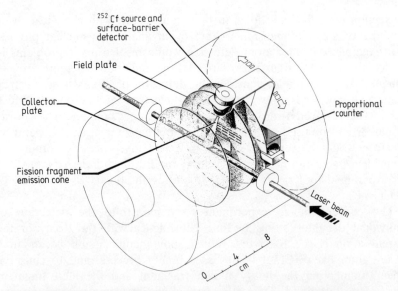

Figure 3.15 Schematic diagram of apparatus used to detect a single atom formed in spontaneous fission. A signal generated in the surface-barrier detector indicated the occurrence of a single fission of ^{252}Cf. After the initial ionisation was swept onto the collector plate, a tunable laser pulse was used to ionise the selected single atom, using the RIS process. The liberated electron was then drifted into a proportional counter and detected as a single event.

was 0.6 cm in diameter and intersected the source–collimator axis at an angle of 60°, was located at a distance of 5 cm from the ^{252}Cf source. With this assembly, and using a chamber pressure of 317 Torr of P-10 gas, 65% of the signalled fragments stopped in the active detector volume of about 1 cm^3.

Direct ionisation of the buffer gas due to the passage of the heavy-mass fragment resulted in the production of more than 10^6 free electrons in the fission ionisation track. These electrons were swept onto a collector plate in about 2 μs. At a time 40 μs after a fission event and 10 μs before probing the chamber with the laser, the collector plate was pulsed negative. It was confirmed by calculations based on electron transport data and by experiment that any photoelectron generated in the active laser-beam volume under these conditions would drift through an aperture in the field plate and into the proportional counter where it would be detected. Since in this apparatus the same gas is used in the proportional counter as is used in the target region, P-10 gas (which is known to work well in counters) was selected. Neither caesium diffusing out of the laser-active volume, nor caesium loss due to chemical reactions, is important on this time-scale (see Chapter 6).

The wavelength of the laser could be tuned to ionise selectively the neutralised fission fragment of interest. In the case of caesium, the laser (which was a grating-tuned, coaxially flashlamp-pumped model manufactured by the Phase-R Corporation) was tuned to either 455.5 or 459.3 nm in order to excite the $7P_{3/2}$ or $7P_{1/2}$ level, respectively. In either case, a second photon of the same wavelength was absorbed to complete the resonance ionisation process by photo-ionisation of the excited atom. Using a laser line width of only 0.4 nm (which was somewhat greater than the pressure-broadened caesium lines that we measured at 317 Torr) and a fluence corresponding to 0.3 J cm^{-2}, saturation was easily achieved. Therefore, one free photoelectron was created each time a caesium atom was injected into the laser beam. The laser line width was broad enough to encompass any reasonable isotope shift in the energy states used in the saturated RIS process; thus, all caesium isotopes produced during fission could be resonantly ionised.

Pulse height discrimination of the proportional counter signal was required to eliminate electrical transients associated with the laser. At the discrimination level used, only 80% of the pulses due to single-electron events could be counted. Combining this counting fraction with the 65% geometrical factor described above, the expected caesium resonant signal is about 7% of N_1, where N_1 is the number of the fission fragments (of light mass) observed in the surface-barrier detector.

In order to establish a tuning curve for the expected caesium RIS effect, eight wavelengths in the interval 450.0 to 462.0 nm were studied. The following procedure was used: for every light-mass and heavy-mass

^{252}Cf fission fragment detected by the surface-barrier detector, the laser was fired after a controlled delay and a counter recorded whether a photoelectron was detected.

The results for the heavy-mass fragment after a background correction (see Kramer *et al* 1978) are shown in figure 3.16. The error bars represent the limit for one standard deviation assuming a correlation between the background at a reference wavelength of 450.5 nm and the other wavelengths investigated. Both neutral caesium resonant line peaks at 455.5 and 459.3 nm stand out at a level exceeding two standard deviations above the background. At these two peaks, the average RIS signal per 100 of the heavy fission fragments is (8.5 ± 2.2), which compares with 7% expected if all the caesium ions are neutralised. The results show quite conclusively that an appreciable fraction, if not all, of the caesium fragments thermalise as neutral atoms in P-10 gas. A similar curve for the light-mass peak showed, as expected, no resonant structure at the wavelengths studied. The light-mass peak contains several kinds of atoms in the region where Z is approximately 43, none of which can be ionised by the wavelengths used.

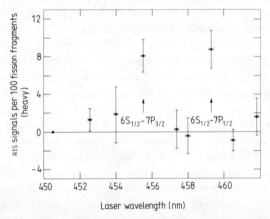

Figure 3.16 Resonance ionisation of Cs atoms formed as products of fission decay of ^{252}Cf. Data points at the indicated wavelengths represent the number of photoelectron events per 100 heavy-mass fission fragments. At wavelengths of 455.5 and 459.3 nm, a resonance ionisation of Cs atoms was observed.

We now need to interpret the significance of the observed neutral atoms. As an energetic positive ion loses its energy in a gas, its charge state is governed by dynamical processes involving primarily electron capture and electron loss, since recombination of the parent ion with free electrons is negligible at the usual concentrations. At high energies, where the particle makes many collisions before losing a significant fraction of its energy, a rate equation formulation based on electron capture and loss cross sections $\sigma_c(E)$ and $\sigma_l(E)$, respectively, is valid for determining the quasi-equilibrium charge state. For the case where the particle can only be in a zero or a $+1$ charge state, the fraction of neutrals at energy E is $f_N(E) = \sigma_c(E)/(\sigma_c(E) + \sigma_l(E))$. Conservation of energy prohibits a positive ion from capturing an electron from the buffer gas when the ion energy drops below a value E_2, as defined in figure 3.17. This requires $\sigma_c = 0$ for $E < E_2$; however, σ_l can remain finite down to a lower energy E_1. Thus, there is a narrow range of particle energy, $E_1 < E < E_2$, where $\sigma_c = 0$ while σ_l can be finite. In the rate equation formulation $f_N = 0$ and without modification would predict no neutral atoms at thermal energy.

However, for energies less than about $100\,\text{eV}$, only a few collisions are required for a particle to lose a large fraction of its energy; thus the rate formulation is no longer valid. In fact, if the cross section for total energy loss, $\sigma_T(E)$, is much less than $\sigma_l(E)$, it is likely that the particle will cross the ionisation gap without charge exchange. We note, in particular, that when a neutral particle at energy $E \geq E_2$ suffers a charge-conserving collision that reduces E below E_2, it must thermalise as a neutral, i.e. the ionisation gap is crossed and the charge state has been frozen. In this 'frozen charge' model the final charge state at thermal energy is then determined by $\sigma_c(E)$ and $\sigma_l(E)$ at E *above the gap*.

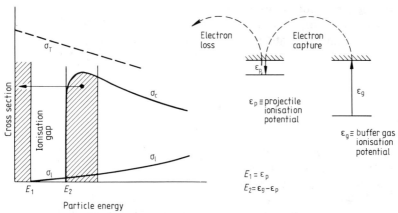

Figure 3.17 Schematic diagram of a model to account for neutral Cs atoms (at thermal energy) resulting from the slowing down of energetic Cs^{n+} ions. Electron loss, but not capture, is energetically possible in the ionisation gap. However, if $\sigma_T \gg \sigma_l$, electron loss is unlikely in the gap; thus a neutral particle passes through the gap without electron loss. (The terms σ_c, σ_l and σ_T are cross sections for electron capture, electron loss, and total energy loss, respectively.)

For the case of identical atoms (symmetric charge transfer), it is generally believed (Rapp and Francis 1962) that $\sigma_c(E)$ becomes larger than $\sigma_l(E)$ for energies just above the ionisation gap; thus we expect a large neutral fraction at thermal energies. In the case of a dissimilar projectile and target (the asymmetric case), the behaviour of $\sigma_c(E)$ and $\sigma_l(E)$ is more complex. Even here, however, an accidental energy degeneracy between the projectile in a +1 charge state and an electronically excited state of the target gas can lead to a large $\sigma_c(E)$ compared with $\sigma_l(E)$ at low energies. A near degeneracy of this type in the case of Cs^+ moving through argon does exist with an electronically excited state in argon, and quite likely with many possible levels in the electronic–vibrational quasicontinuum in CH_4. It should be possible to choose an appropriate buffer gas to ensure a high probability of ion neutralisation; thus, one-atom detection is possible for particles initially produced as energetic ions.

We must add a word of caution here—finding neutral caesium atoms in the track of a fission fragment does not imply that radioactive decay will lead to neutral daughter atoms. There is a sharp contrast between the fission fragment and a recoiling atom as a consequence of, for example, electron capture. In this case, the atom gets only a few electron-volts of energy from the neutrino recoil. Furthermore, if the recoil energy is less than the difference in the ionisation potential of the host gas and that of the recoil atom, energy conservation prevents charge neutralisation. It is the large amount of kinetic energy available that drives the neutralisation process in the case of a fission fragment of low ionisation potential. The search for schemes causing rapid neutralisation of daughter atoms is important, since it could open up new possibilities for one-atom detection in rare nuclear events and in radioactivity.

References

Allen J S 1939 *Phys. Rev.* **55** 966
—— 1947 *Phys. Rev.* **61** 692
Bay Z 1938 *Nature* **141** 284, 1011
Byrne J 1962 *Proc. R. Soc. Edinburgh* **A66** 33
Curran S C, Cockroft A L and Angus J 1949 *Phil. Mag.* **40** 929
Charpak G 1978 *Phys. Today* **31** (10), 23
Corson D R and Wilson R R 1948 *Rev. Sci. Instrum.* **19** 207
Dushman S 1949 *Scientific Foundations of Vacuum Technique* (New York: Wiley) p 20
Frisch O R 1948 *Unpublished lectures*

—— 1959 Fluctuation in Chain Processes *AECL Report No 748* (Chalk River, Ontario: AECL)

Geiger H and Müller W 1928 *Phys. Z.* **29** 839

Genz H 1973 *Nucl. Instrum. Methods* **112** 83

Gold R and Bennett E F 1966 *Phys. Rev.* **147** 201

Greinacher H 1926 *Z. Phys.* **36** 364

Hurst G S, Allman S L, Payne M G, Marshall K A and Soohoo K L 1978 *Nucl. Instrum. Methods* **155** 203–9

Hurst G S and Klots C E 1976 in *Advances in Radiation Chemistry* vol. 5 ed M Burton and J L Magee (New York: Wiley) pp 1–96

Hurst G S, Nayfeh M H and Young J P 1977a *Appl. Phys. Lett.* **30** 229–31

—— 1977b *Phys. Rev.* A **15** 2283–92

Hurst G S, Payne M G, Kramer S D and Young J P 1979 *Rev. Mod. Phys.* **51** 767–819

Hurst G S *et al* 1975 Radiation Physics and Dosimetry—Theoretical Physics of Dosimetry *ORNL Report No ORNL-5046* p 194

Jeffreys H 1948 *Theory of Probability* (Cambridge: Cambridge University Press)

Kramer S D, Bemis C E Jr, Young J P and Hurst G S 1978 *Opt. Lett.* **3** 16–18

Legler W 1961 *Z. Naturforsch.* **16** A, 253

Nayfeh M H, Hurst G S, Payne M G and Young J P 1977 *Phys. Rev. Lett.* **39** 604–7

—— 1978 *Phys. Rev. Lett.* **41** 302–5

Neumann W 1980 in *Seventh Symp. on Microdosimetry* vol. II ed J Booz, H G Ebert and H D Hartfiel (Oxford: Harwood Academic) pp 1067–82

Nygren D R and Marx J N 1978 *Phys. Today* **31**(10), 46

Rapp D and Francis W E 1962 *J. Chem. Phys.* **37** 2631

Rutherford E and Geiger H 1908 *Proc. R. Soc.* **81** A, 141

Snyder H S 1947 *Phys. Rev.* **72** 181

Zeman H D 1974 in *Int. Symp. on Electron and Photon Interactions with Atoms* ed H Kleinpoppen and M R C McDowell (New York: Plenum) pp 581–94

4

The interaction of laser light with atoms

4.1 Introduction

In the first three chapters we have reviewed some of the history of resonance ionisation spectroscopy. Many of the early experiments were carried out in proportional counters where collisional dephasing occurs on a time-scale of the order of 10^{-11} s, and the power density rarely exceeded 10^5 W cm^{-2}. In the latter situation the populations of the ground and excited states change very little within the time over which phase memory is randomised. Consequently, the changes in the wave functions (or elements of the density matrix) for time intervals which are a bit longer than the phase memory add incoherently and can be calculated by perturbation theory. Rate equations are appropriate and were used to guide much of the early experimental work.

Many of the more important applications of RIS involve laser ionisation under conditions of high vacuum. Thus, there is no rapid collisional dephasing to make valid a rate equation treatment based on the Einstein relations. In addition, the current trend is to use lasers with relatively narrow band widths and pulse lengths of the order of a few nanoseconds. Consequently, we develop here a quantum mechanical treatment which can deal with coherent excitation and the related ionisation. Throughout most of this chapter we will assume that the laser either has a band width which is limited by Fourier analysis, or it has only a few cavity modes present in its spectrum. The functional form of the laser field will generally be assumed and the effects of collisions on the laser excitation and magnetic substate redistribution will be ignored in the present chapter.

4.2 Review of electromagnetic fields

The interaction of laser light with atoms is understood in considerable detail in the limit where the laser field is very weak compared with the electrostatic field between the electrons and the nucleus of an atom. Lasers of reasonable quality, operating well above threshold, tend to generate beams in which the beam divergence is very low and the band width is rather narrow. Almost any laser generates beams which have a very large number of photons per cavity mode, and these are just the criteria which must be met in order for it to be valid to treat an electromagnetic wave and many of its effects classically. Consequently, a very large percentage of the phenomena related to the interaction of laser light with gas phase atoms can be understood in terms of the electrons of an atom obeying the time-dependent Schrödinger equation

$$i\hbar\frac{\partial|\psi(t)\rangle}{\partial t} = \hat{\mathcal{H}}|\psi(t)\rangle \tag{4.1}$$

with

$$\hat{\mathcal{H}} = \hat{\mathcal{H}}_0 + \hat{V} \tag{4.2}$$

where $\hat{\mathcal{H}}_0$ is the electronic Hamiltonian of the isolated atom and $\hat{V}$ is the interaction potential between the electrons and a classical electromagnetic field.

At elevated concentrations, the laser field and any fields generated in the medium determine the atomic response, providing source terms in Maxwell's equations. Therefore, the task when the concentration is high enough to modify the incident laser field, or to generate fields at other frequencies, is one of solving the time-dependent Schrödinger equation (or more generally the equations for the density matrix) simultaneously with Maxwell's equations. When only a few atoms are in the laser field one has the simpler problem of solving for the atomic response to a known laser field. We therefore review the elements of classical electromagnetic theory. Details can be found in nearly any book on electromagnetic theory.

The Maxwell equation $\nabla\cdot\boldsymbol{B} = 0$ implies that $\boldsymbol{B}$ can always be written as the curl of a vector $\boldsymbol{A}$ which is called the vector potential:

$$\boldsymbol{B} = \nabla \times \boldsymbol{A} \tag{4.3}$$

Obviously, $\boldsymbol{A}$ is not unique. For any $\boldsymbol{A}$ such that $\boldsymbol{B} = \nabla \times \boldsymbol{A}$ we can add to $\boldsymbol{A}$ the gradient of an arbitrary function. That is,

$$\boldsymbol{A}' = \boldsymbol{A} + \nabla F$$

gives $\nabla \times \boldsymbol{A}' = \nabla \times \boldsymbol{A}$ due to $\nabla \times \nabla F \equiv 0$. In terms of $\boldsymbol{A}$, the Maxwell equation

$$\nabla \times E = -\frac{1}{c}\frac{\partial B}{\partial t}$$

can be written as

$$\nabla \times (E + \frac{1}{c}\frac{\partial A}{\partial t}) = 0$$

implying that $E + (1/c)(\partial A/\partial t)$ can be written as the gradient of a scalar (any vector having a zero curl at all points in a simply connected region of space can be written as the gradient of a scalar). Thus

$$E + \frac{1}{c}\frac{\partial A}{\partial t} = -\nabla\phi$$

where ϕ is the scalar potential. It is evident from the above that the arbitrary nature of A also leads to a related arbitrariness in ϕ. In fact, if $A' = A + \nabla F$ we have

$$E = -\frac{1}{c}\frac{\partial A}{\partial t} - \nabla\phi$$

$$= -\frac{1}{c}\frac{\partial A'}{\partial t} - \nabla\left(-\frac{1}{c}\frac{\partial F}{\partial t} + \phi\right)$$

so that in order for a change in A to $A + \nabla F$ to leave both B and E unchanged and

$$E = -\frac{1}{c}\frac{\partial A'}{\partial t} - \nabla\phi' \tag{4.4}$$

there must be a change in ϕ to $\phi' = \phi - (1/c)(\partial F/\partial t)$. The invariance of E and B to the transformation

$$A' = A + \nabla F$$

$$\phi' = \phi - \frac{1}{c}\frac{\partial F}{\partial t} \tag{4.5}$$

is called gauge invariance, and F is the generating function of the above gauge transformation.

In classical electromagnetic theory the introduction of ϕ and A is a mathematical convenience, and gauge invariance is required because when one considers a system of charged particles interacting by way of electromagnetic fields one uses the Lorentz law

$$dP_i/dt = q_i\, [E(r_i,t) + (V_i/c) \times B(r_i,t)] \tag{4.6}$$

for each particle i, where V_i is the velocity of particle i and $P_i = m dr_i/dt$; while E and B simultaneously satisfy

$$\nabla\cdot B = 0 \tag{4.7a}$$

$$\nabla \times \boldsymbol{E} = -\frac{1}{c}\frac{\partial \boldsymbol{B}}{\partial t} \tag{4.7b}$$

$$\nabla \cdot \boldsymbol{E} = 4\pi \sum_j q_j \delta(\boldsymbol{r} - \boldsymbol{r}_j(t)) \tag{4.7c}$$

$$\nabla \times \boldsymbol{B} = \frac{1}{c}\frac{\partial \boldsymbol{E}}{\partial t} + \frac{4\pi}{c}\sum_i q_i \frac{\mathrm{d}\boldsymbol{r}_i}{\mathrm{d}t}\delta(\boldsymbol{r} - \boldsymbol{r}_i(t)). \tag{4.7d}$$

Obviously, the arbitrariness of $\boldsymbol{A}$ and ϕ must be such that the choice of gauge does not change $\boldsymbol{E}$ or $\boldsymbol{B}$ and, hence, the motion of the charged particles.

We will now demonstrate an important conservation principle for a closed system of charged particles interacting by way of the electromagnetic field. Note that non-relativistically

$$\frac{\mathrm{d}}{\mathrm{d}t}\sum_{i=1}^{N}\frac{m_i}{2}\left(\frac{\mathrm{d}\boldsymbol{r}_i}{\mathrm{d}t}\right)^2 = \sum_{i=1}^{N}\frac{\mathrm{d}\boldsymbol{r}_i}{\mathrm{d}t}\cdot\left(\boldsymbol{E}(\boldsymbol{r}_i(t)) + \frac{1}{c}\frac{\mathrm{d}\boldsymbol{r}_i}{\mathrm{d}t}\times \boldsymbol{B}(\boldsymbol{r}_i(t))\right)q_i$$

$$= \sum_{i=1}^{N}\frac{\mathrm{d}\boldsymbol{r}_i}{\mathrm{d}t}\cdot\boldsymbol{E}(\boldsymbol{r}_i(t))q_i$$

$$= \int \mathrm{d}^3r \sum_{i=1}^{N}\left(\delta(\boldsymbol{r} - \boldsymbol{r}_i(t))q_i \frac{\mathrm{d}\boldsymbol{r}_i}{\mathrm{d}t}\right)\cdot\boldsymbol{E}(\boldsymbol{r})$$

$$= \int \mathrm{d}^3r \boldsymbol{J}(\boldsymbol{r},t)\cdot\boldsymbol{E}(\boldsymbol{r},t)$$

where

$$\boldsymbol{J} = \sum_{i=1}^{N} q_i \frac{\mathrm{d}\boldsymbol{r}_i}{\mathrm{d}t}\delta(\boldsymbol{r} - \boldsymbol{r}_i(t)).$$

Consider

$$\frac{\partial}{\partial t}\int \mathrm{d}^3r \frac{E^2 + B^2}{8\pi} = \frac{1}{4\pi}\int \mathrm{d}^3r \left(\frac{\partial \boldsymbol{E}}{\partial t}\cdot\boldsymbol{E} + \frac{\partial \boldsymbol{B}}{\partial t}\cdot\boldsymbol{B}\right).$$

Now, $\partial \boldsymbol{B}/\partial t = -c\nabla \times \boldsymbol{E}$ and $\partial \boldsymbol{E}/\partial t = c\nabla \times \boldsymbol{B} - 4\pi\boldsymbol{J}$ so that

$$\frac{\partial}{\partial t}\int \mathrm{d}^3r \frac{E^2 + B^2}{8\pi} = \frac{c}{4\pi}\int \mathrm{d}^3r \left(\boldsymbol{E}\cdot\nabla \times \boldsymbol{B} - \boldsymbol{B}\cdot\nabla \times \boldsymbol{E} - \frac{4\pi}{c}\boldsymbol{J}\cdot\boldsymbol{E}\right).$$

Since $\nabla \cdot (\boldsymbol{E} \times \boldsymbol{B}) = -\boldsymbol{E}\cdot(\nabla \times \boldsymbol{B}) + \boldsymbol{B}\cdot(\nabla \times \boldsymbol{E})$, the divergence theorem enables us to convert the integral of $\boldsymbol{E}\cdot(\nabla \times \boldsymbol{B}) - \boldsymbol{B}\cdot(\nabla \times \boldsymbol{E})$ to a surface integral of the Poynting vector over a surface at infinity, thereby showing that its contribution is zero. Thus,

$$\frac{\partial}{\partial t}\int \mathrm{d}^3r \frac{E^2 + B^2}{8\pi} = -\int \mathrm{d}^3r \boldsymbol{J}\cdot\boldsymbol{E}.$$

Finally,

$$\frac{\mathrm{d}}{\mathrm{d}t}\left[\sum_{i=1}^{N}\frac{m_i}{2}\left(\frac{\mathrm{d}r_i}{\mathrm{d}t}\right)^2 + \int \mathrm{d}^3r\frac{E^2 + B^2}{8\pi}\right] = 0 \ . \tag{4.8}$$

It is not difficult to generalise equation (4.8) to the relativistic case.

The interpretation of expression (4.8) is that the sum of the field energy and the particle kinetic energy is constant. To obtain a Hamiltonian from this expression we must deal with the velocity dependence of the force due to the magnetic field. With a force which is expressible as a gradient of a function of position, the 'physical momentum' and the canonical momentum are the same in cartesian coordinates; however, this is not the case with the velocity-dependent magnetic force.

To see how we might formulate a Hamiltonian for the electromagnetic field plus charged particle problem, consider a single charged particle in a known static E and B field. We postulate a Lagrangian which will yield the Lorentz force law. We try

$$L = \frac{m}{2}\left(\frac{\mathrm{d}r}{\mathrm{d}t}\right)^2 - q\phi(r) + \frac{q}{c}\frac{\mathrm{d}r}{\mathrm{d}t}\cdot A \tag{4.9}$$

where ϕ and A are the scalar and vector potentials. If we have made a good guess ($x_1 \equiv x, x_2 \equiv y, x_3 \equiv z$), then

$$\frac{\mathrm{d}}{\mathrm{d}t}\left[\frac{\partial L}{\partial \dot{x}_i}\right] - \frac{\partial L}{\partial x_i} = 0 \tag{4.10}$$

will give the Lorentz force law.

$$\frac{\partial L}{\partial \dot{x}_i} = m\dot{x}_i + (qA_i/c) \tag{4.11}$$

$$\frac{\partial L}{\partial x_i} = -q\frac{\partial \phi}{\partial x_i} + \frac{q}{c}\frac{\mathrm{d}r}{\mathrm{d}t}\cdot\frac{\partial A}{\partial x_i}.$$

Thus,

$$m\frac{\mathrm{d}^2x_i}{\mathrm{d}t^2} = -\frac{q}{c}\frac{\mathrm{d}A_i}{\mathrm{d}t} - q\frac{\partial \phi}{\partial x_i} + \frac{q}{c}\frac{\mathrm{d}r}{\mathrm{d}t}\cdot\frac{\partial A}{\partial x_i}$$

$$= -\frac{q}{c}\frac{\partial A_i}{\partial t} - q\frac{\partial \phi}{\partial x_i} + \frac{q}{c}\frac{\mathrm{d}r}{\mathrm{d}t}\cdot\frac{\partial A}{\partial x_i} - \frac{q}{c}\sum_{k=1}^{3}\frac{\mathrm{d}x_k}{\mathrm{d}t}\frac{\partial A_i}{\partial x_k}.$$

The following identity can be used:

$$V \times B = V \times (\nabla \times A)$$

$$= \nabla(V\cdot A) - (V\cdot\nabla)A \ .$$

Thus,

$$(V \times B)_i = V\cdot\frac{\partial A}{\partial x_i} - (V\cdot\nabla)A_i$$

$$= V\cdot\frac{\partial A}{\partial x_i} - \sum_{k=1}^{3}\frac{\mathrm{d}x_k}{\mathrm{d}t}\frac{\partial A_i}{\partial x_k}.$$

We have

$$m\frac{\mathrm{d}^2 x_i}{\mathrm{d}t^2} = q\left(-\frac{1}{c}\frac{\partial A_i}{\partial t} - \frac{\partial \phi}{\partial x_i}\right) + \frac{q}{c}(V \times B)_i$$

$$= qE_i + \frac{q}{c}(V \times B)_i \qquad (4.12)$$

which indicates that we 'guessed' the proper Lagrangian. In a Langrangian formulation the quantity $P_i = \partial L/\partial \dot{x}_i$ is the component of the canonical momentum conjugate to x_i. The canonical momentum is then

$$P = m\frac{\mathrm{d}r}{\mathrm{d}t} + \frac{q}{c}A . \qquad (4.13)$$

The Hamiltonian is then found by:

$$H = \sum_i P_i \dot{x}_i - L$$

$$= P \cdot \dot{r} - L$$

$$= \frac{m(\dot{r})^2}{2} + q\phi(r) \qquad (4.14)$$

where the $\dot{r}$ are to be replaced in terms of P and r:

$$H = (1/2m)(P - (q/c)A)^2 + q\phi(r) . \qquad (4.15)$$

Equation (4.15) can be generalised (i is now particle number) and we again consider a closed system

$$H = \sum_{i=1}^{N} [P_i - (q/c)A(r_i,t)]^2/2m_i + \int \mathrm{d}^3r \,(E^2 + B^2)/8\pi. \qquad (4.16)$$

Note that H turns out to be the energy, a constant of the motion. It does not involve the magnetic field when expressed in terms of speed, since the speed is never changed by a magnetic field, and the magnetic force is always orthogonal to the direction of motion. It is obvious that just replacing kinetic energy by $P^2/2m$ and applying Hamilton's equations would give incorrect results in which the trajectories do not depend on the presence of the magnetic field. Thus, we could have anticipated that 'physical' and canonical momentum had to turn out to be different.

If E and B are replaced in terms of A and ϕ and A and ϕ are expanded in a Fourier series over the volume of a very large box which surrounds the system, we find that for a gauge in which $\nabla \cdot A = 0$ it is easy to identify canonically conjugate coordinates and momentum for both the electromagnetic field and the particles. This fact has been well known since the derivation of the Rayleigh–Jeans law for black-body radiation. A treatment of all the material outlined above can be found in books on classical electromagnetic theory (Jackson 1962, Panofsky and Phillips 1956, Landau and Lifschitz 1951).

The Maxwell equations

$$\nabla \cdot \boldsymbol{B} = 0$$

$$\nabla \times \boldsymbol{E} - (1/c)(\partial \boldsymbol{B}/\partial t)$$

are statements of the fact that (a) magnetic charge does not occur, and (b) time-changing magnetic fields lead to non-conservative electric fields. A full Hamilton's equation treatment of a system of charged particles yields Maxwell's two other equations (the two having no source terms follow from the relation between $\boldsymbol{E}$ and $\boldsymbol{B}$ and the pair $\boldsymbol{A}$ and ϕ). Consequently, a properly formulated classical Hamiltonian contains the equations of motion for the particles and Maxwell's equations. The classical Hamiltonian for the combined particle–field system is in precisely the form which enables one to quantise the system by the replacement

$$P_i \rightarrow (\hbar/i)(\partial/\partial q_i)$$

for both the field and the particle canonical coordinates. We will not make this quantisation here, but instead we will use the results in formulating a theory in which the field is treated classically. There are theoretical reasons (see Chapter 11) to believe that magnetic monopoles do exist. However, in most experiments, using $\nabla \cdot \boldsymbol{B} = 0$ is a very safe assumption, since many sophisticated experiments have failed to gather evidence for the existence of even one monopole.

From the classical Hamiltonian, it is easy to pick out the terms representing the interaction between the charged particles and the electromagnetic field.

$$\hat{V} = - \sum_i \frac{q_i}{2m_i c} \left(\boldsymbol{P}_i \cdot \boldsymbol{A}(\boldsymbol{r}_i) + \boldsymbol{A}(\boldsymbol{r}_i) \cdot \boldsymbol{P}_i \right) + \sum_i \frac{q_i^2}{2m_i c^2} \boldsymbol{A}^2(\boldsymbol{r}_i). \quad (4.17)$$

For a choice of gauge through $\nabla \cdot \boldsymbol{A} = 0$ we find

$$\nabla \cdot \boldsymbol{E} = 4\pi \sum_j q_j \delta(\boldsymbol{r} - \boldsymbol{r}_j(t))$$

$$= \nabla \cdot [-(1/c)(\partial \boldsymbol{A}/\partial t) - \nabla \phi]$$

$$= -\nabla^2 \phi.$$

Due to the gauge condition $\nabla \cdot \boldsymbol{A} = 0$, the scalar potential satisfies Poisson's equation which can be integrated immediately to give

$$\phi = \sum_i q_i/|\boldsymbol{r} - \boldsymbol{r}_i(t)| . \quad (4.18)$$

The other Maxwell equation with a source term gives

$$\nabla \times \boldsymbol{B} = \frac{1}{c} \frac{\partial \boldsymbol{E}}{\partial t} + \frac{4\pi}{c} \sum_j q_j \frac{\partial \boldsymbol{r}_j}{\partial t} \delta(\boldsymbol{r} - \boldsymbol{r}_j(t))$$

$$= \nabla \times (\nabla \times A) \equiv -\nabla^2 A + \nabla(\nabla \cdot A)$$

$$= -\frac{1}{c^2}\frac{\partial^2 A}{\partial t^2} - \nabla\left(\frac{1}{c}\frac{\partial \phi}{\partial t}\right) + \frac{4\pi}{c}\sum_j q_j \frac{\partial r_j}{\partial t}\delta(r - r_i(t)) .$$

That is

$$\nabla^2 A - \frac{1}{c^2}\frac{\partial^2 A}{\partial t^2} = \nabla\left(\frac{1}{c}\frac{\partial \phi}{\partial t}\right) + \frac{4\pi}{c}\sum_j q_j \frac{dr_j}{dt}\delta(r - r_j(t)) . \quad (4.19)$$

The gauge choice $\nabla \cdot A + (1/c)(\partial\phi/\partial t) = 0$ would eliminate the $\nabla[(1/c)(\partial\phi/\partial t)]$ term, but would make the equation for ϕ more complex. This gauge condition (i.e. $\nabla \cdot A + (1/c)(\partial\phi/\partial t) = 0$) is called the Lorentz gauge. The Lorentz gauge yields equations for A and ϕ such that these quantities transform under the Lorentz transformation like components of a four vector, with ϕ being the time-like component. The Lorentz gauge is a superb choice for generalisation to a completely Lorentz covariant theory.

We have now shown that in a theory where the electromagnetic field is treated clasically and the electrons are treated quantum mechanically, a proper Hamiltonian is

$$\hat{H}_a = \sum_i [\hat{P}_i - (e/c)A_i(r_i,t)]^2/2m - \sum_i \frac{Ze^2}{|r_i|} + \frac{1}{2}\sum_{\substack{i,j \\ i \neq j}} e^2/|r_i - r_j| \quad (4.20)$$

where A is the classical vector potential and ϕ is responsible for the coulomb terms. The radiation part of the laser field is

$$E = -(1/c)(\partial A/\partial t) . \quad (4.21)$$

The scalar potential does not lead to any radiation terms due to its unretarded coulomb form which drops off more rapidly with distance than a radiation field. A further simplification is usually appropriate. Suppose that all transitions to be studied involve transitions where spatial extent of the wavefunctions is only a few times the Bohr radius a_B, while the wavelength of the laser light is greater than 10^{-7} m. Then the $A(r_i,t)$ acts like $A(0,t)$ when the matrix element of $P_i \cdot A(r_i,t)$, $A(r_i,t) \cdot P_i$ or $A^2(r_i,t)$ between two states is evaluated. We can use

$$\hat{H}_a = \sum_i (P_i - (e/c)A(0,t))^2/2m - \sum_i \frac{Ze^2}{r_i} + \frac{1}{2}\sum_{\substack{i,j \\ i \neq j}} e^2/|r_i - r_j| . \quad (4.22)$$

The above operator keeps only the leading terms in an expansion in (a_B/λ), and may break down when the laser is tuned to resonance with a transition allowed by a magnetic dipole or quadrupole. However, near dipole-allowed transitions the approximation is very good even at high laser power. We now introduce the unitary operator

$$\hat{U} = \exp\left(ie \sum_i \boldsymbol{r}_i \cdot \boldsymbol{A}(0,t)/\hbar c\right). \tag{4.23}$$

We subject $\hat{H}_a$ to the unitary transformation

$$\hat{H}'_a = \hat{U}^\dagger \hat{H}_a \hat{U}. \tag{4.24}$$

The eigenvalues of $\hat{H}_a$, as well as any matrix elements of other operators subject to this transformation, will be unchanged. The operator $\hat{U}$ commutes with functions of $\boldsymbol{r}_i$. However,

$$\hat{U}^\dagger \hat{P}_i \hat{U} = \exp(-ie\boldsymbol{r}_i \cdot A(0,t)/\hbar c)\hat{P}_i \exp(ie\boldsymbol{r}_i \cdot A(0,t)/\hbar c)$$

In the position representation $\hat{P}_i = (\hbar/i)\nabla_i$, and it follows that

$$\hat{U}^\dagger \hat{P}_i \hat{U} = \hat{P}_i + eA(0,t)/c. \tag{4.25}$$

Thus,

$$\hat{H}'_a = \sum_i \hat{P}^2/2m - \sum_i Ze^2/r_i + \sum_{\substack{i,j \\ i \neq j}} e^2/2|\boldsymbol{r}_i - \boldsymbol{r}_j|. \tag{4.26}$$

The time-dependent Schrödinger equation changes from $i\hbar\partial|\psi\rangle/\partial t = \hat{H}_a|\psi\rangle$ to $\hat{U}^\dagger \hat{H}_a \hat{U}|\phi\rangle = i\hbar \hat{U}^\dagger[\partial(\hat{U}|\phi\rangle))/\partial t]$, where $|\phi\rangle = \hat{U}^\dagger|\psi\rangle$. We have simply taken the original time-dependent Schrödinger equation and inserted $\hat{U}^\dagger \hat{U} \equiv 1$ before $|\psi\rangle$ and multiplied both sides by $\hat{U}^\dagger$. Letting $\hat{H}'_a = \hat{U}^\dagger \hat{H}_a \hat{U}$ we have:

$$\hat{H}'_a|\phi\rangle = i\hbar \hat{U}^\dagger \left[(\partial \hat{U}/\partial t)|\phi\rangle + \hat{U}(\partial|\phi\rangle/\partial t)\right]$$

$$= i\hbar \hat{U}^\dagger \left[(ie/\hbar c)\left(\sum_i \boldsymbol{r}_i\right)\cdot(\partial A/\partial t)\hat{U} + \hat{U}(\partial/\partial t)\right]|\phi\rangle$$

$$= e\left(\sum_i \boldsymbol{r}_i\right)\cdot \boldsymbol{E}|\phi\rangle + i\hbar(\partial|\phi\rangle/\partial t)$$

where we have used $\boldsymbol{E} = -(1/c)\partial A/\partial t$ for the laser field. Finally,

$$\left(\sum_i [(\hat{P}_i^2/2m) - (Ze^2/r_i)] + \sum_{\substack{i,j \\ i \neq j}} (e^2/2|\boldsymbol{r}_i - \boldsymbol{r}_j|) - \boldsymbol{D}\cdot\boldsymbol{E}\right)|\phi\rangle$$
$$= i\hbar(\partial|\phi\rangle/\partial t). \tag{4.27}$$

We have now arrived at a transformed time-dependent Schrödinger equation in which

$$\hat{V} = -\hat{D}\cdot\boldsymbol{E}$$

$$\hat{D} = e\sum_i \boldsymbol{r}_i$$

and

$$\hat{H} = \hat{H}_0 + \hat{V} \tag{4.28}$$

where $\hat{D}$ is the electric dipole operator and E is the electric field associated with the laser. The similarity transformation that was invoked here amounts to nothing more than a change in phase of the new time-dependent state function relative to the old. We should re-emphasise that equation (4.28) should not be used near allowed quadru-pole or magnetic dipole transitions due to the neglect of any variation of $A(r_i, t)$ over the extent of the eigenfunctions of $\hat{H}_0$. However, it should describe most other situations very well, even with high laser power densities.

4.3 Interaction of a laser field with isolated atoms

Consider the response of an isolated atom to a plane, monochromatic laser field. A classical E field with the functional form

$$E = E_0 \cos(\omega t - kz) \qquad (4.29)$$

represents the laser field. In accord with the discussion of the preceding section, the Hamiltonian for the response of one of the atoms is

$$\hat{H} = \hat{H}_0 - \hat{D} \cdot E \qquad (4.30)$$

where $\hat{H}_0$ is the Hamiltonian of the isolated atom, and the atom–laser field interaction has been chosen to be $\hat{V} = -\hat{D} \cdot E$ where $\hat{D} = e\Sigma_i r_i$ is the electric dipole operator of the atom. As argued earlier, this form for the interaction is expected to be valid for rather strong laser fields, as long as: (a) $|E_0|$ is much weaker than Ze^2/a_B^2; (b) the laser is not tuned near allowed quadrupole or magnetic dipole resonances; and (c) the extent of the radial wave functions is much smaller than the laser wavelength.

This approach to atomic response assumes that $\hat{H}_0$ has a complete set of eigenvectors satisfying

$$\hat{H}_0|n\rangle = \hbar\omega_n|n\rangle \qquad (4.31a)$$

$$= \varepsilon_n|n\rangle$$

$$\langle n|m\rangle = \delta_{n,m} \qquad (4.31b)$$

for discrete states, and

$$\langle n|E_c\rangle = 0 \qquad (4.31c)$$

for the inner product of discrete states with continuum states, and

$$\langle E_c|E_c'\rangle = \delta(E_c - E_c') \qquad (4.31d)$$

for the inner product of continuum states. Other quantum numbers, such as those for angular momentum, have been suppressed. These actually give additional Kronecker deltas multiplying the $\delta(E_c - E'_c)$ and the $\delta_{n,m}$ in equations (4.31b) and (4.31d). Readers should remember the presence of the other quantum numbers which have been suppressed for purposes of a much simpler notation. Equation (4.31d) defines our assumed normalisation of the continuum states.

Before going further, another comment on notation is in order. We will use here Dirac's bra and ket notation. The relation to the Schrödinger wavefunction notation is rather simple. For instance, equation (4.31a) is written in the r representation as

$$\hat{H}_0 \phi_n(r) = \hbar\omega_n \phi_n(r). \tag{4.32}$$

The eigenfunction $\phi_n(r)$ is related to bra and ket vectors by

$$\phi_n(r) = \langle r|n \rangle \tag{4.33}$$

and

$$\int \phi_m^*(r)\phi_n(r)\mathrm{d}^3r = \int \langle m|r \rangle \langle r|n \rangle \, \mathrm{d}^3r \tag{4.34}$$

but in Dirac notation

$$\int |r\rangle\langle r|\mathrm{d}^3r = \hat{1}$$

i.e. bras and kets are complete sets of eigenvectors in any representation. Thus

$$\int \phi_m^*(r)\phi_n(r)\mathrm{d}^3r = \langle m|n \rangle = \delta_{n,m}. \tag{4.35}$$

Recall that the Schrödinger theory can also be formulated in terms of a momentum representation. In the latter case $\hat{H}_0$ must be found by expanding $\phi_n(r)$ in terms of momentum eigenfunctions and identifying what amounts to the Fourier coefficients as momentum representation eigenfunctions. The properties of Fourier transforms enable one to transform equation (4.31a) to the form

$$\hat{H}_0^P \bar{\phi}_n(P) = \hbar\omega_n \phi_n(P) \tag{4.36}$$

where $\hat{H}_0^P$ is the form of $\hat{H}_0$ in the P representation. The eigenvalues of any operator for an observable parameter are independent of representation, and there are many other representations in addition to the r and P representations. What the bra and ket notations do is to enable one to formulate the problem in a way which is independent of representation. Thus,

$$\langle r|\hat{H}_0|n \rangle = \hbar\omega_n \langle r|n \rangle$$

is the same as $\hat{H}_0\phi_n(r) = \hbar\omega_n\phi_n(r)$, and $\langle P|\hat{H}_0|n \rangle = \hbar\omega_n\langle P|n \rangle$ is the same as $\hat{H}_0^P\bar{\phi}_n(P) = \hbar\omega_n\bar{\phi}_n(P)$ and so on. An elementary discussion of the state vector formulation of quantum mechanics is volume three of *Lectures on Physics* by Feynman *et al* (1965). The latter reference puts emphasis on dynamics, rather than upon finding eigenvalues.

Since the eigenvectors of $\hat{H}_0$ are complete time-dependent state vectors in the presence of the laser field, they can be written as

$$|\Psi(t)\rangle = \sum_{\varepsilon_n \in S} a_n(t)e^{-i\omega_n t}|n\rangle \qquad (4.37)$$

where ε_n is an eigenvalue of $\hat{H}_0$ and S is the set of all eigenvalues of $\hat{H}_0$. The sum denotes a sum over discrete states and an integral over the energy for continuum states. The time-dependent state vector contains the dynamics of the atomic response and its time evolution is governed by the time-dependent Schrödinger equation

$$i\hbar\frac{\partial|\Psi(t)\rangle}{\partial t} = (\hat{H}_0 - \hat{D}\cdot E)|\Psi(t)\rangle. \qquad (4.38)$$

It is assumed that the concentration of the vapour is low enough to neglect dephasing, or resonance energy transfer collisions, which would introduce a pressure-broadened width at resonance, but would cause

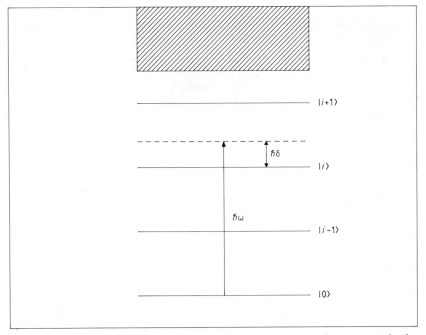

Figure 4.1 The ground state and a few excited states shown for an atom in the laser beam. The laser at frequency ω is off-resonance for all transitions starting from the ground state, but is tuned closest to $|i\rangle$.

almost no effect when the laser is tuned far away from resonance. An energy level diagram showing a few levels is presented in figure 4.1. To make further connections with the Schrödinger Ψ notation, we note that equations (4.37) and (4.38) in an r representation would become

$$\Psi(r,t) = \sum_{\varepsilon_n \in S} a_n(t) e^{-i\omega_n t} \phi_n(r)$$

$$i\hbar(\partial\Psi(r, t)/\partial t) = \hat{H}_r \Psi(r,t)$$

where the latter equations are arrived at by multiplying the left by the bra $\langle r|$. One can identify

$$\phi_n(r) = \langle r|n \rangle$$

$$\Psi(r,t) = \langle r|\Psi(t) \rangle$$

and $\hat{H}_r$ is the r representation of $\hat{H}$. The r is a shorthand notation for the set of coordinates for the atom's electrons relative to the nucleus. Prior to the laser pulse, $\Psi(r,-\infty) = \phi_0(r)$ where $n = 0$ corresponds to the ground state.

Using equation (4.37) in equation (4.38) and multiplying from the left with $\langle m|$

$$i\hbar(da_m/dt) = \sum_{\varepsilon_n \in S} a_n(t) e^{i(\omega_m - \omega_n)t} \langle m|\hat{V}|n \rangle . \tag{4.39}$$

Suppose that ω for the laser is not close to $\omega_m - \omega_0$ for any excited state m. Up to some reasonably high power level we will have $a_0(t) \simeq 1$, if before the laser was turned on $a_0(t) = 1$. In this case, if $m \neq 0$, only one term on the right is important (i.e. the one containing $a_0(t)$). Thus

$$i\hbar(da_m/dt) \simeq e^{i(\omega_m - \omega_0)t} \langle m|\hat{V}|0 \rangle \tag{4.40}$$

where $a_0(t) \simeq 1$. The quantity $|a_m|^2$ is the probability of the electron being found in excited state m, and a_m is the amplitude for being in this state. We will now investigate when the $a_0(t) \simeq 1$ approximation can be applied to get a good result. Since $\Sigma_{\varepsilon_n \in S}|a_n(t)|^2 \simeq 1$, one can only have $|a_0(t)|^2 \simeq 1$ if the $|a_m(t)|^2$ for $m \neq 0$ are all very small. Equation (4.40) becomes

$$da_m/dt = (iD_{m,0} \cdot E_0/2\hbar)[e^{i(\omega_m - \omega_0 + \omega)t} + e^{i(\omega_m - \omega_0 - \omega)t}] \tag{4.41}$$

where it was asumed that at $t = -\infty$, $E_0 = 0$, but that it has grown very slowly up to the present time. Integrating both sides of equation (4.41) with respect to t gives a_m. Note that if $F(t)$ is a very slowly varying function of time such that $F(-\infty) = 0$ and if $e^{i\delta t}[e^{i\delta t} \equiv \cos(\delta t) + i\sin(\delta t)]$ oscillates many times during a time period in which $F(t)$ hardly changes at all, then

$$\int_{-\infty}^{t} F(t')e^{i\delta t}dt' = (F(t)e^{i\delta t}/i\delta) - (1/i\delta)\int_{-\infty}^{t} F'(t')e^{i\delta t}dt'$$

$$= F(t)(e^{i\delta t}/i\delta) + (F'(t)e^{i\delta t}/\delta^2)$$

$$- (1/\delta^2)\int_{-\infty}^{t} F''(t')e^{i\delta t'}dt'$$

where the right-hand result is obtained by integration by parts. Now $2\pi/\delta$ is the time for an oscillation of the real or imaginary parts of $e^{i\delta t}$ and F hardly changes in such a time. Thus, $F'(t)/\delta \ll F(t)$, and the second and third terms of this asymptotic series obtained by repeated integration by parts is very tiny compared with the first. Thus

$$\int_{-\infty}^{t} F(t')e^{i\delta t'}dt' \simeq (f(t)e^{i\delta t}/i\delta). \tag{4.42}$$

During the rest of this chapter the above result will be used many times. Using equation (4.42) in integrating the right-hand side of equation (4.41) gives

$$a_m = (D_{m,0} \cdot E_0/2\hbar)\{[e^{i(\omega_m - \omega_0 + \omega)t}]/[\omega_m - \omega_0 + \omega]$$

$$+ [e^{i(\omega_m - \omega_0 - \omega)t}]/[\omega_m - \omega_0 - \omega]\}. \tag{4.43}$$

Obviously,

$$|a_m|^2 \leqslant |D_{m,0} \cdot E_0|^2/\hbar^2(\omega_m - \omega_0 - \omega)^2. \tag{4.44}$$

For relatively strong translations one frequently has

$$D_{m,0} \cdot E_0/2\hbar \simeq \frac{ea_B E_0}{2\hbar}$$

where a_B is the Bohr radius. For instance, in sodium if m corresponds to the 589.0 nm doublet $D_{m,0} \simeq 3a_B e$. To estimate the magnitude of $ea_B E_0/2\hbar$ note that in cgs units the power density is given by Poynting's theorem ($|E| = |B|$, $E \perp B$ and both E and B are perpendicular to k):

$$I = c\overline{(E \times B)}/4\pi = cE_0^2/8\pi \tag{4.45}$$

where we have averaged over the rapid oscillation of $\cos^2(\omega t - kz)$. The photon flux is

$$\mathscr{F}_\omega = I/\hbar\omega = cE_0^2/8\pi\hbar\omega. \tag{4.46}$$

Thus, with $\mathscr{F}_\omega$ in photons cm^{-2} s^{-1}

$$\frac{D_{m,0} \cdot E_0}{2\hbar} \simeq 10^8 [I(\text{W cm}^{-2})]^{1/2} \tag{4.47}$$

where I is expressed in units of W cm^{-2}, and the units of $D_{m,0}E_0/2\hbar$ are radians s^{-1}. This estimate is for a rather strong transition, but it illustrates the general order of magnitude.

Consider equation (4.44) and assume that the detuning $\omega_m - \omega_0 - \omega$ corresponds to 0.1 eV in terms of a detuning from resonance in photon energy. Using equation (4.47) in equation (4.44) one finds

$$|a_m|^2 \leqslant 2 \times 10^{-12} I(W\,cm^{-2}). \qquad (4.48)$$

Even with a 0.1 eV detuning, $|a_m|^2$ is still small up to $I \simeq 10^{10}$ W cm^{-2}. Most levels will have detunings larger than 1 eV, and most of them will have a much smaller matrix element than the case given here. Correspondingly, the squared amplitudes are at least a factor of 100 smaller for most other transitions. Obviously, away from resonance the power density can be rather high before this simple perturbation theory result fails.

Consider the case where ω is quite close to $\omega_i - \omega_0$. In this near-resonance situation the second term on the right-hand side of equation (4.43) totally dominates the term with the $\omega_i - \omega_0 + \omega$ denominator. We have

$$a_i \simeq D_{i,0} \cdot E_0 e^{i(\omega_i - \omega_0 - \omega)t} / 2\hbar(\omega_i - \omega_0 - \omega) . \qquad (4.49)$$

In carrying out the integration to obtain a_i note that the exp $[i(\omega_i - \omega_0 - \omega)t]$ term oscillates very slowly for $\omega \simeq \omega_i - \omega_0$, while the exp $[i(\omega_i - \omega_0 + \omega)t]$ term oscillates very rapidly and thereby tends to average any contribution to zero. In the integration process only one part of the $\cos(\omega t - kz) = (1/2)\{\exp[i(\omega t - kz)] + \exp[-i(\omega t - kz)]\}$ makes an appreciable contribution. Keeping only the resonant term from $\cos(\omega t - kz)$ in even more general circumstances is called the rotating wave approximation. We will use this approximation frequently in what follows. The other concept to be learned here is that if the laser is tuned very much closer to $\omega_i - \omega_0 - \omega = 0$ (for some i, as in figure 4.2) than for any other level, then $|a_i|^2$ for that level completely dominates $|a_{i'}|^2$ for any other level other than the ground state. This suggests that a good approximation might be obtained by including only near-resonance terms in the expansion of $|\Psi(t)\rangle$ in terms of the eigenvectors of $\hat{H}_0$. In fact, much of our understanding of laser field–atom interactions is based on extensive use of such a 'truncated basis' in situations where one or more lasers are tuned near one-photon absorption resonances.

Before proceeding to a discussion of situations where this first-order time-dependent perturbation theory approach fails, we will pause to derive a useful result. We would like to calculate the macroscopic polarisability of the vapour at the laser frequency. Thus, we need to determine the expectation value of D with respect to the time-dependent wavefunction and multiply this by the concentration N. The time-dependent expectation value of D is the average time-dependent dipole

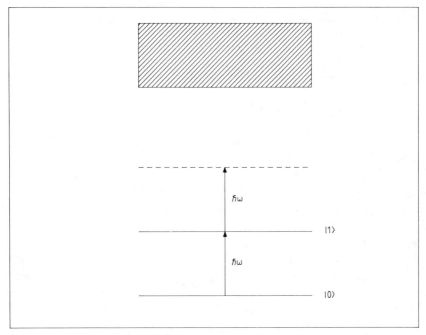

Figure 4.2 The laser at angular frequency ω is tuned on, or very close to, one-photon resonance between states $|0\rangle$ and $|1\rangle$. The laser is assumed to be either weak, or at too long a wavelength to produce appreciable ionisation.

per atom, which we will presently see is proportional to the laser field within the region of applicability of first order perturbation theory. Thus,

$$\mathcal{P}_\omega = N \langle \Psi(t)|\hat{D}|\Psi(t)\rangle$$

$$= N \sum_{\varepsilon_n \in S} \sum_{\varepsilon_m \in S} \langle n|\hat{D}|m\rangle \, a_n^* a_m \, e^{i(\omega_n - \omega_m)t} \tag{4.50}$$

where equation (4.37) was used. Using perturbation theory results, in which $|a_0|^2 \simeq 1$ and $|a_0 a_m| \gg |a_m|^2$ for $m \neq 0$, we have

$$\mathcal{P}_\omega = Ni \sum_{\varepsilon_m \in S} \left[\frac{|(D_x)_{m,0}|^2}{\hbar(\omega_m - \omega_0 - \omega)} + \frac{|(D_x)_{m,0}|^2}{\hbar(\omega_m - \omega_0 + \omega)} \right] E_0 \cos(\omega t - kz)$$

$$= (2NE/\hbar) \sum_{\varepsilon_m \in S} |(D_x)_{0,m}|^2 (\omega_m - \omega_0)/[(\omega_m - \omega_0)^2 - \omega^2] \tag{4.51}$$

where plane-polarised light, polarised in the x direction, with the wave propagating in the z direction, was assumed. Introducing the absorption oscillator strength F_m

$$F_m = \frac{2m}{e^2\hbar} \frac{(\omega_m - \omega_0)}{2J_0 + 1} \sum_{M_{J_0}} | \langle E_0, J_0, M_{J_0} | \hat{D}_x | E_m, J_m, M_{J_m} \rangle |^2 .$$

Averaged over the degeneracy of the ground state, one finds:

$$\mathcal{P}_\omega = (Ne^2E/m) \sum_{\varepsilon_m \in S} F_m/[(\omega_m - \omega_0)^2 - \omega^2] . \tag{4.52}$$

We will now find the refractive index of the medium. The only current density for a neutral vapour is

$$J = \partial\mathcal{P}/\partial t \tag{4.53a}$$

and

$$\rho = 0. \tag{4.53b}$$

Since $\nabla\cdot E = 0$ we can take the curl of both sides of $\nabla \times E = -(1/c)\partial B/\partial t$ and use

$$\nabla \times (\nabla \times E) \equiv \nabla(\nabla\cdot E) - \nabla^2 E = -\nabla^2 E = -(1/c)(\partial\nabla \times B/\partial t) .$$

Since

$$\nabla \times B = (1/c)(\partial E/\partial t) + (4\pi/c) J$$

we get,

$$\nabla^2 E - (1/c^2)(\partial^2 E/\partial t^2) = (4\pi/c^2)(\partial^2\mathcal{P}/\partial t^2) . \tag{4.54}$$

Using the relationship between $\mathcal{P}_\omega$ and E, as given by equation (4.52) and letting $\mathcal{P}_\omega = \chi_0(\omega)E$ gives

$$\chi_0(\omega) = (Ne^2/m) \sum_{\varepsilon_m \in S} F_m/[(\omega_m - \omega_0)^2 - \omega^2] . \tag{4.55}$$

Then

$$\nabla^2 E - (1 + 4\pi\chi_0(\omega)/c^2)(\partial^2 E/\partial t^2) = 0$$

is a wave equation for E, but with a modified phase velocity. If $v(\omega)$ is the phase velocity, $v(\omega)^{-2} \equiv (n(\omega)/c)^2$. Comparing with the wave equation (4.55): $n(\omega)^2 = 1 + 4\pi\chi_0(\omega)$. Assuming $|4\pi\chi_0(\omega)| \ll 1$,

$$n(\omega \simeq 1 + 2\pi\chi_0(\omega)$$

$$= 1 + (2\pi Ne^2/m \sum_{\varepsilon_m \in S} F_m/[(\omega_m - \omega_0)^2 - \omega^2] . \tag{4.56}$$

Much of our later discussion of pulse propagation and non-linear optics will be based on equation (4.54), but with more complicated forms of $\mathcal{P}$ in which the atomic response must be included and solved for simultaneously with equation (4.54). Equation (4.56) will also be considered further in a later chapter. In the non-resonant case just considered the results are correct even if the laser has a broad band width, and the concentration is reasonably high. This is a consequence of being far from resonance where the response is weak, at modest power densities, and the atomic response adiabatically follows the laser field. The adiabatic nature permits one to write down the laser field with the effect of the media taken into account by using a modified phase velocity. The density does, of course, have to be low enough so that the refractive index is close to unity.

4.4 The two-state model

We have seen in the last section that when the la er is tuned very close to a one-photon resonance, the amplitude of the near-resonance state dwarfs those of all other excited states. We restrict the power density so that if another photon could ionise the excited state, the probability of the ionisation is small. In the region very near a one-photon resonance simplifying equation (4.37) to the following should still give an accurate result:

$$|\psi(t)\rangle = a_0 e^{-i\omega_0 t}|0\rangle + a_1 e^{-i\omega_1 t}|1\rangle \tag{4.57}$$

where $|1\rangle$ is the near-resonant excited state as shown in figure 4.2. Using equation (4.39) to obtain differential equations for a_0 and a_1:

$$i\hbar \frac{da_0}{dt} = \langle 0|\hat{V}|1\rangle a_1 e^{i(\omega_0 - \omega_1)t}$$

$$i\hbar \frac{da_1}{dt} = \langle 1|\hat{V}|0\rangle a_0 e^{-i(\omega_0 - \omega_1)t}. \tag{4.58}$$

Unlike the off-resonant case studied in the last section, the resonance case is very sensitive to the band width of the laser and to any collisional dephasing effects that are present.

Assume that there are no collisional effects so that the atomic response is that of a single isolated atom. With this model equations (4.58) and their complex conjugates can be used to show

$$(d/dt)[a_0^* a_0 + a_1^* a_1] = 0$$

so that

$$|a_0|^2 + |a_1|^2 = 1. \tag{4.59}$$

Thus, a_0 and a_1 are complex numbers with an absolute value less than 1. Consequently,

$$|da_0/dt| \leqslant |\langle 0|\hat{V}|1\rangle|/\hbar \tag{4.60a}$$

$$|da_1/dt| \leqslant |\langle 0|\hat{V}|1\rangle|/\hbar \tag{4.60b}$$

with the equality only holding when the probability for being in the other state is unity. We examine the matrix element more carefully assuming that the laser is either a single longitudinal mode continuous wave laser or a pulsed laser with a transform-limited band width. That is, we take

$$E = iE_0(t)\cos(\omega t - kz + \phi) \qquad (4.61)$$

$$\langle 0|\hat{V}|1\rangle /\hbar = -(D_x)_{0,1}E_0(t)\cos(\omega t - kz + \phi)/\hbar.$$

We have taken $(D_x)_{0,1}E_0/2\hbar$ to be approximately equal to $10^8(I)^{1/2}$ with I in $W\,cm^{-2}$. This estimate is based on a fairly strong transition in which $|(D_x)_{0,1}|$ is approximately ea_B. The $\hat{D}$ matrix elements can be determined from measured oscillator strengths and angular momentum algebra. Note that even a transition with an oscillator strength of approximately 0.01 at 600 nm would still give a value greater than $10^7 (I)^{1/2}$. Table 4.1 shows a typical range for $\Omega \equiv (D_x)_{0,1}E_0/2\hbar$ at several power densities.

Table 4.1 Ranges of Ω.

$I(W\,cm^{-2})$	$\Omega\ (s^{-1})$
0.01	10^5–10^7
1.0	10^6–10^8
10^4	10^8–10^{10}
10^{10}	10^{11}–10^{13}

Each range of Ω covers a range of oscillator strengths from about 0.3 at the high end, to 0.00003 at the low end for photons in the 600.0 nm range of the spectrum.

With the above limits on Ω, equation (4.60) can be used to put rather stringent limits on how rapidly a_0 and a_1 can change with time. With these facts in mind,

$$\cos(x) = (e^{ix} + e^{-ix})/2$$

can be used to rewrite equation (4.58):

$$da_0/dt = i\bar{\Omega}e^{i\delta t}a_1$$
$$da_1/dt = i\bar{\Omega}^*e^{-i\delta t}a_0 - (\gamma/2)a_1 \qquad (4.62)$$

where

$$\delta = \omega - \omega_1 + \omega_0 \qquad (4.63)$$

is the detuning from exact resonance between $|0\rangle$ and $|1\rangle$. We have absorbed $\exp[i(\phi - kz)]$ into $\bar{\Omega}$ and have introduced a phenomenological damping term to simulate some of the averaged effects of spontaneous decay on the atomic response. Only the most resonant contribution to the equations of motion has been kept, in accord with our previous discussion in relation to equation (4.49). By the resonant term, we mean that the cosine in the E field has been broken into two complex exponential parts, with each combining with the $\exp(i(\omega_1 - \omega_0)t)$ in the equations of motion to give terms with very different characteristics. The first, or resonant term, oscillates slowly for small δ while the other term oscillates with an angular frequency close to 2ω. The fast oscillating term changes between $+1$ and -1 so rapidly that its average effect is zero. However, the slowly varying (resonant) term can permit large changes in $|a_0|$ or $|a_1|$ when $|\bar{\Omega}_0| \geq |\delta|$. In the latter situation the coupling is sufficiently large so that the amplitudes can change a lot in a time which is short compared with the time of oscillation of $\exp(i\delta t)$. The coupling can never be strong enough to cause large changes in the amplitudes in the time that $\exp(2i\omega t)$ oscillates without violating the whole concept of the atoms having well defined discrete states, with only a few of the amplitudes being significant. In the visible part of the spectrum the time-scale of this oscillation is less than 10^{-15} s. Retaining the resonance term, while neglecting the off-resonance part of the cosine, is the rotating wave approximation.

We now differentiate both sides of the second equation and replace da_0/dt by using the first equation:

$$\frac{d^2 a_1}{dt^2} + [i\delta - (d/dt)\ln \bar{\Omega}^* + \gamma/2](da_1/dt)$$
$$+ [(i\delta\gamma/2) + |\bar{\Omega}|^2 - (\gamma/2)(d\ln \bar{\Omega}^*/dt)] a_1 = 0. \qquad (4.65)$$

First let us take the case where $\bar{\Omega}^*$ is constant. This is most closely satisfied with single-mode continuous wave lasers, but is not completely applicable due to atomic motion through the beam. We find

$$a_1 = 2i\bar{\Omega}^*\exp\{(-it/2)[\delta-(i\gamma/2)]\}\{4\Omega^2 + [\delta + (i\gamma/2)]^2\}^{-1/2}$$
$$\times \sin((t/2)\{[\delta + (i\gamma/2)]^2 + 4|\Omega|^2\}^{1/2}). \qquad (4.67)$$

The inclusion of spontaneous decay is somewhat artificial in that it allows for decay of the upper state, but no return to the ground state, and thereby the total population of the two levels decays if $|\Omega| \gg |\delta|$ and $|\Omega| \gg \gamma/2$. For periods of time which are short compared with $1/\gamma$ we have for $|\Omega| \gg \gamma/2$,

$$|a_1|^2 = [4|\Omega|^2/(4|\Omega|^2 + \delta^2)]\sin^2[(t/2)(\delta^2 + 4|\Omega|^2)^{1/2}]. \qquad (4.68)$$

For $I > 10^4$, $|\Omega| \simeq 10^8 - 10^{10}$ s, which is large compared with $\gamma/2$ for most visible transitions. Thus, for small detuning

$$|a_1|^2 = \sin^2(|\Omega|t)$$
$$|a_0|^2 = \cos^2(|\Omega|t). \tag{4.69}$$

The population coherently oscillates between 0 and 1 with a period $\pi/|\Omega|$. The quantity Ω is $1/2$ of the Rabi flopping frequency ω_R, which was originally introduced in connection with oscillating magnetic fields interacting with nuclear spin systems. The line width (averaged over a time of several Rabi cycles) of the resonance is obtained from

$$|a_1|^2 = 2|\bar{\Omega}|^2/(\delta^2 + 4|\Omega|^2). \tag{4.70}$$

Thus, the averaged upper state population responds with a Lorentzian line shape with a full width at half maximum (FWHM) of $4|\Omega|$. This dependence of the excitation line width on laser power is commonly called power broadening. It results from the fact that any perturbation which can change the state vector by a sizeable factor in a time τ_p will lead to a width of the order of $1/\tau_p$. In the case of the $3s \rightarrow 4p$ transition in sodium, the power-broadened width approximately is $5 \times 10^8 (\bar{I})^{1/2}$, where the width is in $\mathrm{rad\,s^{-1}}$ (i.e. angular frequency units) and $\bar{I}$ is the power density in $\mathrm{W\,cm^{-2}}$. For $\bar{I} = 10^8\,\mathrm{W\,cm^{-2}}$ FWHM $= 5 \times 10^{12}\,\mathrm{rad\,s^{-1}} \simeq 30\,\mathrm{cm^{-1}} \simeq 1\,\mathrm{nm}$.

We return to equation (4.65) and consider the response of atoms to a pulsed laser having a transform-limited band width. That is, assume that the E field of the laser is of the form

$$E = kE_0 g(t) \cos(\omega t - kx + \phi_0) \tag{4.71}$$

where $g(t)$ starts to grow from zero after the triggering of the laser, growing to a height of unity at $t = 0$ before decaying to zero at large positive times. The shape of $|g(t)|^2$ mirrors the power density so that this quantity can be regarded as the laser pulse shape function. The band width of the laser field is determined completely by the time dependence of $g(t)$, which represents the only deviation from a monochromatic source. In terms of $g(t)$ equation (4.65) becomes

$$d^2a_1/dt^2 + \{i\delta - [d\ln(g(t))/dt]\}(da_1/dt + |\bar{\Omega}|^2 g^2(t)a_1 = 0 \tag{4.72}$$

where $\bar{\Omega}_0 \equiv (D_z)_{0,1}E_0/2\hbar$. Assume that

$$|\bar{\Omega}_0|g(t) \gg |d\ln(g(t))/dt| \tag{4.73a}$$

and

$$|\delta| \gg |d\ln(g(t))/dt|. \tag{4.73b}$$

We do not assume that $|\delta| > |\bar{\Omega}_0|$, and $|\bar{\Omega}_0|$ can be very much larger than either the natural line width or the laser band width, which is related to $|d\ln(g(t))/dt|$. For large $|\bar{\Omega}_0|$ the region of $|\delta|$ such that $|a_1|^2$ is appreciable will be determined by $\bar{\Omega}_0$, which determines the power broadening of the transition. Equation (4.72) can be written as

$$[(d/dt) + g_1(t)][(d/dt) + g_2(t)]a_1 = 0 \qquad (4.74)$$

providing that g_1 and g_2 are chosen to satisfy

$$g_1(t) + g_2(t) = i\delta - d\ln(g(t))/dt$$
$$g_1(t)g_2(t) + dg_2(t)/dt = |\bar{\Omega}_0|^2 g^2(t). \qquad (4.75)$$

When equations (4.75) are satisfied equation (4.74) is exactly equivalent to equation (4.72). If g_1 and g_2 can be found in some accurate approximation the solution to equation (4.74) becomes trivial.

One type of approximation can be arrived at by noting that if $|\delta|$ is fairly large and the laser pulse length is very long then the rate of change of $|\ln(g(t))|$ is very small. If $g(t)$ did not change at all the solutions for g_1 and g_2 could be arrived at by neglecting both $|d\ln(g(t))/dt|$ and $dg_2(t)/dt$, so that

$$\bar{g}_1 + \bar{g}_2 = i\delta \qquad (4.76)$$
$$\bar{g}_1\bar{g}_2 = |\bar{\Omega}_0|^2 g^2(t).$$

We now derive a correction to the solutions of equation (4.76) which takes the rate of change of $g(t)$ into account. If the corrections are very small, we expect that this type of solution is meaningful. Let

$$g_1 = \bar{g}_1 + \varepsilon_1$$
$$g_2 = \bar{g}_2 + \varepsilon_2. \qquad (4.77)$$

Substituting into equations (4.75) and neglecting $d\varepsilon_2/dt$ and $\varepsilon_2\varepsilon_1$,

$$\varepsilon_1 + \varepsilon_2 \simeq d\ln(g(t))/dt$$
$$\bar{g}_1\varepsilon_2 + \bar{g}_2\varepsilon_1 + (d\bar{g}_2/dt) \simeq 0. \qquad (4.78)$$

Solving for $\bar{g}_1$ and $\bar{g}_2$ as slowly varying continuous functions of time,

$$\bar{g}_1 = (i\delta/2) + isJ$$
$$\bar{g}_2 = (i\delta/2) - isJ \qquad (4.79)$$

where

$$s = \text{sgn}(\delta)$$
$$J = [(\delta/2)^2 + |\bar{\Omega}|^2 g^2(t)]^{1/2}.$$

We find for ε_1 and ε_2

$$\varepsilon_1 = -(1/2)\{d\ln[\bar{g}_2(\bar{g}_2 - \bar{g}_1)]/dt\}$$
$$\varepsilon_2 = -(d\ln(g(t))/dt) - \varepsilon_1. \qquad (4.80)$$

The corrections to $\bar{g}_1$ and $\bar{g}_2$ are very small if $|\delta\tau| \gg 1$, even when $|\bar{\Omega}_0|$ is very large compared with δ. The term τ is the pulse length of the laser.

We will now see how $\bar{g}_1$ and $\bar{g}_2$ can be used to arrive at solutions for a_1 and a_2. Thus, let

$$Z = (\mathrm{d}a_1/\mathrm{d}t) + g_2(t)a_1 \tag{4.81}$$

and note that according to equation (4.74)

$$(\mathrm{d}Z/\mathrm{d}t) + g_1(t)Z = 0. \tag{4.82}$$

Equation (4.82) can be integrated immediately and the resulting Z serves as an inhomogeneous term in equation (4.81), which can be integrated to yield a_1. When $|\delta|\tau$ is large the quantity

$$\exp[\int_{-T}^{t}(g_1(t') - g_2(t'))\mathrm{d}t')]$$

oscillates many times during a laser pulse and the second integral can be evaluated asymptotically to yield

$$a_1 = \bar{g}_2(t)/[\bar{g}_2(t)(\bar{g}_2(t) - \bar{g}_1(t))]^{1/2}\exp\left(-\int_{-T}^{t}\bar{g}_1(t')\mathrm{d}t'\right). \tag{4.83}$$

Using the algebraic properties of g_1 and g_2, one finds that

$$\begin{aligned}|a_1|^2 &= (1/2)[1 - (|\delta|/2J)] \\ |a_0|^2 &= (1/2)[1 + (|\delta|/2J)].\end{aligned} \tag{4.84}$$

With the smoothly varying laser pulse a very different type of solution was obtained compared to the cw laser. Subject to $|\delta\tau| \gg 1$ where τ is the laser pulse length, we have found that even though $|\bar{\Omega}_0|$ may be a thousand times larger than $1/\tau$, nevertheless whenever $|\delta|\tau > 10$ the upper and lower state populations are now non-oscillatory. When $|\delta|\tau < 10$ the 'adiabatic' type of approximation used here fails, and at the centre of the line one again obtains oscillatory amplitudes similar to the cw case, except that the period depends on the instantaneous power. Note that when $|\bar{\Omega}_0|\tau > 100$ almost all of the excitation line shape is given accurately by equation (4.84), with only a tiny region near the centre of the line exhibiting deviations. Even near the centre of the line, if the irregular Rabi oscillations are time averaged, we find the averaged $|a_1|^2$ is equal to the averaged $|a_0|^2$, and both are 1/2, just as predicted by equation (4.84) during the intense part of the laser pulse. A very interesting aspect of the 'adiabatic' approximation is that following the laser pulse there is no population left in the excited state. Indeed, the central criterion for the adiabatic approximation is that there be no overlap between the frequency spectrum of the laser and the resonance. This could never be satisfed if the amplitude of the laser changed instantaneously as assumed in deriving equations (4.67)–(4.70). With such a discontinuity the spectrum of the laser has very long, slowly decreasing wings which overlap resonance with finite amplitude for any detuning of line centre from resonance.

Before leaving the adiabatic approximation we will consider two special cases and compare the approximations of equations (4.84) with numerical calculations. In the first example assume that the laser field is of the form

$$E = kE_0 e^{-(t/\tau)^2} \cos(\omega t - kx). \qquad (4.85)$$

Particular values for the laser intensity and the laser pulse length permit the analytical approximation to be compared with numerical calculations for various detunings from resonance. Our choice of laser power is chosen to make the peak value of $|\bar{\Omega}| = 10^{10}\,\text{s}^{-1}$, and the pulse length $\tau = 10^{-8}\,\text{s}^{-1}$. With a strong transition such an $|\bar{\Omega}|$ is achieved with a power density around $10^4\,\text{W}\,\text{cm}^{-2}$, and the chosen pulse length is typical of a dye laser pumped by an XeCl excimer laser, or a harmonic of a Q-switched Nd–YAG laser.

Figure 4.3 shows $|a_1|^2$ and $|a_0|^2$ as functions of time for the case

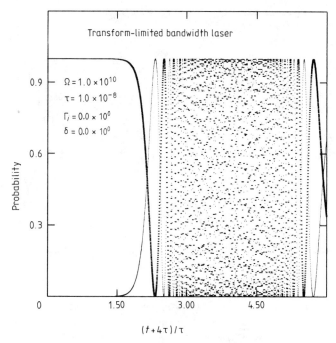

Figure 4.3 Graphs of $|a_0|^2$, the heavy curve, and $|a_1|^2$ for the case of exact resonance. The laser line width is Fourier-transform-limited, with a pulse length of about 13 ns. The peak Rabi frequency is $2.0 \times 10^{10}\,\text{s}^{-1}$.

$\delta = 0$. In this case the adiabatic solution is not shown since nearly 100 complete oscillations are expected, while an adiabatic solution is non-oscillatory for this laser field. Figure 4.4 shows the atomic response for $\delta\tau = 5$. Some of the main features of an adiabatic response are just starting to appear. Figures 4.5 and 4.6 show that as δ increases the adiabatic and numerical solutions approach each other very closely.

The example of the adiabatic approximation given on the previous pages is a very simple and well known one. It is less well known that even multimode lasers can be described by an adiabatic approximation providing the band width of the laser is small compared with the detuning of line centre from resonance (i.e. no laser photons overlap the resonance). We now consider one of the simpler examples of adiabatic behaviour for a laser having three equal amplitude modes. Specifically, assume

$$E = kE_0 e^{-(t/\tau)^2}\{\cos[(\omega - \Delta\omega)t] + \cos(\omega t) + \cos[(\omega + \Delta\omega)t]\}. \quad (4.86)$$

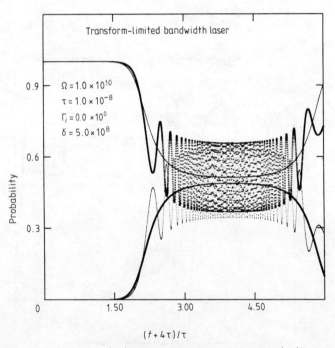

Figure 4.4 Graphs of $|a_0|^2$ (the upper curves) and $|a_1|^2$ for a detuning of $5 \times 10^8\,\mathrm{s}^{-1}$. All other parameters are the same as in figure 4.3. The smooth, non-oscillatory curves are adiabatic approximations for the absolute square of the amplitudes based on equation (4.84). Note that if one averages out the very rapid oscillations in the numerical solutions, something very close to the adiabatic solution is obtained.

Had this laser field been used in deriving equations (4.62), and δ had been measured from the central mode, then we would have to identify

$$\bar{\Omega} = \bar{\Omega}_0 e^{-(t/\tau)^2}[1 + 2\cos(\Delta\omega t)]. \tag{4.87}$$

Introducing a new $g(t)$ for this case:

$$g(t) = e^{-(t/\tau)^2}[1 + 2\cos(\Delta\omega t)]. \tag{4.88}$$

The entire analysis required in deriving equations (4.84) goes through and the latter equations apply with

$$J = \{(\delta/2)^2 + |\Omega|^2 \exp(-2t^2/\tau)[1 + 2\cos(\Delta\omega t)]^2\}^{1/2} \tag{4.89}$$

and with $\Omega \equiv \bar{\Omega}_0$. Figures 4.7 and 4.8 show a comparison of numerical calculations with the adiabatic solution for $|\Omega| = 10^{10}\,\text{s}^{-1}$ and $\tau = 10^{-8}\,\text{s}^{-1}$.

The validity of the adiabatic approximation requires that the laser band width does not overlap the resonance. The Rabi frequency can even be a factor of 100 times larger than $|\delta|$ and equations (4.84) will still hold for $\delta\tau \gg 1$. The off-resonance cases where the excited state

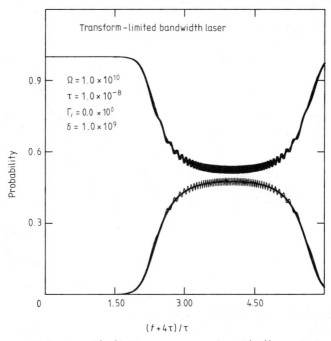

Figure 4.5 Graphs of $|a_0|^2$ (the upper curves) and $|a_1|^2$ as calculated numerically and by the adiabatic approximation for a detuning of $10^9\,\text{s}^{-1}$. The other parameters are identical to those of figures 4.3 and 4.4. The very smooth curves are the adiabatic approximations, while the numerical results still show rapid, small amplitude oscillations about the adiabatic result.

amplitudes become comparable with those of the ground state are very difficult to calculate numerically, but they can be determined precisely by an adiabatic approximation. The validity of adiabatic approximations when δ is much larger that the laser band width enables one to see very clearly that effects such as power broadening exist for laser pulses with a large number of longitudinal modes present. A wide body of literature (see, for example, Krylov and Bogolyubov 1947, Armstrong and Baker 1980) has been devoted to the exploitation of adiabatic behaviour. Other names have even been coined for some of the general methods. One of the more prevalent terms used in the literature is 'multiple time-scale perturbation theory'. Such mhods have been very useful in non-linear problems, as well as in quantum mechanics.

One useful extension of equations (4.84) is to consider

$$da_0/dt = i\bar{\Omega}e^{i\delta t}a_1$$
$$da_1/dt = i\bar{\Omega}^*e^{-i\delta t}a_0 - \Gamma_i(t)a_1/2 \tag{4.90}$$

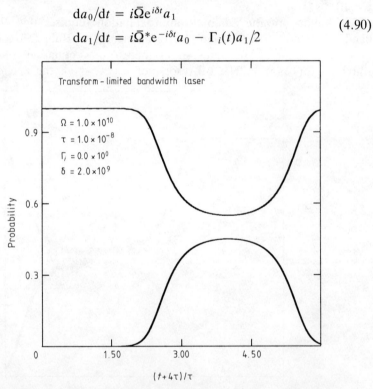

Figure 4.6 Graphs of $|a_0|^2$ (upper curve) and $|a_1|^2$ for a detuning of $\delta = 2.0 \times 10^9$ s^{-1}. The other parameters for the one-photon excitation are the same as in figures 4.3 to 4.5. Note that the solution is non-oscillatory and that the numerical solution cannot be distinguished from the adiabatic approximation. For larger detunings the adiabatic approximation is even closer to the numerical results.

where $|\bar{\Omega}| \gg |\Gamma_i|$. The adiabatic solution becomes:

$$|a_1(t)|^2 = |a_1^0(t)|^2 \exp\left(-\int_{-\infty}^t dt' \Gamma_i(t')|a_1^0(t')|^2\right)$$

$$|a_0(t)|^2 = |a_0^0(t)|^2 \exp\left(-\int_{-\infty}^t dt' \Gamma_i(t')|a_1^0(t')|^2\right).$$

(4.91)

In equation (4.91) the quantities $|a_1^0(t)|^2$ and $|a_0^0(t)|^2$ are just the solutions to equation (4.90) with $\Gamma_i(t) = 0$. These quantities are then given by equations (4.84). The physical significance of equations (4.91) is that the very strong coupling between the two states keeps a type of equilibrium while the slower decay rate causes both to decay together. This result will turn out to be very important in understanding pulse shape effects on the line shape in laser ionisation.

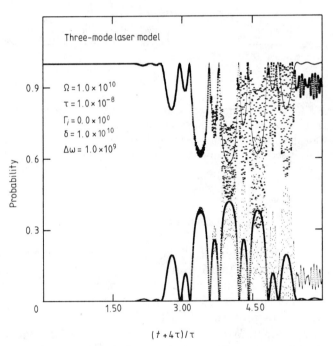

$$(t + 4\tau)/\tau$$

Figure 4.7 Graphs of $|a_0|^2$ and $|a_1|^2$ for $\delta = 1.0 \times 10^{10}$ s^{-1}. The laser has three equal modes separated by $\Delta\omega = 10^9$ s^{-1} and a pulse length close to 13 ns. The smooth curves are adiabatic approximations based on equations (4.89) and (4.84). Note that the adiabatic approximation is reasonably good until the power becomes rather high, giving enough resonance overlap to cause oscillations to appear and the adiabatic approximation to fail.

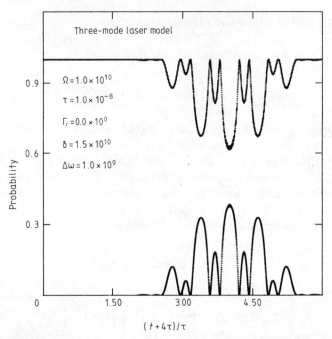

Figure 4.8 Graphs of $|a_0|^2$ and $|a_1|^2$ for a detuning of $\delta = 1.5 \times 10^{10}$ s^{-1}. The laser is a three-mode laser and all of the parameters except the detuning are the same as in figure 4.7. Note that at this detuning the numerical solution and the adiabatic solution based on equations (4.84) and (4.89) cannot be distinguished.

4.5 Excitation involving three bound states

This is an appropriate point to discuss an effect which occurs when two dye lasers are used with the first one tuned to resonance between states $|0\rangle$ and $|1\rangle$ and the second one tuned to very near resonance between $|1\rangle$ and a third bound state $|2\rangle$. The situation is shown in figure 4.9.

To approach this problem add a term in $|2\rangle$ to equation (4.57) and apply equation (4.39). We then obtain three simultaneous equations for amplitudes for the occupancy of $|0\rangle$, $|1\rangle$, and $|2\rangle$. After approximations that are in the same spirit as the rotating wave approximation, we obtain

$$da_0/dt = i\Omega_0(0 \to 1)g(t)e^{i\delta t}a_1 \tag{4.92}$$

$$da_1/dt = i\Omega_0^*(0 \to 1)g(t)e^{-i\delta t}a_0 + i\Omega_0(1 \to 2)g(t)e^{i(\omega' + \omega_1 - \omega_2)t}a_2$$

$$da_2/dt = i\Omega_0^*(1 \to 2)g(t)e^{-i(\omega' + \omega_1 - \omega_2)t}a_1.$$

Above, $\delta = \omega - \omega_1 + \omega_0$, $\Omega_0(0 \to 1)$ is half of the peak Rabi frequency

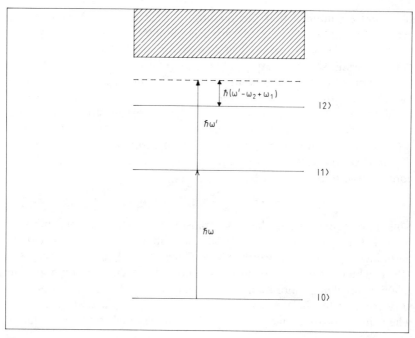

Figure 4.9 A laser at angular frequency ω is tuned to exact resonance between $|0\rangle$ and $|1\rangle$, while a second laser at angular frequency ω' is tuned very near a second resonance between $|1\rangle$ and $|2\rangle$. In our discussion the laser at ω is assumed to pump the resonance between $|0\rangle$ and $|1\rangle$ quite hard, while the second laser at ω' is much weaker so that the Rabi frequency for pumping the second transition is much smaller than that for the first resonance.

of the $|0\rangle \rightarrow |1\rangle$ transition, $\Omega_0(1 \rightarrow 2)$ is half of the peak Rabi frequency for the $|1\rangle \rightarrow |2\rangle$ transition and $g(t)$ is a laser pulse shape function. Assume the same pulse length and shape for the two lasers. Assuming that $\Omega_0(1 \rightarrow 2)$ is small, take $\delta = 0$ and neglect the pumping of the second transition on the populations of the lower levels. Letting $v = \int_{-\infty}^{t} dt' g(t')$, one finds

$$a_1(t) \simeq i(\Omega_0^*(0 \rightarrow 1)/|\Omega_0(0 \rightarrow 1)|) \sin\left(|\Omega_0(0 \rightarrow 1)| \int_{-\infty}^{t} dt' g(t')\right) \quad (4.93)$$

In order to understand some aspects of the three-state problem we can use this amplitude on the right-hand side of the equation for a_2:

$$da_2/dt = i\Omega_0^*(1 \rightarrow 2)g(t)a_1(t) \exp\left[-i(\omega' + \omega_1 - \omega_2)t\right].$$

Since in this approximation $a_1(t)$ is known, we can simply integrate both sides of the equation for a_2 and use the fact that at $t = -\infty$ its value is zero. We find

$$a_2(t) \propto \int_{-\infty}^{t} dt' g(t')e^{-(\omega' - \omega_2 + \omega_1)t'} \sin\left(|\Omega_0(0 \rightarrow 1)| \int_{-\infty}^{t'} g(t'')dt''\right). \quad (4.94)$$

It should be noticed that the quantity $\sin(|\Omega_0(0 \to 1)| \int_{-\infty}^{t} g(t') dt')$ can oscillate thousands of times during a laser pulse if the power density of the first laser is fairly large. The sine factor can be broken up into two parts by using $\sin(x) = [\exp(ix) - \exp(-ix)]/2i$. The product of one of these exponential factors with $\exp[-i(\omega' - \omega_2 + \omega_1)t]$ will oscillate more slowly than the other and at some time during the pulse will oscillate very slowly. For large $\Omega_0(0 \to 1)\tau$ nearly all of the contribution to a_2 originates from times very near $(\omega' - \omega_2 + \omega_1) = \pm|\Omega_0(0 \to 1)|g(t)$. If the second laser is tuned to exact resonance between $|1\rangle$ and $|2\rangle$ and $|\Omega_0(0 \to 1)|\tau \gg 1$ the integral for a_2 is very small. The largest contribution to a_2 occurs when

$$\omega' - \omega_2 + \omega_1 = \pm|\Omega_0(0 \to 1)|.$$

This means that when the first transition is pumped very hard the second transition is split so that two absorption peaks occur for detunings from the unperturbed resonance of $\pm|\Omega_0(0 \to 1)|$. This is an effect which must be avoided in choosing excitation or ionisation schemes involving more than one resonance step. The situation becomes very complicated in any case where successive resonances are pumped, when the Rabi frequency for one resonance is much larger than that of the other.

4.6 A more general adiabatic method

Earlier in this chapter we discussed an adiabatic solution for the two-state problem in which the system of simultaneous equations was reduced to a single higher order differential equation, which was then factored in the sense of equations (4.74) and (4.75). The latter method is quite easy to implement for a two-state system, but becomes awkward when applied to three or more simultaneous equations. Since the adiabatic method is very powerful in dealing with a class of problems which are difficult to deal with numerically, a more general version of adiabatic theory will be described.

In studies of near-resonant laser fields interacting with atoms, one usually assumes that some number, N, of the discrete states have by far the largest amplitudes and a set of N simultaneous differential equations are obtained for the probability amplitudes. We write the equations in matrix form

$$d\mathbf{a}/dt = i\mathbf{B}(t)\mathbf{a} \qquad (4.95)$$

where $\mathbf{a}(t)$ is the column matrix of probability amplitudes for the dominant states and $\mathbf{B}(t)$ is an $N \times N$ square matrix. Usually the square matrix $\mathbf{B}$ has the property that when $i \neq j$: $B_{ij} = B_{ji}^*$. In fact, in the absence of the inclusion of spontaneous emission or laser ionisation, the matrix $\mathbf{B}(t)$ is Hermitian. In Chapter 5 we show that one can frequently include the effects of laser ionisation by having diagonal elements of $\mathbf{B}(t)$ which are complex, and the imaginary part is positive and proportional to the rate of ionisation of the state designated by the row number. Consider a method of solution for the case where $\mathbf{B}$ is time independent. In order to put the equations in a form where the coefficients are time independent for the cw laser model, or slowly varying for a pulsed laser, it is necessary to get rid of complex exponential factors by introducing new amplitudes which differ from those which would be arrived at from equations (4.39) and the rotating wave approximation by complex exponential terms of the form $\exp(i\delta\omega_n t)$. By proper choices for $\delta\omega_n$, the B_{ij} become time independent for the cw case, or slowly varying for pulsed lasers.

Let $\mathbf{a}_n$ be a set of eigencolumns of $\mathbf{B}$ corresponding to the set of eigenvalues λ_n, with $1 \leqslant n \leqslant N$, where N is the dimension of the square matrix $\mathbf{B}$. Thus,

$$\mathbf{B}\mathbf{a}_n = \lambda_n\mathbf{a}_n. \tag{4.96}$$

Let $\boldsymbol{\beta}_n$ be a set of eigenrow vectors of $\mathbf{B}$ defined by

$$\boldsymbol{\beta}_n\mathbf{B} = \lambda_n'\boldsymbol{\beta}_n \tag{4.97}$$

where λ_n' is an eigenvalue corresponding to the eigenrow $\boldsymbol{\beta}_n$. If one writes out the characteristic determinants involved in finding the two sets of eigenvalues it is soon realised that the matrix for which one is doing the determinant in the case of λ_n' is just the transpose of the one involved in finding the λ_n eigenvalues. It is well known that the transpose of a matrix has the same determinant as does the original matrix. Consequently, the eigenvalues are identical for the two eigenvalue problems. Now consider

$$\begin{aligned}\boldsymbol{\beta}_m\mathbf{B}\mathbf{a}_n &= \lambda_n\boldsymbol{\beta}_m\mathbf{a}_n \\ &= \lambda_m\boldsymbol{\beta}_m\mathbf{a}_n.\end{aligned} \tag{4.98}$$

Thus,

$$(\lambda_m - \lambda_n)\boldsymbol{\beta}_m\mathbf{a}_n = 0.$$

We have used the fact that the eigenvalues in the two problems are the same, and the ones having equal values are assumed to be numbered the same. If there is no degeneracy, when $n \neq m$,

$$\boldsymbol{\beta}_m\mathbf{a}_n = 0$$

so that $\boldsymbol{\beta}_m$ is orthogonal to $\mathbf{a}_n$ when $n \neq m$. The normalisation of $\mathbf{a}_n$ and $\boldsymbol{\beta}_n$ is chosen so that

$$\boldsymbol{\beta}_n \boldsymbol{a}_m = \delta_{n,m} \tag{4.99}$$

where $\delta_{n,m}$ is the Kronecker delta. We can now write down an obvious solution to the initial value problem when we imagine a laser (or lasers) to be switched on at $t = 0$:

$$\boldsymbol{a}(t) = \sum_{n=1}^{N} c_n \boldsymbol{a}_n \exp{(i\lambda_n t)}. \tag{4.100}$$

Taking the time derivative of both sides of equation (4.100) and noting that $\lambda_n \boldsymbol{a}_n = \boldsymbol{B} \boldsymbol{a}_n$, the simultaneous equations of (4.95) are satisfied. We now show how the constants c_n can be chosen in order to satisfy the initial conditions. Multiplying by $\boldsymbol{\beta}_m$ on both sides of equation (4.100) evaluated at $t = 0$ gives

$$c_m = \boldsymbol{\beta}_m \boldsymbol{a}(t = 0). \tag{4.101}$$

Equations (4.100) and (4.101) represent a full solution to the initial value problem.

Imagine that the matrix $\boldsymbol{B}$ has large elements at all times, but that the components are slowly varying with time. In this case the eigenvalues are time dependent, but one can still find time dependent $\boldsymbol{a}_n(t)$ and $\boldsymbol{\beta}_m(t)$ which are completely analogous to those defined in equations (4.96) and (4.97). With the time dependences involved we number the eigenvalues and eigenvectors at early times, and as time increases the numbering is made unique by requiring that both the eigenvalues and the eigenvectors evolve continuously in time. We now try a solution of the form

$$\boldsymbol{a}(t) = \sum_{n=1}^{N} c_n(t) \boldsymbol{a}_n(t) \exp{\left(i \int_{-\infty}^{t} dt' \lambda_n(t') \right)} \tag{4.102}$$

where the $c_n(t)$ are no longer constants defined by a set of initial conditions, but are n new variables to be found by applying the equations of motion to equation (4.102), which is used to see what differential equations the $c_n(t)$ must satisfy in order to solve equations (4.95). To find equations for the c_n note that

$$d(\boldsymbol{\beta}_m \boldsymbol{a}(t))/dt \equiv (d\boldsymbol{\beta}_m/dt)\boldsymbol{a}(t) + \boldsymbol{\beta}_m(d\boldsymbol{a}(t)/dt)$$

$$= (d\boldsymbol{\beta}_m/dt)\boldsymbol{a}(t) + \boldsymbol{\beta}_m \boldsymbol{B} \boldsymbol{a}. \tag{4.103}$$

From the orthogonality properties of $\boldsymbol{\beta}_m$ and $\boldsymbol{a}_n$ and equation (4.102) we can write

$$\boldsymbol{\beta}_m \boldsymbol{a} = c_m(t) \exp{\left(i \int_{-\infty}^{t} \lambda_m(t')dt' \right)} \tag{4.104}$$

$$\boldsymbol{\beta}_m \boldsymbol{B} \boldsymbol{a} = \lambda_m(t) c_m(t) \exp{\left(i \int_{-\infty}^{t} \lambda_m(t')dt' \right)}.$$

so that

$$dc_m(t)/dt = \sum_{n=1}^{N} c_n(t)(d\boldsymbol{\beta}_m/dt)\boldsymbol{a}_n \exp\left(i\int_{-\infty}^{t}(\lambda_n(t') - \lambda_m(t'))dt'\right).$$

(4.105)

If the $\lambda_n(t)$ quantities are very large, the complex exponentials oscillate many times during a laser pulse. Thus, terms on the right-hand side (except for the term with $n = m$) will tend to oscillate rapidly and average to zero. Just how well the rapid oscillations suppress the contributions for $n \neq m$ determines the accuracy of the adiabatic approximation. If the criteria are well satisfied we have

$$dc_m(t)/dt \simeq c_m(t)(d\boldsymbol{\beta}_m/dt)\boldsymbol{a}_m.$$ (4.106)

This is a great simplification. We no longer have simultaneous equations to solve, and the solution will yield a slowly varying quantity. Even situations which are too complex for analytical results are amenable with some of the powerful routines available for numerical matrix analysis.

Consider the following two-state problem. Let

$$d\boldsymbol{a}/dt = i\boldsymbol{B}(t)\boldsymbol{a}$$ (4.107)

with $\boldsymbol{B}(t)$ given by

$$\boldsymbol{B} = \begin{pmatrix} 0 & \Omega(t) \\ \Omega^*(t) & \Delta(t) + i\Gamma \end{pmatrix}.$$ (4.108)

Assume that $\Omega(-\infty) = 0$, and $\Delta(-\infty) = \delta$. We find two eigenvalues

$$\lambda_1 = [(\Delta(t) + i\Gamma(t))/2] + \text{sgn}(\delta)J$$
$$\lambda_2 = [(\Delta(t) + i\Gamma(t))/2] - \text{sgn}(\delta)J$$

(4.109)

where

$$J = [\Omega^2(t) + (\Delta(t)/2)^2 - (\Gamma(t)/2)^2 + i(\Delta(t)\Gamma(t)/2)]^{1/2}.$$

It is now simple to find $\boldsymbol{a}_n$ and $\boldsymbol{\beta}_n$ normalised according to equation (4.99) for all t. It is then necessary to integrate equation (4.106) and make use of the initial conditions on $c_n(t)$ as dictated by $c_n(-\infty) = \boldsymbol{\beta}_n(-\infty)\boldsymbol{a}(-\infty)$. One finds

$$\boldsymbol{a} = \left(\frac{\lambda_1 + \lambda_2^*}{\lambda_1 - \lambda_2}\right)\left(\begin{array}{c} i\lambda_2^{1/2}/(\lambda_1 + \lambda_2^*)^{1/2} \\ \lambda_1^{1/2}/(\lambda_1 + \lambda_2^*)^{1/2} \end{array}\right)\exp\left(i\int_{-\infty}^{t}dt'\lambda_1(t')\right).$$ (4.110)

We have used $a_1(-\infty) = 1$ and $a_2(-\infty) = 0$ as initial conditions. Finally,

$$|a_1(t)|^2 + |a_2(t)|^2 = \exp\left(-2\int_{-\infty}^{t}dt'\text{Im}\lambda_1(t')\right).$$ (4.111)

Equation (4.111) will be useful in Chapter 5 when we discuss two-photon ionisation near a one-photon intermediate resonance.

4.7 Multiphoton excitation

In the last section we have seen how equation (4.39) can be combined with a truncated basis to deal with saturation effects in laser excitation. The applications of the time-dependent Schrödinger equation are straightforward even when several lasers tuned near a sequence of one-photon resonances are involved. The situation is not so easy when higher order resonances are used, since nearly all states of the atom can be important as virtual states in dealing with multiphoton excitation. This makes an approach with equation (4.39) and a truncated basis quite tedious. We will develop here a formalism which enables one to easily apply a truncated basis to the formulation of the multiphoton excitation problem.

We again consider a two-state model of excitation by lasers. However, we now generalise our treatment to deal with multiphoton excitation. In order to do this we will develop a formalism to make the 'bookkeeping' much simpler. Assume that the absorption of N photons is close to satisfying the conservation of energy between a lower state $|0\rangle$ and an excited state $|1\rangle$, as shown in figure 4.10. In that figure δ is defined through

$$\hbar\delta = \hbar\sum_{i}^{N}\omega_{l,i} - \hbar(\omega_1 - \omega_0) \qquad (4.112)$$

where $\hbar\omega_1$ is the energy of the upper level, $\hbar\omega_0$ is the energy of the lower level, and $\hbar\omega_{l,i}$ are the individual photon energies at line centre for the lasers used for the N-photon excitation. If the N photons are all absorbed from a single laser beam, $\sum_{i}^{N}\hbar\omega_{l,i} \rightarrow N\hbar\omega_l$, etc. Let $|\Psi(t)\rangle$ be the state vector of the atom in the presence of the laser fields; then

$$\hat{\mathcal{H}}|\Psi(t)\rangle = i\hbar(\partial|\Psi(t)\rangle/\partial t$$

where $\hat{\mathcal{H}} = \hat{\mathcal{H}}_0 + \hat{V}$. Here $\hat{\mathcal{H}}_0$ is the Hamiltonian of the isolated atom and $\hat{V}(t)$ represents the interaction between the atom and the laser fields, described as classical electromagnetic fields. Initially, $|\Psi(-\infty)\rangle = |0\rangle$, and as the laser pulse arrives at the atom $|\Psi(t)\rangle$ evolves according to $|\Psi(t)\rangle = \hat{T}(t)|0\rangle$, where $\hat{T}(t)$ is the time evolution operator. In standard quantum mechanics text books (Messiah 1966) it is shown that if

$$\hat{T}(t) = \exp(-i\hat{H}_0 t/\hbar)\hat{S}(t) \qquad (4.113)$$

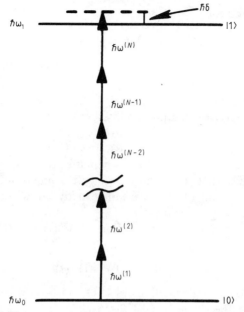

Figure 4.10 Energy level diagram for a two-state model of N-photon excitation. The detuning from resonance δ is defined by $\hbar\delta = \Sigma_{p=1}^{N}\hbar\omega_p - \hbar(\omega_1 - \omega_0)$. It is assumed that δ is much smaller than any k-photon resonance with $k < N$ and that the detuning from any lower order resonance is also smaller than the laser band widths or the lower order Rabi frequencies.

then $\hat{S}(t)$ satisfies

$$\hat{S}(t) = 1 + (i\hbar)^{-1} \int_{-\infty}^{t} \hat{V}_H(t')\hat{S}(t')dt' \tag{4.114}$$

where $\hat{V}_H(t) = \exp(i\hat{H}_0t/\hbar)\hat{V}(t)\exp(-i\hat{H}_0t/\hbar)$. Equation (4.113) is obtained by using equation (4.112) in the time-dependent Schrödinger equation to give

$$i\hbar(\partial(\hat{S}(t)|0\rangle/\partial t) = \hat{V}_H(t)\hat{S}(t)|0\rangle. \tag{4.115}$$

On integration, equation (4.114) follows. By iterating equation (4.114), one arrrives at the following equation, which is equivalent to equation (4.114):

$$\hat{S}(t) = \sum_{k=0}^{p-1} \hat{S}_k(t) + (i\hbar)^{-p}\int_{-\infty}^{t} dt_p \int_{-\infty}^{t_p} dt_{p-1}\hat{V}_H(t_{p-1})\ldots$$
$$\ldots \int_{-\infty}^{t_2} dt_1 \hat{V}_H(t_1)\hat{S}(t_1) \tag{4.116}$$

where $\hat{S}_0 = 1$ and for $k > 1$,

$$\hat{S}_k(t) = (i\hbar)^{-k} \int_{-\infty}^{t} dt_k \hat{V}_H(t_k) \int_{-\infty}^{t_k} dt_{k-1} \hat{V}_H(t_{k-1}) \cdots$$

$$\cdots \int_{-\infty}^{t_2} dt_1 \hat{V}_H(t_1). \tag{4.117}$$

Equations (4.116) and (4.117) hold for any integer p. One can find equations of motion for the probability amplitudes for being in state $|0\rangle$ and $|1\rangle$, i.e. for $C_0(t) = \exp(i\omega_0 t) \langle 0|\Psi(t)\rangle = \langle 0|\hat{S}(t)|0\rangle$ and $C_1(t) = \exp(\omega_1 t) \langle 1|\Psi(t)\rangle = \langle 1|\hat{S}(t)|0\rangle$. In defining $C_0(t)$ and $C_1(t)$, the phase factors were introduced for mathematical convenience and do not change the values of $|C_0(t)|^2$ and $|C_1(t)|^2$. It is important to realise that equations (4.114) and (4.115) are still exactly equivalent to the time-dependent Schrödinger equation.

We now derive equations of motion of $C_0(t)$ and $C_1(t)$. Equation (4.115) immediately yields

$$i\hbar(\partial C_0/\partial t) = \langle 0|\hat{V}_H(t)\hat{S}(t)|0\rangle. \tag{4.118}$$

Operator methods using equations (4.114) and (4.116) can be employed in manipulating the quantity $\langle 0|\hat{V}_H(t)\hat{S}(t)|0\rangle$ to derive a very general two-state approximation to the laser excitation problem where the required approximations are clearly evident. The situation with $N = 1$ will be treated separately. Note that if $\hat{H}_0|n\rangle = \hbar\omega_n|n\rangle$, then the unit operator can be written as

$$\hat{1} = \sum_{\varepsilon_n \in S} |n\rangle\langle n|$$

with $\sum_{\varepsilon_n \in S}$ indicating a sum over discrete states and an integral over the continuum. The notation $\varepsilon_n \in S$ indicates a sum over all energies ε_n in the spectrum of $\hat{H}_0$ which is indicated by S. Thus, for $N = 1$ we have, using $\langle 0|\exp(i\hat{H}_0/\hbar) = \langle 0|\exp(i\omega_0 t)$ and $\exp(-i\hat{H}_0 t/\hbar)|n\rangle = \exp(-i\omega_n t)|n\rangle$, just equation (4.39) as derived in a different way. Neglecting the amplitudes of off-resonant excited states, we can write

$$i\hbar(\partial C_0/\partial t) = \langle 0|\hat{V}|1\rangle \, e^{i(\omega_0 - \omega_1)t} C_1$$
$$i\hbar(\partial C_1/\partial t) = \langle 1|\hat{V}|0\rangle \, e^{-i(\omega_0 - \omega_1)t} C_0. \tag{4.119}$$

Equation (4.119) is standard and, in general, simple to derive by the earlier formalism.

When $N > 1$ is considered, the derivation of equations analogous to equation (4.119) is cumbersome; it is here that the operator method greatly simplifies the derivation. Begin with equation (4.118) and use equation (4.114) to replace $\hat{S}(t)$:

$$i\hbar(\partial C_0/\partial t) = \langle 1|\hat{V}_H(t)\left(1 + (i\hbar)^{-1}\int_{-\infty}^{t} dt' \hat{V}_H(t')\hat{S}(t')\right)|0\rangle \tag{4.120}$$

$$= (i\hbar)^{-1}\langle 0|\hat{V}_H(t)\int_{-\infty}^{t}\hat{V}_H(t')\hat{S}(t')|0\rangle dt'.$$

The last form follows because $\langle 0|\hat{V}_H(t)|0\rangle = 0$ by parity considerations. We let $\hat{Y} = \hat{1} - |0\rangle\langle 0|$ and insert the unit operator between $\hat{V}_H$ and $\hat{S}$ in equation (4.120):

$$i\hbar(\partial C_0/\partial t = (i\hbar)^{-1}\,\langle 0|\hat{V}_H(t)\int_{-\infty}^{t}\hat{V}_H(t')|0\rangle C_0(t')dt' \qquad (4.121)$$

$$+ (i\hbar)^{-1}\langle 0|\hat{V}_H(t)\int_{-\infty}^{t}\hat{V}_H(t')\hat{Y}\hat{S}(t')|0\rangle dt'.$$

The first term on the right-hand side has been separated off because it will eventually give rise to the AC Stark shift term. We also expect to eventually get a term involving C_1 on the right-hand side and a product of N of the $\hat{V}_H$ interaction terms because the lowest-order term which conserves energy involves the absorption of N photons. Replace $\hat{S}(t')$ by equation (4.116) with $p = N - 2$ to obtain

$$i\hbar(\partial C_0/\partial t) = (i\hbar)^{-1}\int_{-\infty}^{t}\langle 0\,|\hat{V}_H(t)\hat{V}_H(t')|0\rangle\,C_0(t')dt' \qquad (4.122)$$

$$+ (i\hbar)^{-1}\sum_{k=0}^{N-3}\int_{-\infty}^{t}\langle 0|\hat{V}_H(t)\hat{V}_H(t')\hat{Y}\hat{S}_k(t')|0\rangle\,dt'$$

$$+ (i\hbar)^{-N+1}\langle 0|\int_{-\infty}^{t}dt_{N-1}\hat{V}_H(t)\hat{V}_H(t_{N-1})\hat{Y}$$

$$\times \int_{-\infty}^{t_{N-1}}dt_{N-1}\hat{V}_H(t_{N-2})\cdots$$

$$\cdots\int_{-\infty}^{t_2}dt_1\hat{V}_H(t_1)\hat{S}(t_1)|0\rangle.$$

This complicated equation can be simplified by recognising and estimating some of the terms. A two-state approximation will hold only if the middle set of terms involving $\langle 0|\hat{V}_H(t)\hat{V}_H(t')\hat{Y}\hat{S}_k(t')|0\rangle$ can be neglected, and if, after inserting $\hat{1} = |1\rangle\langle 1| + \Sigma_{\varepsilon_n\in S, n\neq 1}|n\rangle\langle n|$ between $\hat{V}_H(t_1)$ and $\hat{S}(t_1)$ in the last term, the non-resonance terms coming from $\Sigma_{\varepsilon_n\in S, n\neq 1}$ can be neglected. As in the one-photon excitation case, the neglected terms can be estimated. All of the terms, in the absence of any other near resonances of the same or lower order, will be found to be either very small or small and multiplied by a rapidly oscillating complex exponential whose effect averages to near zero unless the laser power density is extremely large. It is advisable to be sure that the neglected terms are negligible in any case where the two-state approximation is used. It is important to note that before these terms are thrown out the relation is still exact. In the two-state approximation,

$$i\hbar(\partial C_0/\partial t) = (i\hbar)^{-1}\int_{-\infty}^{t}\langle 0|\hat{V}_H(t)\hat{V}_H(t')|0\rangle C_0(t')dt' \qquad (4.123)$$

$$+ (i\hbar)^{-N+1} \int_{-\infty}^{t} dt_{N-1} \langle 0| \hat{V}_H(t) \hat{V}_H(t') \hat{Y}$$

$$\times \int_{-\infty}^{t_{N-1}} dt_{N-2} \hat{V}_H(t_{N-2}) \ldots \int_{-\infty}^{t_2} dt_1 \hat{V}_H(t_1) |1\rangle C_1(t_1).$$

Equation (4.123) can be simplified further by noting that for a slowly varying function F multiplied by a rapidly oscillating complex exponential:

$$\int_{-\infty}^{t} F(t') e^{i\Omega t'} dt' \simeq e^{i\Omega t} F(t)/(i\Omega). \tag{4.124}$$

Equation (4.124) is identical with equation (4.42) which was derived earlier in this chapter. On inserting $\hat{1}$ between the $\hat{V}_H$ factors and using $\langle n| \exp(i\hat{H}_0 t/\hbar) = \langle n| \exp(i\omega_n t)$, and $\exp(-i\hat{H}_0 t/\hbar)|m\rangle = \exp(-i\omega_m t)|m\rangle$, together with the time dependences of the laser fields, it is found that equation (4.124) can be applied to all the time integrations in equation (4.123) in the same situations where the neglected terms are small. The final effect is that $C_0(t')$ and $C_1(t_1)$ can be removed from the integrals and evaluated at t. The same type of scheme with similar approximations also works for the equation $i\hbar(\partial C_1/\partial t)$. We get

$$\partial C_0/\partial t = i\Delta_0(t) C_0 + i\Omega_N(t) \exp(i\delta t) C_1$$
$$\partial C_1/\partial t = i\Delta_1(t) C_1 + i\Omega_N^*(t) \exp(-i\delta t) C_0 \tag{4.125}$$

where

$$\Omega_N(t) = -i(i\hbar)^{-N} \exp(-i\delta t) \tag{4.126}$$

$$\times \langle 0| \hat{V}_H(t) \int_{-\infty}^{t} dt_{N-1} \hat{V}_H(t_{N-1}) \hat{Y} \int_{-\infty}^{t_{N-1}} dt_{N-2} \hat{V}_H(t_{N-2}) \ldots$$

$$\times \int_{-\infty}^{t_2} dt_1 \hat{V}_H(t_1) |1\rangle$$

and, for $i = 0$ and 1,

$$\Delta_i(t) = -i(i\hbar)^{-2} \int_{-\infty}^{t} dt_1 \langle i| \hat{V}_H(t) \hat{V}_H(t_1) |i\rangle. \tag{4.127}$$

The quantities $\Omega_N(t)$ and $\Delta_i(t)$ are the N-photon Rabi frequency and the AC Stark shift of $|i\rangle$, respectively. In evaluating equations (4.126) and (4.127), it must be remembered that the same approximations used in removing $C_0(t)$ and $C_1(t)$ from the integrals must be employed. Thus, unit operators are inserted between the $\hat{V}_H(t_i)$, and equation (4.124) is applied repeatedly. With this understanding, equations (4.126) and (4.127) represent a very compact and general mathematical form in which the lasers can have any state of polarisation, any direction of propagation, any band width consistent with our approximations, and N is general.

Even though higher order absorption processes are not used with great frequency in RIS studies, equations (4.125)–(4.127) are valuable in estimating multiphoton Rabi freuqencies and AC Stark shifts. These equations will also be used extensively in a later chapter on the use of non-linear processes in extending the wavelength range covered by dye lasers and conventional doubling and mixing crystals.

Nearly the same type of operator manipulation can be used to extend the treatment to multiple resonances, ionisation and effects of degeneracy, as well as collisional effects. However, the resulting theories are not two-state approximations. The two-state approximation has been discussed many times and is included in many standard reference books (see, for example, Sargent *et al* (1974), or Allen and Eberley (1975)). An elementary discussion including the effect of phase-changing collisions and the resulting line-broadening effects can be found in Hurst *et al* (1979).

References

Allen L and Eberley J H 1975 *Optical Resonance and Two-level Atoms* (New York: Wiley)

Armstrong L and Baker H C 1980 *J. Phys. B: At. Mol. Phys.* **13** 4727

Feynman R P, Leighton R B and Sands M 1965 *The Feynman Lectures on Physics* vol III (Reading, MA: Addison-Wesley)

Hurst G S, Payne M G, Kramer S D and Young J P 1979 *Rev. Mod. Phys.* **51** 767

Jackson J D 1962 in *Classical Electromagnetic Theory* (Reading, MA: Addison-Wesley)

Krylov N and Bogolyubov N 1947 *Introduction to Nonlinear Mechanics* (Engl. Transl. S Lefshetz) (Princeton, NJ: Princeton University Press)

Landau L and Lifshitz E 1951 *The Classical Theory of Fields* (Reading, MA: Addison-Wesley)

Messiah A 1966 *Quantum Mechanics* vols I & II (New York: Wiley)

Panofsky W K H and Phillips M 1956 *Classical Electricity and Magnetism* (Reading, MA: Addison-Wesley)

Sargent III M, Scully M O and Lamb Jr W E 1974 in *Laser Physics* (Reading, MA: Addison-Wesley)

5

Theory of resonance ionisation spectroscopy

5.1 Introduction

In this chapter we will discuss the use of multistep laser ionisation as part of an ultrasensitive and spectroscopically selective detection scheme for atoms and small molecules. Here the emphasis will be on the study of selective ionisation schemes which yield nearly 100% ionisation of the selected species over a sizeable volume, thereby making possible the detection of very small numbers of atoms. Since the emphasis in this chapter is on the detection of very small numbers of atoms, we will neglect any modification of the laser field due to the presence of the medium. Some of the specific topics which will be covered are:

(i) the realm of validity of rate equations, and the quantum mechanical interpretation of the Einstein relations for the absorption and emission of electromagnetic radiation;
(ii) incorporation of laser ionisation into the theory of the interaction of laser fields with atoms;
(iii) loss of selectivity with increasing laser power densities;
(iv) general RIS schemes that work for most elements;
(v) estimation of effective volumes of ionisation.

Some topics will be discussed here which were not covered in our earlier review papers (Hurst *et al* 1979, Payne *et al* 1981, Hurst *et al* 1985) while other topics covered earlier have been omitted. Consequently, the review papers make good supplementary reading for the reader who wants to extend the study.

5.2 Thermodynamic arguments concerning the absorption and emission of radiation by an atomic vapour

The first discussions of the interaction of light with atoms were based upon rate equations, with the rates being determined by the Einstein relations. Such a description is still widely used in describing the interaction of laser light with atoms. For these reasons it is particularly important to understand Einstein's arguments and the limitations of the rate analysis method. We now present a derivation of the Einstein relations.

Consider an atomic vapour in thermodynamic equilibrium with the walls of a black body cavity. It is well known that the electromagnetic radiation density is given by the Planck distribution,

$$U(\omega)d\omega = (\hbar\omega^3 d\omega/\pi^2 c^3)[1/(e^{\hbar\omega/kT} - 1)]. \tag{5.1}$$

where $U(\omega)d\omega$ is the energy per unit volume with angular frequency in the range $\omega \leq \omega_1 \leq \omega + d\omega$. In terms of wavelength of the black body radiation, the Planck function has its maximum when $\lambda_m T = 0.29$. Consequently, at $T = 3000$ K the most abundant wavelength is around $\lambda_m = 1$ μm. In the latter situation many photons are present from the visible part of the spectrum, and light escaping from the cavity through a pinhole is quite visible to the eye.

If the walls of the black body are opaque, the Planck distribution is independent of the material which makes up the walls of the cavity. Also, the distribution in frequency is the same in the presence of various vapours in the cavity. This independence of the materials of the wall, or in the cavity, requires that the atoms in any intercavity vapour should emit and absorb light in such a way as to replace any light absorbed at a resonance line by an equal amount of light emitted into the same frequency region. In providing this balance to preserve the Planck distribution, the atoms will be distributed among their excited states in a way dictated by statistical mechanics.

We consider two states of an atom, $|1\rangle$ and $|u\rangle$, with the notation referring to the *lower* and *upper* states for some allowed one-photon resonance. The populations of the two states are related by

$$N_u/N_1 = (g_u/g_1)e^{-\hbar\omega_r/kT}. \tag{5.2}$$

The quantities $g_u = 2J_u + 1$ and $g_1 = 2J_1 + 1$ are statistical weight factors, with J_u and J_1 being the total angular momentum quantum numbers of the atomic states under consideration. Let $\sigma_a(\omega_r)$ be the absorption cross section for light at the resonance frequency, and $\sigma_s(\omega_r)$ be a cross section for the possibility of incident light *stimulating* an atom to emit a photon at the resonance frequency. Atoms in an excited state are known to spontaneously emit photons that have frequency distributions centred on or near the resonant frequency. We let the rate of spontaneous emission for the transition be $\gamma_{u,1}$, and the distribution of this light be given by $P(\omega)d\omega$, where $P(\omega)d\omega$ is the fraction of the light emitted in the range $\omega \leqslant \omega_1 \leqslant \omega + d\omega$. A photon at frequency ω, which we assume to be near resonance, has a probability $N_1\sigma_a(\omega)cdt$ of being absorbed in a time dt. Similarly, it has a probability $N_u\sigma_s(\omega)cdt$ of stimulating an emission at the same frequency ω in the time dt. Also, in the time dt there will be $N_uP(\omega)d\omega\gamma_{u,1}dt$ spontaneously emitted photons per cm^3 in the frequency region between ω and $\omega + d\omega$. If we consider a volume V with dimensions much larger than cdt, and write an equation which expresses the balance between energy emitted in the frequency range between ω and $\omega + d\omega$ against that absorbed, we have

$$V\hbar\omega N_uP(\omega)d\omega\gamma_{u,1}dt + VU(\omega)d\omega N_u\sigma_s(\omega)cdt = VU(\omega)d\omega N_1\sigma_a(\omega)cdt.$$
$$(5.3)$$

Using the ratio of populations given by equation (5.2), and solving for $U(\omega)$ we find

$$U(\omega) = (\hbar\omega P(\omega)\gamma_{u,1}/c\sigma_s(\omega))[e^{\hbar\omega/kT}g_1\sigma_a(\omega)/(g_u\sigma_s(\omega) - 1)]^{-1}. \quad (5.4)$$

The right-hand side of equation (5.4) must be equivalent to the Planck distribution quite independently of the two levels chosen, or even of the element chosen. This requires that

$$\sigma_s(\omega) = (\lambda^2/4)\gamma_{u,1}P(\omega) \quad\quad\quad (5.5)$$

and

$$g_1\sigma_a(\omega) = g_u\sigma_s(\omega). \quad\quad\quad (5.6)$$

In equation (5.5) $\lambda = 2\pi c/\omega$. These equations show that the line shapes of absorption, stimulated emission, and spontaneous emission are all very nearly the same; and, further, their magnitudes are closely related.

These remarkable relationships were first derived by Einstein, who applied the principle of detailed balance in more detail than described above, to arrive at relations similar to equations (5.5) and (5.6). The reader should notice that without postulating the existence of stimulated emission processes it would have been impossible to make equation (5.3) reduce to the Planck distribution. At the time of Einstein's work in 1917 the existence of stimulated processes was unknown either from experiment or theory. The entire reason for postulating the process was that it was required to give agreement with the Planck relationship.

Integrating both sides of equation (5.6) over ω and using the fact that $P(\omega)$ integrates to unity gives

$$\int \sigma_s(\omega)d\omega = \lambda^2\gamma_{u,1}/4$$

$$\simeq \sigma_s(\omega_r)\Gamma. \tag{5.7}$$

In equation (5.7) Γ is the width of the absorption or emission line (they are the same by equations (5.5) and (5.6)). We now have an estimate of the stimulated emission cross section at line centre:

$$\sigma_s(\omega_r) = \lambda^2 \gamma_{u,1}/4\Gamma. \tag{5.8}$$

In a situation at room temperature there will be very few black body photons which can pump an atomic transition, but if weak light with a spectral width much narrower than the absorption width for a transition is incident on a vapour which is otherwise in thermal equilibrium, this light should still be absorbed at resonance according to the above relationships, provided that there is a fast collisional mechanism to keep the magnetic sub-levels of the two states equally populated, or if the incident light is unpolarised. If plane or circularly polarised light is used in a collision-free situation, the above relationships fail (see the following section).

It is useful to use equation (5.8) to estimate the stimulated emission cross section at line centre. Suppose that $\gamma_{u,1} = 8.0 \times 10^7\,\text{s}^{-1}$, $\lambda = 6.0 \times 10^{-5}$ cm, and that Γ is just a Doppler width corresponding to a parallel component of velocity of $5.0 \times 10^4\,\text{cm s}^{-1}$, $\Gamma \simeq 5 \times 10^9\,\text{s}^{-1}$. Thus, $\sigma_s(\omega_r) \simeq 1 \times 10^{-11}\,\text{cm}^2$. Consequently, very little concentration of a vapour is required to cause the medium to be very opaque to light which is resonant for a transition starting from the atomic ground state.

In the limit where equations (5.5) and (5.6) apply, an incident flux of photons $\mathscr{F}$, with a frequency distribution $W(\omega)$, promotes atoms between the ground state $|0\rangle$ and an excited state $|1\rangle$ at a rate per cm^3 of

$$N_0 r(0, 1) = N_0 \mathscr{F} \int W(\omega)\sigma_a(\omega)\,\text{d}\omega$$

$$\simeq (g_1/g_0)N_0 \mathscr{F} W(\omega_r)(\gamma_{1,0}\lambda^2/4)$$

where N_0 is the concentration of the ground state population, and it was assumed that the width of $W(\omega)$ is very large compared with the width of $\sigma_a(\omega)$. A similar relationship can be written for the rate at which atoms in $|1\rangle$ are stimulated to emit, thus providing a source term for the ground state which is proportional to the population of the excited state. Spontaneous emission is responsible for another process which depopulates the excited state and provides a source term for the ground state. The above discussion provides a basis for the rate equation analysis of selective laser ionisation studies carried out in the presence of a high-pressure buffer gas, with a broad band width laser operated with low power densities, but long pulse lengths. The rate equations used in our discussion of the He(2^1S) experiment in Chapter 2 are based directly on the use of equations with rates given by the Einstein relations.

5.3 Density matrix formulation of atomic response

In Chapter 4 on the interaction of laser light with atoms we considered a very idealised situation, where the initial electronic state of the atom was a pure state, the atom was at rest, and the laser generated a beam which had a temporal profile and band width which repeated perfectly from shot to shot, yielding a transform-limited band width. Correspondingly, the approach was to determine the atomic response by solving the time-dependent Schrödinger equation. However, the situation is not usually so simple in most experiments. For instance, if there is a degeneracy in the lower state of the atoms which interact with the laser beam the atoms are generally in a mixed state in which the different degenerate states are initially equally populated. Further, the atoms are generally moving with some velocity distribution, and thereby photons with an angular frequency ω in the laboratory frame appear to have a frequency $\omega' = \omega[1 - (v_\parallel/c)]$ in the rest frame of an atom. If the concentration of the atoms is high, or if there is a high concentration of a buffer gas, there may be collisions which produce phase changes in the atomic wavefunction or the collisions may produce changes in the magnetic quantum number. The collisions occur at random times which are entirely out of control of the experimentalist. Finally, the laser which is being used may have a cavity gain which is not selective enough to pick a single longitudinal mode of the cavity. There could then be many frequency modes present, each of which started at a nearly random time dictated by a properly directed spontaneous emission at a frequency which can be amplified to high intensity. In the above situation the laser pulses are made up of many frequency modes which may be nearly randomly phased on a given pulse, and these phases do not repeat from pulse to pulse. It is clear that something like a density matrix formulation is needed in describing the atomic response.

If the dye laser pump, the dye, the nuclear motion of the atoms of interest and the electronic states of the atoms were all dealt with quantum mechanically, we could write equations for the density matrix and calculate proper averages of various observables as a trace over the states of the entire system of the product of the density operator and the operator representing the observable. However, a considerable simplification is achieved by taking a more modest approach in which the laser field is treated as classical; but it is assumed to have some reasonable statistical characteristics governing phase and amplitude fluctuations. Also, it is often appropriate to treat nuclear motion as occurring along classical trajectories. A truncated basis will usually be used in dealing with the electronic transitions quantum mechanically.

Consider an atom with a particular velocity and position in space. If the atom is initially in a state with quantum numbers α_i, m_i, J_i and interacts with buffer gas atoms and a laser field which will be seen to have a particular time profile, the time-dependent state vector evolves according to the time-dependent Schrödinger equation. Expanding the state vector in terms of the states of the unperturbed atom gives

$$|\Psi(t)\rangle = \sum a(\alpha_1, m_1, J_1, \chi, t)|\alpha_1, m_1, J_1\rangle \qquad (5.9)$$

where χ represents the functional dependence on the stochastic properties of the laser field and the collisional interactions. These, along with the initial positions, electronic states and velocities, will need to be averaged in ascertaining the behaviour of any observable which is determined by the atomic response. The expectation value of any observable for this particular initial state, velocity, position, and for the particular time histories for collisions and laser field, is

$$Q(\alpha_i, m_i, J_i, \chi, t) = \langle \Psi(t)|\hat{Q}|\Psi(t)\rangle$$

$$= \sum\sum a^*(\alpha_1, m_1, J_1, \chi, t)a(\alpha_p, m_p, J_p, \chi, t)\langle \alpha_1, m_1, J_1|\hat{Q}|\alpha_p, m_p, J_p\rangle$$

where $\hat{Q}$ is the quantum mechanical operator for the observable. To obtain what is measured as an average response for an ensemble of atoms experiencing collisions and subject to different laser pulses it is necessary to carry out the following average

$$\bar{Q}(t) = \sum\sum \rho(\alpha_1, m_1, J_1; \alpha_p, m_p, J_p, t)\langle \alpha_1, m_1, J_1|\hat{Q}|\alpha_p, m_p, J_p\rangle.$$

$$(5.10)$$

Here the $\rho(\alpha_1, m_1, J_1; \alpha_p, m_p, J_p, t)$ are the elements of the density matrix defined by

$$\rho(\alpha_1, m_1, J_1; \alpha_p, m_p, J_p, t)$$

$$= \langle\langle a^*(\alpha_1, m_1, J_1, \chi, t)a(\alpha_p, m_p, J_p, \chi, t)\rangle\rangle \qquad (5.11)$$

and $\langle\langle \ldots \rangle\rangle$ indicates the appropriate averages over initial electronic state, position, and velocity, along with the proper functional averages over the time histories of the laser field and the collisions. Now let us consider a special case which will illustrate some aspects of the density matrix approach.

5.4 Finite band width effects in a two-state model

Consider a low concentration of atoms interacting with a broad band width laser which is tuned very near a one-photon resonance between the ground state and an excited state. Assume that the laser band width is large compared with the Doppler width of the resonance transition under consideration, so that the velocity of the atoms can be ignored. Also, assume that the atoms are in a collision-free environment so that only the initial distribution among states, the position distribution, and the stochastic properties of the laser are of importance.

The ground state can be degenerate, with the degeneracy factor given by the usual $g_i = 2J_i + 1$. We take the laser to be plane polarised with polarisation along the z axis and direction of propagation along the x axis. Thus,

$$E(\rho, x, t) = e_z E_0(\rho, t) \cos(\bar{\omega}t - k_\omega x + \phi(t)) \qquad (5.12)$$

where $\phi(t)$ is the fluctuating phase, $E_0(\rho, t)$ is the fluctuating amplitude and $\bar{\omega}$ is the central frequency of the laser pulse which is chosen so that the time average of $\phi(t)$ is zero. Even a laser field of the type

$$E(\rho, x, t) = e_z \sum_i E_i(\rho, t) \cos(\omega_i t - k_i x + \phi_i)$$

can be put into the form of equation (5.12) by identifying the sum as the total component of a sum of vectors of length $E_i(\rho, t)$ along a fictitious axis from which they are oriented at angles $\theta_i = \omega_i t - k_i x + \phi_i$. We assume here that there are many closely spaced modes, generated in a cavity which does not have ideal optical properties. These modes can actually overlap and give rise to a continuous frequency spectrum, as will be assumed here. Write the degenerate lower states as $|\alpha_0, m_0, J_0\rangle$ and the upper states as $|\alpha_1, m_1, J_1\rangle$. The plane-polarised light will only couple upper and lower states with the same magnetic quantum numbers. Consequently, with short pulses, where spontaneous emission does not couple states with different m, the equations of motion are just like those of a two-state system. Using the rotating wave approximation and the selection rules for $\hat{D}_z$, the time-dependent Schrödinger equation gives

$$da(\alpha_0, m_0, J_0, t)/dt = i\Omega_1 e^{i\delta t} a(\alpha_1, m_0, J_1, t) \qquad (5.13a)$$

$$da(\alpha_1, m_0, J_1, t)/dt = i\Omega_1^* e^{-i\delta t} a(\alpha_0, m_0, J_0, t). \qquad (5.13b)$$

In these,

$$\Omega_1 = \langle \alpha_0, m_0, J_0 | \hat{D}_z | \alpha_1, m_0, J_1 \rangle E_0(\rho, t) \exp[i(\phi(t) - k_\omega x)]/(2\hbar)$$
$$(5.14a)$$

$$\delta = \bar{\omega} - \omega_r \qquad (5.14b)$$

where Ω_1 is related to the conventional Rabi frequency by $\Omega_R = 2\Omega_1$ and δ is the detuning between the central frequency of the laser and the unperturbed one-photon resonance frequency. The amplitudes used here are for an interaction situation, while those used in the discussion of the density matrix were in the Schrödinger system. The only difference between the two is a time-dependent phase factor which depends only on the relative position of the unperturbed energy levels and t. The latter phase factor is unaffected by the averaging which must be carried out.

These elements of the density matrix are properly averaged bi-linear products of amplitudes for the unperturbed atomic states. We now introduce a convenient set of bi-linear products, that is

$$W = a^*(\alpha_1, m_0, J_1, t)a(\alpha_0, m_0, J_0, t) \tag{5.15a}$$

$$Z = |a(\alpha_1, m_0, J_1, t)|^2 - |a(\alpha_0, m_0, J_0, t)|^2. \tag{5.15b}$$

Note that after proper averaging W differs only by a phase factor from the off-diagonal elements of the density matrix, while Z is the difference between two diagonal elements of the density matrix. Using equations (5.13) and their complex conjugates one finds

$$dW/dt = i\Omega_1 e^{i\delta t} Z \tag{5.16a}$$

$$dZ/dt = 4\text{Re}(i\Omega^* e^{-i\delta t} W). \tag{5.16b}$$

Integrating equation (5.16a) and using the fact that before the laser pulse W is zero, we have

$$W = i\int_{-\infty}^{t} \Omega_1(t')e^{i\delta t'} Z(t')dt'. \tag{5.17}$$

Using equation (5.17) in equation (5.16b) gives

$$dZ/dt = -4\text{Re}\int_{-\infty}^{t} \Omega_1^*(t)\Omega_1(t')e^{-i\delta(t-t')} Z(t')dt'. \tag{5.18}$$

We restrict the power density of the laser to levels such that $E_0(\rho, t)$ and $\phi(t)$ change a great deal during the time required for Z to change appreciably; i.e. Z is assumed to change very little in a time equal to the reciprocal band width of the laser in angular frequency units. To incorporate this assumption quantitatively, imagine carrying out pulse-to-pulse averaging on the quantity $E_0(\rho, t')E_0(\rho, t)\exp[i(\phi(t') - \phi(t))]$. We define

$$g(t_1, t_2) = \langle\langle E_0(\rho, t_1)e^{i\phi(t_1)} E_0(\rho, t_2)e^{-i\phi(t_2)}\rangle\rangle. \tag{5.19}$$

Equation (5.19) defines the *laser field autocorrelation function*. Before proceeding with the simplification of equation (5.18) we make a brief digression to discuss another application of the concept of time autocorrelation functions for physical quantities.

Autocorrelation functions play an important role in many areas of physics. For instance, consider a particle diffusing through a gas. In this case the velocity of the particle is constant between collisions, but when it passes within a few angstroms of another molecule its velocity undergoes a very rapid change in both direction and magnitude. As a result, after a few momentum-changing collisions, the memory of both the magnitude and direction of the initial velocity is totally lost. The displacement vector from the initial position to the position after a time such that many collisions have occurred is

$$R(t) = \int_0^t V(t_1)dt_1. \tag{5.20}$$

We now take the dot product of the displacement vector at time t with itself and average over a large number of particles, all starting from the same point and having a thermal distribution of initial velocities given by

$$\langle R(t)^2 \rangle = \int_0^t dt_2 \int_0^t \langle V(t_2) \cdot V(t_1) \rangle \, dt_1. \tag{5.21}$$

The quantity $\langle V(t_2) \cdot V(t_1) \rangle$ is the velocity autocorrelation function. The velocity autocorrelation should depend only on $t_2 - t_1$, and not upon the values of t_1 and t_2 individually. Further, the velocity autocorrelation function should decrease to nearly zero in the time required for only a few collisions. If $|t_2 - t_1|$ is many hundreds of times larger than the time between collisions, the integral over t_1 will only give contributions for t_1 very close to t_2. Let

$$g|t_2 - t_1| = \langle V(t_1) \cdot V(t_2) \rangle$$
$$\simeq \langle V^2 \rangle e^{-\Gamma_c |t_2 - t_1|}. \tag{5.22}$$

The quantity Γ_c is a measure of the rate of decay of the velocity autocorrelation function. Using $M\langle V^2 \rangle/2 = 3kT/2$ and equations (5.21) and (5.22) gives

$$\langle R(t)^2 \rangle = 6kTt/M\Gamma_c. \tag{5.23}$$

For comparison, the diffusion equation gives for the same situation $\langle R(t)^2 \rangle = 6Dt$, where D is the diffusion constant. It is obvious that $D = kT/(M\Gamma_c)$, in terms of the decay of the velocity autocorrelation function. A crude estimate of Γ_c is just the reciprocal time for one collision, which is $\Gamma_c \simeq \langle nv\sigma \rangle$, where n is the concentration, σ is the momentum transfer cross section and v is the speed.

We now return to the consideration of the laser field autocorrelation function of equation (5.19). In early commercial pulsed dye lasers the optical components were of poorer quality than those found in present day systems. The result was laser beams with poor beam divergence, band widths of several cm^{-1} and a frequency spectrum which showed few signs of a discrete mode structure. The reader should not assume that all dye lasers are automatically described by the model that follows, since the lasing process tends to work against some of the basic assumptions that will be made.

Our model is based on the assumption that the dye laser has a long cavity with a very low reflectance for the output coupler. Further, the 'flatness' of the optical components is poor and the grating permits reasonable amplification over a rather wide range of frequencies. The result is that the output of the laser has a beam divergence many times larger than the diffraction limit set by the waist of the output beam, and the frequency spectrum is continuous. The output present at any time is the result of amplification which started with a very large number of separate spontaneous emissions, each initiating a part of the output which is randomly phased relative to output initiated by another spontaneous emission. In the model we write

$$E(\rho, x, t) = e_x \int_0^\infty d\omega E(\rho, \omega, t) \cos(\omega t - k_\omega x + \phi(\omega)) \quad (5.24)$$

where the phase factors $\phi(\omega)$ satisfy

$$\langle\langle \exp[i(\phi(\omega') - \phi(\omega))]\rangle\rangle = \delta(\omega' - \omega). \quad (5.25)$$

This assumption is the limiting case of no phase correlation if the frequencies differ at all. Such an electromagnetic field is sometimes called a *chaotic field*. Real laser outputs are never quite as 'chaotic' as assumed in this model. The time dependence in $E(\rho, \omega, t)$ is a very slow time dependence characteristic of the pulsed pumping of the dye. Within the model the power density is

$$I(\rho, t) = (c/8\pi) \int_0^\infty d\omega |E(\rho, \omega, t)|^2 \quad (5.26)$$

$$= \hbar \bar{\omega} \mathscr{F}$$

where $\mathscr{F}$ is the photon flux in photons per cm^2 per second and $\bar{\omega}$ is the central frequency of the laser. In deriving equation (5.26) we have used the power density as the average of the Poynting vector over a few cycles. Thus, averaging $I = (c/4\pi)E^2$ over a few cycles and using equation (5.25) results in equation (5.26). The amplitude function $E(\rho, \omega, t)$ is assumed to peak at a frequency $\bar{\omega}$ and on applying equation (5.25) the field autocorrelation function becomes

$$g(t_1, t_2) = \int_{-\infty}^\infty d\varepsilon |E(\rho, \bar{\omega} + \varepsilon, t)|^2 e^{i\varepsilon(t_1 - t_2)}. \quad (5.27)$$

Thus the laser field autocorrelation function is proportional to the Fourier transform of the angular frequency spectrum of the laser field. If the frequency spectrum is symmetric about $\bar{\omega}$ the autocorrelation function will depend only on $|t_2 - t_1|$. Consequently, the time difference $|t_2 - t_1|$ over which the autocorrelation function decays is of the order of $1/\Delta\omega$ where $\Delta\omega$ is the band width of the laser. A Lorentzian line shape (this is rarely appropriate) would lead to

$$g(t_1, t_2) = (8\pi/c)I(\rho, t)e^{-\Gamma_L|t_1 - t_2|} \quad (5.28)$$

where Γ_L is the half width at half maximum of the frequency spectrum of the laser.

Approximations in equation (5.18) lead to rate equations. With the broad band laser described above operating at sufficiently low power densities so that Z cannot change appreciably in the time that is required for the decay of the laser field autocorrelation function, the average Z is determined by changes which have accumulated many laser coherence times earlier, while the rate of change of the average is governed by the statistical properties of the laser during just the last few coherence times. Thus, the average of the product of Z and the quantities dependent on the laser field should factorise into a product of averages. This requires that only certain average features of the laser should repeat accurately from pulse to pulse. Letting $\langle\langle Z \rangle\rangle \equiv \bar{Z}$ and using the fact that $\bar{Z}$ changes very little in a time $1/\Gamma_L$,

$$d\bar{Z}/dt = -(8\pi I |D_1|^2/ch^2)\text{Re}\int_{-\infty}^{t} dt' \exp[-i\delta(t - t') - \Gamma_L|t - t'|]$$
$$\times \bar{Z}(\rho, t') \tag{5.29}$$
$$= -(8\pi|D_1|^2\Gamma_L\bar{\omega}\mathscr{F}(\rho, t)/\hbar c)(\delta^2 + \Gamma_L^2)^{-1}\bar{Z}.$$

With the notation $D_1 = \langle\alpha_0, m_0, J_0|\hat{D}_z|\alpha_1, m_0, J_1\rangle$, and the realisation that

$$\bar{Z} = \rho(\alpha_1, m_0, J_1; \alpha_1, m_0, J_1, t) - \rho(\alpha_0, m_0, J_0; \alpha_0, m_0, J_0, t) \tag{5.30a}$$

$$1 = \rho(\alpha_1, m_0, J_1; \alpha_1, m_0, J_1, t) + \rho(\alpha_0, m_0, J_0; \alpha_0, m_0, J_0, t) \tag{5.30b}$$

$$W_s(\omega) = (\Gamma_L/\pi)[(\omega - \bar{\omega})^2 + \Gamma_L^2]^{-1} \tag{5.30c}$$

where $W_s(\omega)$ is the spectral function of the laser, we find the rate equations

$$d\rho_{1,1}/dt = R\rho_{0,0} - R\rho_{1,1} \tag{5.31a}$$

$$d\rho_{0,0}/dt = R\rho_{1,1} - R\rho_{0,0} \tag{5.31b}$$

Here,

$$R = (4\pi^2|D_1|^2\bar{\omega}\mathscr{F}/\hbar c)W_s(\omega_r). \tag{5.32}$$

Equation (5.32) is more general than the derivation based on a Lorentzian line shape. We have also used the following notation for the elements of the density matrix for this initial magnetic substate m_0:

$$\rho_{1,1} = \rho(\alpha_1, m_0, J_1; \alpha_1, m_0, J_1, t)$$

$$\rho_{0,0} = \rho(\alpha_0, m_0, J_0; \alpha_0, m_0, J_0, t).$$

In order to compare these results with the rate equations which result from the Einstein relations, one must examine some results from quantum electrodynamics and from the quantum theory of angular momentum. Spontaneous decay rates cannot be calculated in terms of atomic parameters without the quantisation of the electromagnetic field. However, the calculation of the spontaneous decay rate is the most elementary problem considered with quantised fields. The spontaneous transition rate between states $|\alpha_1, m_1, J_1\rangle$ and $|\alpha_0, m_0, J_0\rangle$ is

$$\gamma_s = 4\omega^3 \sum_{m_0,m_1} |\langle \alpha_1, m_1, J_1|\hat{D}_z|\alpha_0, m_0, J_0\rangle|^2[(2J_1 + 1)\hbar c^3]^{-1} \quad (5.33)$$

where J_1 is the total angular momentum quantum number of the upper state, and 0 and 1 refer to the lower and upper states, as in the last few pages. Equation (5.33) will be used later to demonstrate how the D_1 matrix elements can be determined from a knowledge of the spontaneous decay rate for the transition.

In the degenerate case, different magnetic substates can have very different dipole matrix elements, which complicates the relationship between the spontaneous decay rate of the upper state and the individual excitation and stimulated emission rates. Note that the coupling on the right-hand side of equation (5.31) can be thought of as a rate expressed as a product of an effective cross section and the flux of photons. The effective cross section is then given by

$$\sigma = 4\pi^2 \bar{\omega} |D_1|^2 W_s(\omega_r)/\hbar c. \quad (5.34)$$

The ratios of cross sections for pumping the populations for different m_0 are ratios of the squares of Clebsch–Gordon coefficients given by the Wigner–Eckert theorem as applied to the z component of a vector operator. Since these rates can be quite different, the saturation of the transition can give a very confusing power dependence.

Results from the theory of angular momentum are related to the calculation of rates of excitation and stimulated emission appearing in rate equations like equations (5.31). According to the Wigner–Eckert theorem (Edmonds 1960)

$$\langle \alpha', J', m'|\hat{D}_z|\alpha, J, m\rangle = (-1)^{J'-m'}\begin{pmatrix} J' & J & 1 \\ m' & m & 0 \end{pmatrix}\|\hat{D}_z\| \quad (5.35)$$

where $\|\hat{D}_z\|$ is the reduced matrix element of $\hat{D}_z$, which is independent of m' and m. The quantity in brackets is a Wigner 3j symbol, which is closely related to the Clebsch–Gordon coefficients. Treatments of the quantum theory of angular momentum are given in several quantum mechanics books (Merzbacher 1970, Messiah 1966). The orthogonality relations for the 3j coefficients yield

$$\gamma_s = (4\omega^3/3\hbar c^3)\|D_z\|^2/(2J_f + 1) \quad (5.36)$$

where J_f is the total angular momentum of the upper state and

$$\sum_{m,\,m'}\left|\langle\alpha',J',m'|\hat{D}_z|\alpha,J,m\rangle\right|^2=\|\hat{D}_z\|^2\sum_m\begin{pmatrix}J'&J&1\\-m&m&0\end{pmatrix}^2=\frac{\|\hat{D}_z\|^2}{3}.$$

The absorption oscillator strength, $F_{l\mapsto u}$, satisfies the following relationships:

$$F_{l\mapsto u}\equiv\left(\frac{2m_e(\omega_r)}{\hbar e^2}\right)\left(\frac{1}{2J_1+1}\right)\sum_{m_1,m_u}\left|\langle\alpha_1,J_1,m_1|\hat{D}_z|\alpha_u,J_u,m_u\rangle\right|^2$$

$$=(2m_e\omega_r/\hbar e^2 g_1)\|\hat{D}_z\|^2. \tag{5.37}$$

The spontaneous decay rate of the upper state and the absorption oscillator strength for the transition are related by

$$\gamma_s=8\pi^2(e^2/m_ec)(g_1/g_u)(F_{l\mapsto u}/\lambda_r^2).$$

For $J=J'$, but $J\neq 0$ (Edmonds 1960):

$$|\langle\alpha',J,m'|\hat{D}_z|\alpha,J,m\rangle|^2=\{4m^2/[2J(2J+1)(2J+2)]\}\|\hat{D}_z\|^2\delta_{m,m'}. \tag{5.38}$$

For $|J'-J|=1$, and with J_m being the larger of J and J':

$$|\langle\alpha',J',m'|\hat{D}_z|\alpha,J,m\rangle|^2$$

$$=\{(J_m^2-m^2)/[J_m(2J_m-1)(2J_m+1)]\}\|\hat{D}_z\|^2\delta_{m,m'}. \tag{5.39}$$

Equation (5.37) can be used to find the reduced matrix elements of $\hat{D}_z$ in terms of the absorption oscillator strength, and equations (5.38) and (5.39) give the $\hat{D}_z$ matrix elements starting from different magnetic substates as required in the rate equations. More specifically, we apply the above results to the case of a non-degenerate lower state.

To be non-degenerate $|0\rangle$ must be a state with $J=0$. Since with $J=0$, $J_f\neq 0$, thus $J_f=1$. Equation (5.33) becomes, for this special case,

$$\gamma_s=(4\omega^3/9\hbar c^3)\|\hat{D}_z\|^2 \tag{5.40}$$

for $J=0$, $J_f=1$. From equation (5.39)

$$|D_1|^2\equiv|\langle\alpha_1,0,1|D_z|\alpha_0,0,0\rangle|^2=\|D_z\|^2/3. \tag{5.41}$$

Substituting into equation (5.34) for the non-degenerate lower state case

$$\sigma=(3\pi^2c^2\gamma_s/\omega_r^2)W_s(\omega_r)$$

$$=(3\lambda^2\gamma_s/4)W_s(\omega_r). \tag{5.42}$$

It should be noted that equation (5.42) implies an absorption coefficient which is identical to that given by the Einstein relations. However, in the case considered here the stimulated emission cross section is equal to the absorption coefficient, while the Einstein relations give a value which is three times smaller than that for absorption. The basic difference is that there are no collisions here to mix magnetic substates. With plane-polarised light, any population of the upper state sub-levels with $m_1 = \pm 1$ would not be stimulated to go to the ground state. The Einstein relations assume rapid collisions to keep all magnetic substates equally populated; and with plane-polarised light only, the $m = 0$ state is stimulated to emit. This accounts for the factor of three difference.

In the high-pressure case, a rate analysis is valid because collisional dephasing causes loss of phase memory on a time-scale which is short compared to the time during which the populations change appreciably. Thus, perturbation theory can be used to calculate changes in the density matrix over a time longer than the time of decay of the phase memory. These changes add incoherently and rate equations are obtained. Above, we have seen that rate equations can result because of the randomness in the phase of effects caused by the laser beam itself. An analysis of this case neglects collisions and obtains an absorption rate identical to that implied by the Einstein relations. In the study of the $He(2^1S)$ population in Chapter 2, an analysis based on assuming rapid redistribution among magnetic sub-levels is definitely valid at high pressures (Payne *et al* 1975), but the inclusion of the degeneracy factors may not be appropriate at lower pressures. In the low-pressure study, rate equations would still be valid because of the extreme incoherence of the laser.

Before proceeding further it is worthwhile noting that the definition of the autocorrelation function implies for a Lorentzian line shape

$$\langle\langle \Omega_1^*(t')\Omega_1(t)\rangle\rangle = \langle\langle |\Omega_1(t)|^2\rangle\rangle e^{-\Gamma_L|t-t'|}.$$

Using this relation in equation (5.18) gives another form for R:

$$R = 2\pi\langle\langle |\Omega_1(t)|^2\rangle\rangle W_s(\omega_r).$$

At line centre

$$R = 2(\langle\langle |\Omega_1(t)|^2\rangle\rangle/\Gamma_L).$$

Clearly, the above relationships can be used to calculate the Rabi frequency based on an absorption oscillator strength for the transition. From the material in §4.5, one sees that rate equations could be applied equally well to two- or three-photon excitation when the laser band width exceeds the multiphoton Rabi frequency, any AC Stark shifts in the transition and the Doppler width of the transition. The excitation rate is then similar to the above expression for R, but with the Ω_1 replaced with the corresponding multiphoton quantity given by equation (4.126). The major modification would have to do with the proper inclusion of photon statistics for the multiphoton case. See Payne *et al* (1981) for some examples of two-photon excitation.

At this point we can say quite clearly what is required in order for a rate equation analysis to be correct. The pumping by the light source must be so weak that (either due to the coherence of the light, or due to some memory destroying mechanism such as collisional dephasing or resonance energy transfer) the atoms totally lose phase memory in a time interval during which only a very small change in the state populations is induced. In this case, the change in state populations during successive time periods (long times compared with the time of retention of state phase information) can be calculated by perturbation theory and added incoherently; thereby leading to a set of simultaneous equations for the diagonal elements of the density matrix. With a much stronger laser field, such that for much of the pulse $|D_1 E_0(t)/\hbar| \gg \Gamma_L$, the changes in the amplitude can be of the order of unity in time intervals which are short compared with the laser coherence time or any collisional dephasing effect. In this situation the line shape is dominated by power broadening (even for a large band width laser) and a rate equation analysis is incorrect. We will presently see that adding ionisation into the laser–atom interaction problem usually leads to equations which are very similar to the ones obtained in the absence of ionisation. The major difference in the equations of motion with ionisation included is that damping terms which are related to the ionisation rate enter the equations of motion. The damping terms destroy memory and actually help in making rate equations valid.

To get some indication of the effects that degeneracy can cause suppose that the lower state to be excited has $J_0 = 1$, and that the upper state is chosen to have $J_1 = 0$. If there are no collisions, and plane-polarised light is used, only the $m = 0$ substate can be excited. Consequently, if the upper state can be ionised by another photon there is an upper limit of $1/3$ on the ionisation probability. Obviously, degeneracy requires great care in choosing ionisation schemes. Care must also be taken in a collision free situation with the state of polarisation of the light. An unlikely example will illustrate this point. Suppose that the ground state of an atom has $J_0 = 0$ and that one-photon resonance excitation is carried out with circularly polarised light. If a second resonance transition is pumped between the excited state and a second excited state with $J_1 = 0$, it will be found that with light in a cross propagating beam polarised parallel to the direction of propagation of the first beam, excitation to the second excited state does not occur. Only $m_1 = \pm 1$ states are made by the first laser, while only the $m_1 = 0$ substate can be pumped to the second excited state by the second laser. The situation changes if there is a different angle between the two laser beams. Of course, laser beams are never exactly plane polarised, nor can one make purely circularly polarised light. In the above situations, if the power density was made sufficiently high, the small component of the other state of polarisation would eventually come into play and the other magnetic substates would finally be pumped. However, the power density required to saturate the transition(s) would appear to be anomalously high.

The reader will have noticed by now that equations (5.34) to (5.40) also permit the calculation of Rabi frequencies for magnetic substates when plane-polarised light is used. Analogous results exist to permit the calculation of Rabi frequencies when circularly polarised light is employed.

5.5 The incorporation of laser ionisation into the equations of motion

As an example of how laser ionisation can be included in the theory of the interaction of laser fields with atoms (see, for example, Choi and Payne (1977) and Hurst *et al* (1979)), we consider the simplest of all selective ionisation schemes. Assume that a laser is tuned on, or very near, a one-photon resonance between state $|0\rangle$ and state $|1\rangle$ (we suppress J and other quantum numbers except M_J when dealing with the discrete states). Suppose further that either photons from the first laser can produce one-photon ionisation of state $|1\rangle$, or that a second laser beam is present which can produce one-photon ionisation of state $|1\rangle$. The situation is shown schematically in figure 5.1.

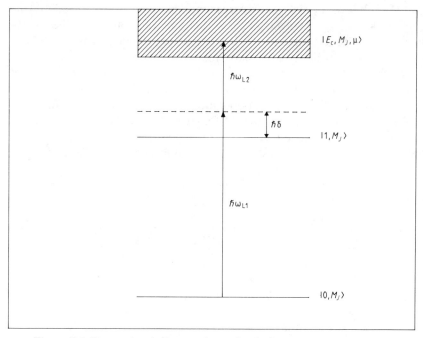

Figure 5.1 Energy level diagram for a simple laser ionisation scheme.

Very little power density is required to saturate a discrete–discrete transition, while the power density (for a given pulse length) must be much higher for ionisation, thus a two colour laser scheme usually makes a superior RIS method. This is particularly true if both wavelengths are chosen so that they are far from resonance with any one-photon transition other than the $|0\rangle \rightarrow |1\rangle$ transition which we desire to pump. Frequently, a good RIS scheme results by making the power density of the first laser just sufficient to saturate the discrete–discrete transition, but with the photon energy relatively high, so that the much more powerful laser used for ionisation is in the visible or infrared region of the spectrum. In this way only the long wavelength laser is capable of appreciably pumping multiphoton processes, and its wavelength is long so that only high-order multiphoton ionisation (MPI) processes of other elements (that might be present) could lead to interfering ionisation signals. The second laser might, for instance, be the fundamental or second harmonic of a Nd–YAG laser. In what follows assume:

(i) there is no collisional mixing of magnetic substates;
(ii) the laser light is plane polarised;
(iii) the laser pulse lengths are very short compared with spontaneous decay rates out of magnetic substates of $|1\rangle$.

With the above assumptions the M_J sub-level of $|0\rangle$ will only couple to the M_J sub-level of $|1\rangle$; and correspondingly only M_J sub-levels in the continuum will be involved. Thus, equations of motion for the amplitudes of different magnetic sub-levels are not coupled. This leads to a two-state plus ionisation continuum model for each of the M_J sub-levels, in which the M_J population of $|0\rangle$ is coupled to the M_J population of $|1\rangle$ and the latter is coupled to M_J amplitudes in the ionisation continuum; but different M_J populations are uncoupled. If J for state $|1\rangle$ is chosed to be smaller than J for $|0\rangle$, then part of the population of $|0\rangle$ will not be excited except at much higher power densities where the imperfections in the state of polarisation of the laser become important.

We pick a particular M_J and assume the time-dependent state vector to be of the form

$$|\Psi(t)\rangle = a_0(t)e^{-i\omega_0 t}|0, M_J\rangle + a_1(t)e^{-i\omega_1 t}|1, M_J\rangle$$

$$+ \sum_\mu \int_{C_{M_J}} dE_c A(E_c, \mu, t)e^{-iE_c t/\hbar}|E_c, M_J, \mu\rangle \quad (5.43)$$

where $|E_c, M_J, \mu\rangle$ is a continuum state corresponding to energy E_c, and μ allows for coupling to more than one J state in the continuum. The continuum states are orthogonal and are normalised so that

$$\langle E'_c, \mu' | E_c, \mu \rangle = \delta_{\mu', \mu} \delta(E'_c - E_c). \tag{5.44}$$

The continuum states are also orthogonal to $|0, M_J \rangle$ and $|1, M_J \rangle$. We apply the time dependent Schrödinger equation to equation (5.43) and make use of equation (5.44), and the fact that discrete states are orthonormal to obtain:

$$da_0/dt = i \exp[i(\omega_0 - \omega_1 + \omega_{L1})t]\Omega_1(0 \to 1)a_1$$

$$da_1/dt = i \exp[-i(\omega_0 - \omega_1 + \omega_{L1})t]\Omega^*_1(0 \to 1)a_0$$

$$+ i\sum_\mu \int_{C_{M_J}} dE_c \exp\{i[\omega_1 - (E_c/\hbar) + \omega_{L2}]t\}$$

$$\times A(E_c, \mu, t)(E_2\langle 1, M_J | \hat{D}_z | E_c, M_J, \mu \rangle / 2\hbar)$$

$$dA(E_c, \mu, t)/dt$$

$$= i \exp\{-i[\omega_1 - (E_c/\hbar) + \omega_{L2}]t\}a_1(E_2\langle E_c, M_J, \mu | \hat{D}_z | 1, M_J \rangle / 2\hbar). \tag{5.45}$$

At first glance equation (5.45) appears to be very complicated. By adding the possibility of ionising $|1, M_J \rangle$ we have replaced two simultaneous equations by a non-denumerable infinity of simultaneous equations. Already we have made several approximations. We have truncated our basis by using only two discrete states, we have used the rotating wave approximation, and we have neglected the coupling of continuum states to other continuum states. If the power densities are not too high these are all good approximations. The Rabi frequency $\Omega_1(0 \to 1) = E_1(t)e^{i\phi_1(t)}D_z(0,1,M_J)/(2\hbar)$, where E_1 is the amplitude of the first laser and $\phi_1(t)$ is the fluctuating phase of the first laser. It has been assumed that the second laser totally dominates the coupling to the continuum states. There are $2J_0 + 1$ sets of equations like equation (5.45), with the Rabi frequency and the discrete–continuum matrix elements depending on the M_J for state $|0, M_J \rangle$ being described.

Obviously, a simplification must be found if equations (5.45) are to be solved. Let $A_1 = \exp[i(\omega_0 - \omega_1 + \omega_{L1})t]a_1$ and transform equations (5.45) accordingly. We can now proceed with our simplification knowing that when the laser is tuned off the one-photon resonance, unlike a_1, there will be no rapid oscillation in A_1. The first step is to integrate the third equation from a time before the laser pulse up to t. The resulting formal expression for $A(E_c, \mu, t)$ can then be used to replace the continuum amplitude in the second equation in terms of $A_1(t)$. The second equation becomes

$$dA_1/dt = i\delta A_1 + i\Omega^*_1 a_0 - (1/4\hbar^2)\int_{-\infty}^t dt' A_1(t')E_2(t')E_2(t)Q(t - t') \tag{5.46}$$

where $\delta = \omega_{L1} - \omega_1 + \omega_0$ and

$$Q(t - t')$$

$$= \int_{C_{M_J}} dE_c S(E_c, M_J) \exp\{-i[(E_c/\hbar) - \omega_0 - \omega_{L2} - \omega_{L1}](t - t')\} \quad (5.47)$$

with

$$S(E_c, M_J) \equiv \sum_\mu |\langle 1, M_J| \hat{D}_z |E_c, M_J, \mu\rangle|^2. \quad (5.48)$$

Assume that in the region of energy very near $E_{c0} = \hbar(\omega_0 + \omega_{L1} + \omega_{L2})$, $S(E_c, M_J)$ is very constant over a region of 0.001 eV. This precludes the energy conserving part of the ionisation continuum from being extremely close to an auto-ionising resonance; but, otherwise, this will generally be the case. Note that if the integral over E_c in equation (5.47) is broken into an integral over a small range given by $-\varepsilon_1 \leqslant E_c - \hbar(\omega_0 + \omega_{L1} + \omega_{L2}) \leqslant \varepsilon_1$, plus the integral over the rest of the continuum, and if S is constant over the $2\varepsilon_1$ region about the point of energy conservation, the contribution to Q is a quantity which decreases rapidly for $|t - t'| > 1/\varepsilon_1$. In fact, if $R(t)$ is a function which only changes appreciably over periods of time larger than 10^{-12} s, then

$$\int_{-\infty}^t dt' R(t') Q(t - t')$$

$$\simeq \pi \hbar S[\hbar(\omega_0 + \omega_{L1} + \omega_{L2}), M_J] R(t)$$

$$- iR(t)\hbar\rho \int dE_c \, S(E_c, M_J)/[E_c - \hbar(\omega_0 + \omega_{L1} + \omega_{L2})]. \quad (5.49)$$

Note that

$$E_2(t)^2 = (8\pi\hbar\omega_{L2}/c)\mathscr{F}_2$$

$$\sigma_I = (4\pi^2/c)\sum_\mu |\langle 1, M_J| \hat{D}_z |\hbar(\omega_0 + \omega_{L1} + \omega_{L2}), M_J, \mu\rangle|^2 \quad (5.50)$$

where $\mathscr{F}_2$ is the photon flux for laser two, and σ_I is the photo-ionisation cross section of the excited state with magnetic quantum number M_J. Using equations (5.49) and (5.50) in equation (5.46) one finds

$$dA_1/dt = i[\delta + \Delta_2(t) + (i\sigma_I \mathscr{F}_2/2)]A_1 + i\Omega_1^*(0 \to 1)a_0$$

$$da_0/dt = i\Omega_1(0 \to 1)A_1. \quad (5.51)$$

The quantity $\Delta_2(t)$ is a small AC Stark shift related to the principle value integral which arises when equation (5.49) is applied. It is apparent that the effect of including the photo-ionisation of $|1, M_J\rangle$ is to introduce a damping term related to the rate of photo-ionisation and an AC Stark shift into the equation for A_1. Otherwise the continuum states are absent from the equations of motion and we again have a two-state problem for the amplitudes of a lower state and a state being excited.

One can prove from equations (5.45) that for all t:

$$|a_0(t)|^2 + |A_1(t)|^2 + \sum_\mu \int_{C_{M_J}} dE_c |A(E_c, \mu, t)|^2 = 1. \qquad (5.52)$$

The ionisation probability is the term in equation (5.52) involving the integral over continuum states evaluated at $t = \infty$. It then follows that the ionisation probability for an atom with magnetic quantum number M_J is

$$P_I = 1 - |a_0(\infty)|^2 - |A_1(\infty)|^2. \qquad (5.53)$$

The above analysis can be generalised to cases where more than one resonance transition is used before ionisation. For instance, if three discrete states are involved the problem can often be reduced to a three-state problem with damping terms related to photo-ionisation rates. Also, if the coupling between the discrete transitions involves two-photon (or higher order) excitation, the inclusion of ionisation proceeds in the same way and modifies the equations for the discrete state problem with no ionisation by introducing damping terms equal to half the photo-ionisation rate for the state and by introducing AC Stark shifts into the equations for the amplitudes of the discrete states. Similarly, none of the above argument is dependent on the coupling of the discrete states by way of one-photon processes. For instance, with two-photon resonance coupling and three-photon ionisation one obtains two-state equations like equation (5.51), with the quantity $\Omega_1(0 \rightarrow 1)$ replaced by half of the two-photon Rabi frequency. The equations of motion are hardly complicated at all by including the photo-ionisation of excited states.

5.6 Near-resonant two-photon ionisation

In this section we present the effects of high power densities on two-photon ionisation yields when the laser is tuned through a one-photon resonance. The simplest of all RIS schemes involves the two-photon ionisation of isolated atoms by a pulsed laser having a Fourier-transform-limited band width. An analysis of this scheme will be the subject of the present section. The main purpose of this section is to demonstrate several effects which lead to a loss of spectroscopic selectivity when the power densities are increased well above the levels required to bring about saturation of the discrete–discrete transitions and saturation of the ionisation step.

Assume that the dye laser generates linearly polarised light with a Fourier-transform-limited band width. With linearly polarised light (and in the absence of collisions) M_J is preserved in both absorption and ionisation. Consequently, if the pulse length is short compared with the lifetime of the excited state against spontaneous decay, the equations of motion for atoms initially in state $|0, M_J\rangle$ involve only those amplitudes for other resonance and continuum states with the same M_J. This is in contrast to the same problem with laser pulses which are long compared with spontaneous decay rates, or with collisional mixing of the magnetic substates, where there would be coupling between states with different magnetic quantum numbers and the previous arguments would not hold. Doppler shifts will also be ignored since we will be discussing cases where the power broadening of the discrete–discrete transition is large compared with the Doppler width.

In the case of only one resonance and two-photon ionisation one obtains for short pulses $2J_0 + 1$ sets of two-state problems—one for each possible initial value of the magnetic quantum number M_J. The reduction to a two-state problem involves the arguments presented in the last section in order to eliminate the continuum amplitudes. Thus, for each initial substate one has an energy level diagram as indicated in figure 5.2.

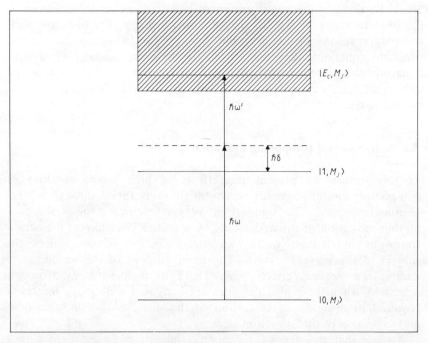

Figure 5.2 Energy level diagram for atoms initially in $|0, M_J\rangle$. The laser is tuned near one-photon resonance between $|0\rangle$ and $|1\rangle$ and with linearly polarised light M_J does not change so that different two-state plus ionisation continuum models apply for each initial M_J.

Assume that the transform-limited band width laser has a pulse shape function of the form

$$g(t) = \exp[-(t/\tau)^2]. \tag{5.54}$$

Thus,

$$E = kE_0 g(t) \cos(\omega t + \phi_0)$$

where k is a unit vector in the z direction and E_0 is the peak amplitude for the laser field. If the dominant laser in pumping the ionisation step is actually a separate laser it is assumed to have the same pulse shape function, but a different peak amplitude and frequency. Using the rotating wave approximation, along with the techniques of the last section for dealing with the amplitudes of the ionisation continuum states, one finds for equations of motion $((\mathbf{a})_0 \equiv a_0$ and $(\mathbf{a})_1 \equiv A_1)$:

$$d\mathbf{a}/dt = i\mathbf{B}(t)\mathbf{a} \tag{5.55}$$

where

$$\mathbf{B} = \begin{pmatrix} 0 & \Omega_0 g(t) \\ \Omega_0^* g(t) & \delta + i(\Gamma_0/2)g^2(t) \end{pmatrix}. \tag{5.56}$$

Above, Ω_0 is the peak value of half the Rabi frequency for the M_J under consideration, $\Gamma_0 \equiv \sigma_i \mathscr{F}_0$ is the photo-ionisation rate out of $|1, M_J\rangle$ and $\delta \equiv \omega - \omega_1 + \omega_0$. $\mathscr{F}_0$ is the peak photon flux and σ_i is the photo-ionisation cross section of the state $|1, M_J\rangle$. The derivation of equations (5.55) and (5.56) exactly parallels the last section.

In Chapter 4 it was seen that modest laser power densities can make a one-photon Rabi frequency very large. For instance, with $I = 10^6$ W cm^{-2} the quantity Ω_0 is sometimes as large as 10^{11} s^{-1}. For $\tau \approx 10^{-8}$ s, even when $\delta \approx 10^9$ s^{-1}, then an adiabatic solution would be valid. The small region where the adiabatic approximation does not hold is only a fraction of a percent of the power-broadened width of the ionisation line shape. Using equation (5.53) from the present chapter and equation (4.111) we find for $|\Omega_0| \gg \Gamma_0$

$$P_I =$$
$$1 - \exp\left(-\Gamma_0 \tau \int_{-\infty}^{\infty} dx \exp(-2x^2)\left(1 - (|\delta|/2)[(\delta/2)^2 + |\Omega_0|^2 \exp(-2x^2)]^{-1/2}\right)\right). \tag{5.57}$$

Equation (5.57) can be put into a simpler form

$$P_I = 1 - \exp\left(-\sigma_i \mathscr{F}_0 \tau Q2|\Omega_0|/|\delta|\right) \tag{5.58}$$

where

$$Q(x) = \int_0^{\infty} dy \, e^{-2y^2}\left[1 - (1 + x^2 e^{-2y^2})^{-1/2}\right]. \tag{5.59}$$

The function $Q(x)$ has the following limiting properties:

$$Q(x) \simeq \pi^{1/2}x^2/8 \qquad x \ll 1$$
$$\simeq (\pi/8)^{1/2} \qquad x \gg 1. \qquad (5.60)$$

Whenever $|\Omega_0|\tau > 20$ and $|\Omega_0| \gg \Gamma_0$ the entire line shape for P_I is given very accurately by equations (5.58) and (5.59). At high power the expression will finally fail due to a breakdown of the two-state approximation—a failure which occurs when the width of the resonance starts to overlap another resonance.

Figure 5.3 shows a numerically generated plot of $Q(x)$ and compares it with a least square fit to a function of the form:

$$Q(x) \simeq (\pi^{1/2}/8)x^2[1 + c_1x + (x^2/2^{3/2})]^{-1}. \qquad (5.61)$$

The least square fit of a rational function of this type to numerically generated values of $Q(x)$ yields $c_1 = 0.392$. A basis for such an approximation can be found from either the general methods for constructing rational approximations, or by considering a laser pulse

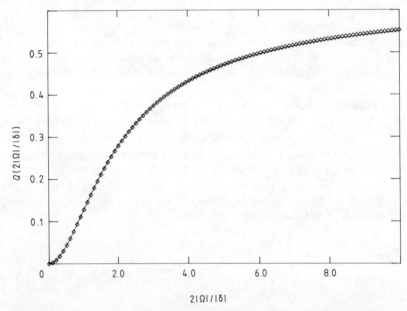

Figure 5.3 Plot of the function $Q(x)$ versus x. The discrete points were generated numerically from equation (5.59). The solid line is a rational function of the form $Q_0(x) = 0.2216x^2(1 + 0.392x + 0.3536x^2)^{-1}$. The coefficient of the linear term in the denominator of the rational function was chosen by a least square fit. The other two parameters were chosen so as to make the limiting values for $x \ll 1$ and for $x \gg 1$ agree with equation (5.60).

shape which rises rather quickly at $t = 0$ and stays rather flat until the time $t = \tau$. For a $g(t)$ with this characteristic the integral would get very little contribution except when $0 < t < \tau$, and from this interval the value is just the integrand times τ. This consideration could lead to an effective $Q(x)$ which is Lorentzian in δ. The addition of a linear term in the denominator gives an extra parameter in the fit.

When the parameter $\sigma_i \mathcal{F}_0 \tau \gg 1$ the ionisation probability can be close to unity even when the laser is detuned much further than the power-broadened width from line centre and the occupation probability of the excited state is always much less than 1/2. Figure 5.4 shows the line shape of P_I for various values of $\sigma_i \mathcal{F}_i \tau$.

When $\sigma_i \mathcal{F}_0 \tau > 20$ the product of Q and this quantity will be $\ln(2)$ for a value of δ which is considerably larger than Ω_0. In this case, Q has the $x \ll 1$ limiting form from equation (5.60) and one finds for this limit:

$$\delta_{\text{FWHM}} = 2|\Omega_0|[(\pi^{1/2}/2\ln(2))\sigma_i \mathcal{F}_0 \tau]^{1/2}$$

$$\simeq 1.13|\Omega_0|(\sigma_i \mathcal{F}_0 \tau)^{1/2}. \tag{5.62}$$

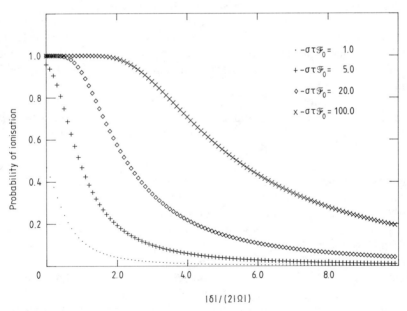

Figure 5.4 Line shapes for ionisation for different values of $\sigma_i \mathcal{F}_0 \tau$. The curves were calculated from equation (5.58) with the rational approximation to $Q(x)$ being used to speed the calculation. These line shapes still do not represent what would be observed in most experiments with narrow band width pulsed lasers, due to the fact that we have not included the spatial variation of the laser field amplitude.

Equation (5.62) is in very good agreement with figure 5.4 for the case where $\sigma_i \mathscr{F}_0 \tau$ is greater than 20.

Some of the early studies involving RIS tended to make the technique look easier than it actually is due to the use of long pulse dye lasers under circumstances where rate equations applied and there was almost no chance of loss of selectivity due to multiphoton ionisation or power broadening. In particular, in some of the early work Cs atoms were ionised in the presence of a very large concentration of Ar and CH_4 (Hurst *et al* 1977, Kramer *et al* 1978, Grossman *et al* 1977). In these a single flash lamp pumped dye laser was used for both excitation and ionisation. In the idealised situation there was almost no chance of accidental interference, due to the fact that neither Ar nor CH_4 has resonance absorptions which are lower in energy than 10 eV. Thus, an accidental four-photon absorption resonance or an off-resonance five-photon absorption would have been required to ionise methane. Six photons at 459 nm are required to ionise Ar. The lasers used in the Cs study had a 1 μs pulse length so that even though photon fluences greater than 10^{17} cm^{-2} were used, the power densities were only 10^5 W cm^{-2}. In contrast, most recent applications of RIS lasers have pulse lengths about 100 times shorter. Consequently, if a single laser scheme is used for ionisation the laser power density will need to be about 100 times higher than in the early ORNL experiments in order to make ionisation probabilities close to unity. A fifth-order background would be increased by ten orders of magnitude over the studies with microsecond pulses.

In most detection problems the situation is not nearly as contrived as the one described above, and the use of a single dye laser which is sufficiently powerful to both excite and ionise is not a good idea. It is rare to have an application where the atom to be detected can be excited by one photon and ionised by two, while all of the more abundant species require five photons for ionisation. To demonstrate the problem, note that most good dye lasers have pulse lengths of less than 10^{-8} s, while a typical photo-ionisation cross section is 10^{-18} s. In order for $\sigma \mathscr{F}_0 \tau > 3$ (for P_I values near unity), we must have a photon fluence of approximately 3×10^{18} cm^{-2}. Since a typical ionisation potential is around 8 eV, this fluence corresponds to nearly 2 J cm^{-2}, or to a power density of 2×10^8 W cm^{-2}. With power densities this high it is not unusual to have power-broadened ionisation line widths as wide as 10 cm^{-1}. At power densities as high as 10^8 W cm^{-2} the Rabi frequency is approximately 10^{12} s^{-1}, which is large compared with a band width of approximately 0.5 cm^{-1} for a typical broad band width dye laser. For detunings much larger than the band width, similar power-broadening effects should be observed for broad band width lasers. Ideally, a dye laser would be restricted to power densities which are just sufficient to power broaden over the Doppler profile, while the second laser should have a much longer wavelength. With this ionisation method the high-power laser can only produce a background signal by an off-resonance, high-order multiphoton ionisation process.

In an earlier review (Payne *et al* 1981) we have pointed out some of the relative advantages which can be achieved in carrying out single colour laser ionisation if the RIS process is started with Doppler-free (Vasilenko *et al* 1970), two-photon excitation. In the latter case the power density required to ionise is similar to that required to saturate typical two-photon transitions. However, the required wavelength is usually longer than when one starts with one-photon excitation, so that interferences either require higher order processes or an accidental resonance. Doppler-free, two-photon absorption requires counter propagating beams, but the Doppler-free absorption process, in which one photon is absorbed from each beam, can be used in order to greatly reduce the loss of selectivity due to the Doppler effect (Payne *et al* 1981, Vasilenko *et al* 1970). Doppler effects are large in many applications of laser ionisation in which atomisation of the sample is achieved by ion sputtering or laser ablation: see Chapter 8.

It may be useful to give an actual example of the determination of the Rabi frequency, $2|\Omega_0|$. In §5.4 of this chapter the theory of angular momentum was used to relate matrix elements of $\hat{D}_z \equiv \Sigma_i e z_i$ between two atomic states to the absorption oscillator strength for the transition. Equations (5.38) and (5.39), together with $\|D_z\|^2 = (\hbar e^2 g_1 F_{1 \to u})(2 m_e \omega_r)$, are particularly useful when combined with

$$|\Omega_0|^2 \equiv |\langle 1, J_f, M_f | \hat{D}_z | 0, J_i, M_i \rangle|^2 E_0^2 / (4\hbar^2) \tag{5.63}$$

$$= (2\pi \omega_r \mathcal{F}_0(\omega)/\hbar c) K(J_m, M_i) \delta_{M_F, M_i} (\hbar e^2 g_1 F_{1 \to u} / 2 m_e \omega_r)$$

where ω_r is the resonance angular frequency and $\mathcal{F}_0(\omega)$ is the peak photon flux for the first laser. The units at this point are cgs. The quantity J_m is the larger of the two total angular momentum quantum numbers involved in the transition, and $K(J_m, M_i)$ is given by

$$K(J_m, M_i) = 4M_i^2 / [(2J_m)(2J_m + 1)(2J_m + 2)] \quad \text{for } \Delta J = 0 \text{ and } J_m \neq 0 \tag{5.64}$$

$$= (J_m^2 - M_i^2) / [J_m(2J_m - 1)(2J_m + 1)] \quad \text{for } |\Delta J| = 1.$$

The term ΔJ is the change in total angular momentum quantum number for the transition. If we simplify equation (5.63) and introduce the power density in W cm^{-2} by multiplying $\mathcal{F}_0(\omega)$ by the photon energy in joules, then

$$|\Omega_0|^2 / I(\text{W cm}^{-2}) = 1.336 \times 10^{13} K(J_m, M_0) \lambda g_1 F_{1 \to u}, \tag{5.65}$$

where $|\Omega_0|$ is in radians per second, λ is the resonant wavelength in angstrom units and I is the power density in $W \, cm^{-2}$. Consider the $3s(J = 1/2) \rightarrow 4p(J = 3/2)$ transition in Na. The National Bureau of Standards tables of atomic transition probabilities give $\lambda = 5889.95$ and $F_{1 \rightarrow u} = 0.63$. Using $g_i = 2$ we find from equation (5.65) that

$$|\Omega_0|(I)^{-1/2} = 1.31 \times 10^8.$$

Equation (5.65), along with (5.63), predicts that in transitions where the total angular momentum quantum number changes, the states with the smallest $|M_J|$ are easiest to pump; while for $\Delta J = 0$ transitions the states with the largest $|M_J|$ have the largest Rabi frequencies.

Arguments which are similar to those used above for the Rabi frequency can be used to relate photo-ionisation cross sections for different M_J to measurements or calculations which tabulate the average of the cross section at the same photon energy over the magnetic substates of the state being ionised. One simply uses the fact that the photo-ionisation cross section is proportional to the square of a $\hat{D}_z$ matrix element and equations (5.38) and (5.39) hold equally well for discrete–continuum transitions.

5.7 Methods of RIS using commercial lasers

5.7.1 Laser systems

Several good commercial dye lasers suitable for RIS are available, including various dye laser systems pumped by either the XeCl excimer laser, or harmonics of the Nd–YAG. With both of these pump sources several companies offer dye lasers with pulse lengths between 2 ns and 20 ns and band widths (without the use of intercavity etalons) of $0.1 \, cm^{-1}$ to $0.5 \, cm^{-1}$ in the visible part of the spectrum. With both pump lasers, the dye laser output is in the range of tens of mJ in the visible region of the spectrum. With a 1 mm beam diameter this translates to greater than $1 \, J \, cm^{-2}$, or to a power density greater than or equal to $10^8 \, W \, cm^{-2}$. With frequency doubling and stimulated Raman used to extend the frequency range, both dye laser pumps can be used to generate at least 1 mJ for wavelengths in the region $265 \leqslant \lambda \leqslant 1500$ nm. The Nd–YAG pumped dye lasers have an advantage over the excimer pumped devices in the region $215 \leqslant \lambda \leqslant 260$ nm due to the possibility of frequency-doubling the output from a dye laser (using a highly efficient red dye) and then frequency-summing the doubled light with the fundamental of the Nd–YAG. On the other hand, the excimer pumped dye laser can only be frequency doubled with conversion efficiencies less than 1% to cover this wavelength region. Consequently, the Nd–YAG systems have outputs of approximately

1 mJ in this region, while excimer pumped systems typically have outputs of the order of a few hundred μJ.

With either of the above dye laser systems, stimulated anti-Stokes processes in H_2 can yield 10^8–10^{14} photons per pulse in the region $150 \leq \lambda \leq 215$ nm (Schomberg *et al* 1983). Through most of this wavelength region the output is greater than 10^{11} photons per pulse, which is sufficient to saturate a strong one-photon transition if a 1 mm beam diameter is used and the pulse length and band width correspond to that of the commercially available dye lasers described above. All of the above techniques for extending the wavelength region to cover 150 to 1500 nm require only standard commercial options supplied by the companies which market the dye laser systems. Control systems are also provided which permit scanning the laser in wavelength while frequency doubling or frequency summing is being carried out.

An application of RIS can be accomplished with the band widths described above, and if one-photon transitions can be reached using photons with energy in the range 0.7 to 7.5 eV, then commercial dye lasers are quite adequate for both the excitation and ionisation steps. If narrower band widths are required, an intracavity etalon can be added to decrease the band width by an order of magnitude, with less than a factor of two decrease in output power in the wavelength region 217 to 1000 nm. The wavelength region can be extended downward to approximately 110 nm by making use of four-wave mixing in inert gases and mercury vapour (Payne 1987). At most wavelengths between 110 and 146 nm at least 10^{10} photons can be generated per pulse with a dye laser. The generation of vacuum ultraviolet light by four-wave mixing will be discussed in Chapter 9. Even limited outputs in this wavelength region can be quite useful, for instance in the RIS of noble gases (see Chapters 9 and 10).

A commercial system which permits effective ionisation of most elements is a Nd–YAG pump with three dye lasers, doubling and mixing crystals and a Raman cell. The harmonics of the Nd–YAG are not only useful for pumping of the dyes, but also for providing intense beams for use in the photo-ionisation of the highest excited state used in an ionisation scheme. The main disadvantages of Nd–YAG systems are price and repetition rate. The system described here would cost about $150\,000$ (1987), and the repetition rate would generally be either 10 or 30 Hz. An excimer pumped dye laser system with three dye lasers would be somewhat less expensive and would operate at variable repetition rates up to several hundred hertz, with some decrease in the output per pulse. The Nd–YAG systems may improve greatly in the near future with the advent of slab lasers pumped by laser diodes. These systems promise variable repetition rates as high as 1000 Hz with extremely high average power. Until slab-type Nd–YAG lasers are available, the best alternative for a high repetition rate dye laser pump is the copper vapour laser which can reach more than 5000 Hz, with an output of the order of 10 mJ per pulse. With copper vapour lasers the range for good tunable output is roughly 217 to 1000 nm, permitting the effective ionisation of most elements with ionisation potentials less than 9.5 eV. In mass spectroscopy applications the effectiveness of the copper vapour laser could frequently be improved by using two resonance steps, with the last being to a Rydberg state with principle quantum number of 15: these states can be efficiently ionised by photons from a continuous wave CO_2 laser.

5.7.2 Ionisation schemes

When the general view of RIS (Hurst *et al* 1979) was written, the optics and crystals for extending the wavelength region attainable by a dye laser were not commonly supplied with commercial systems. Consequently, we suggested a number of ionisation schemes which specified the technique to be used to generate the tunable output. A periodic table which suggested ionisation schemes for most of the elements was drawn and is shown in figure 5.5.

Today, the commercial sector supplies nearly everything needed to extend the range of tunability to the point where only elements with ionisation potentials higher than 11 eV need special techniques for their efficient ionisation. Since the use of frequency doubling, stimulated Raman processes and frequency sum and difference mixing is now standard with commercial dye lasers, one no longer needs to distinguish between ionisation methods which differ only in the details used to generate light. We will now discuss two rather general RIS schemes.

If the tunable sources described in §5.7.1 are used with a 1 mm beam diameter, the photon fluence is greater than 10^{12} cm^{-2}. With incoherent light having a band width Γ_L the absorption cross section at resonance is $\sigma_a = (3\lambda^2\gamma_s)/(4\Gamma_L)$ where λ is the resonance wavelength and γ_s is the spontaneous decay rate. We estimate this cross section for $\lambda = 110$ nm $= 1.1 \times 10^{-5}$ cm, with $\gamma_s = 3.0 \times 10^8$ s^{-1} and $\Gamma_L = 4.0 \times 10^{10}$ s$^{-1} = 0.2$ cm^{-1}. We find, with the broad band source and a transition which is strong in this part of the electromagnetic spectrum that $\sigma_a \simeq 7.0 \times 10^{-13}$ cm^2. The product of the cross section and the photon fluence is near unity so that a sizeable fraction of the atoms would be excited. Obviously, with a slightly smaller beam waist the discrete–discrete transition would be strongly saturated. This calculation suggests that if a strong one-photon transition exists for photon energy less than 11 eV; a very plausible ionisation scheme using commercially available lasers can start with a one-photon transition to an excited state. Following this initial excitation there are two general alternatives

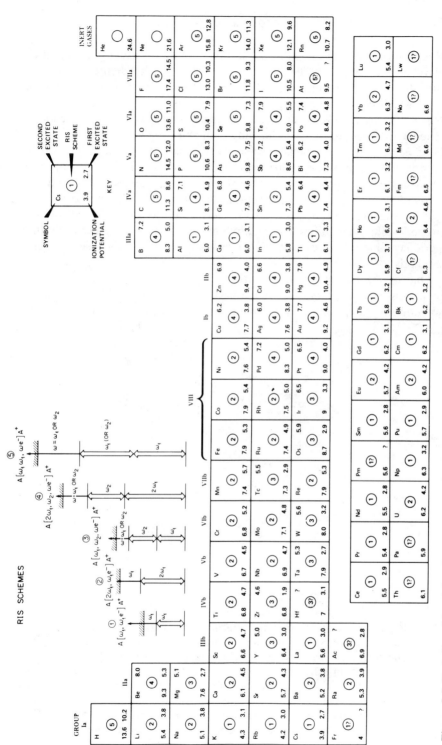

Figure 5.5 Periodic table of the elements suggesting ionisation potentials, lowest excited states and suggested ionisation schemes for most of the elements. For a detailed description of how to use the table see Hurst *et al* 1979.

(see figure 5.6). In scheme A another photon, usually at another wavelength, completes the ionisation process. With scheme B another tunable dye laser promotes the first excited state population to a higher level which could, for example, be ionised with the fundamental of the Nd–YAG laser. There are several reasons why one might choose scheme B. The first is that the only available first excited states might be s states, which typically have very small photo-ionisation cross sections. A second reason for using two resonance steps is to improve the selectivity and make possible the use of a non-tunable red or infrared (IR) laser for the ionisation step. For example, if the second excited state has $n \simeq 15$, a cw CO_2 laser could ionise nearly all of the excited state population. There are only four or five elements in the periodic table which cannot be ionised effectively by the use of these methods.

One of the major problems with RIS has always been related to the high power requirements of the ionisation step. One widely discussed solution to the problem is to make use of field ionisation from high

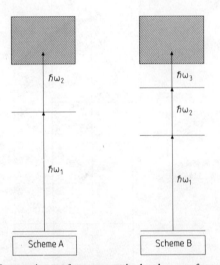

Figure 5.6 Comparison of two practical schemes for RIS using commercial laser systems. Scheme A involves only one resonance step and could be carried out with a single colour. It is preferable to use two colours in Scheme A in order to avoid loss of selectivity due to strong pumping of the resonance. In Scheme B two resonant steps are used in order to achieve a situation where either a non-tunable red or IR laser can be used for the ionisation step, or to avoid the necessity of ionising a state with a small photo-ionisation cross section.

Rydberg states (Hurst *et al* 1979). Field ionisation has been used as a detector of Rydberg states for many years by individuals (Bayfield and Koch 1974) carrying out collision studies or microwave spectroscopic studies of Rydberg states. The techniques were already quite sophisti- cated in 1974 (Bayfield and Koch 1974). The Oak Ridge group was strongly influenced to incorporate field ionisation and collisional ionisa- tion into RIS schemes by the work of the Stebbings (Stebbings *et al* 1975) group at Rice University and the Bayfield programme at Yale (Bayfield and Koch 1974). In applying field ionisation to RIS, sequential excitation is used. The excitation is carried out in the absence of an electrostatic field, but shortly after the laser pulse such a field is switched on. If the effective quantum number of the Rydberg state is n^* then the field in V cm^{-1} required to ionise the state is

$$E \simeq 3 \times 10^8/(n^*)^4.$$

Starting around $n^* = 30$ the field that needs to be pulsed on is only $E \simeq 300 \text{ V cm}^{-1}$. In principle, field ionisation is simple, but in some mass spectroscopic studies possible perturbations on the ion optics should be considered carefully. Also, when CW lasers are being used it is not easy to pump Rydberg transitions with $n^* = 30$. Recent reviews of the properties of Rydberg states have been written by Haroche and Raimond (1985) and by Gallas *et al* (1985). A very valuable earlier review is by Feneuille and Jacquinot (1981).

Most applications of RIS to mass spectroscopy have used stepwise excitation culminating in photo-ionisation. For this reason it is useful to provide practical guidelines for choosing the upper state in the RIS process. Before making such a list we will mention some relevant facts related to the photo-ionisation of excited states. Excited states with orbital angular momentum quantum number $l = 0$ tend to penetrate inside the ion core, leading to discrete–continuum matrix elements which have a zero near the ionisation threshold for nearly all elements except the very lightest such as H, He and Li. In most heavier elements the related Cooper minima in the cross section lead to unpredictable cross sections that are nearly always small. Consequently, it is usually best to avoid the photo-ionisation of excited s states. As a rule of thumb excited s states (other than Rydberg states) tend to have photo- ionisation cross sections which never get much above 10^{-18} cm^2 and are frequently smaller than 10^{-19} cm^2. Photo-ionisation cross sections of excited states with $l \geqslant 1$ are largest near the ionisation threshold and decrease rapidly as the ratio of the ionisation potential of the excited state to the energy of the photoelectron decreases. Of course, there can be auto-ionising resonances over which the photo-ionisation cross sec- tion is much larger. Such resonances in the ionisation continuum can be quite useful in reducing the power requirements for RIS.

With some of the lowest excited d states, the cross section near threshold frequently exceeds 10^{-17} cm^2. In the case of states with $l \geqslant 2$ it is often found that as n^* increases the threshold photo-ionisation cross section becomes very large, increasing approximately proportional to n^*. For instance, in alkali atoms for $n^* > 13$ a d state will have a photo-ionisation cross section greater than 10^{-16} cm^2. This statement applies only to near-threshold photo-ionisation where the energy of the photoelectron is small compared with the ionisation potential of the Rydberg state in question. With a fixed laser wavelength one finds as n^* increases that finally the energy of the photoelectron becomes much larger than the ionisation potential of the Rydberg state and the photo-ionisation cross section starts to decrease as $(n^*)^{-3}$. Thus, photo-ionisation is easiest for large n^*, providing light is supplied near the photo-ionisation threshold.

It has been known for some time that by the time $n^* > 40$ even the black body radiation in an apparatus can lead to substantial photo-ionisation in the lifetime of the state. This is partially due to the greatly increased lifetime against spontaneous emission and partially due to a very large photo-ionisation cross section in the region near threshold. The availability of low-cost, high-power, cw CO_2 lasers makes possible an appealing ionisation scheme. In this scheme one pumps with two resonant steps a state with $n^* \simeq 15$ and $l \geqslant 2$, and the excited state is ionised with laser radiation with $\lambda \simeq 10$ μm. Bushaw *et al* (1987) have recently reported very promising results based on such a scheme.

5.8 Effective volumes of ionisation

Up to this point we have discussed the laser power dependence of the probability of ionisation for an atom in the presence of a designated laser pulse. This would represent the power dependence of the observed ionisation signal if all of the atoms being ionised were exposed to the same laser field. However, the power density seen by an atom at a given time depends on the position of the atom in the laser beam. We now discuss some of the effects of the position dependence of the intensity on the number of observed ions.

Let $n(x,y,z,t)$ be the concentration of selected atoms at x,y,z at the time t, $P_I(x,y,z)$ be the ionisation probability for an atom at x,y,z (the position dependence enters through the amplitude of the laser field), and $\varepsilon(x,y,z)$ be the detection efficiency of an ion produced at x,y,z. If N_I is the number of observed ions,

$$N_I = \int_V \mathrm{d}x\mathrm{d}y\mathrm{d}z\, n(x,y,z,t)P_I(x,y,z)\varepsilon(x,y,z) \qquad (5.66)$$

where the integral is carried out over a volume V in which $n(x,y,z)$,

$\varepsilon(x,y,z)$ and the laser intensities are non-zero. We assume that $n(x,y,z,t)$ changes very little during a laser pulse so that atomic motion in the laser beam is only a relevant factor because of the Doppler effect, which is ignored since we assume that the power-broadened width of the discrete–discrete transition is large compared with the Doppler width. We are also suppressing the average over initial quantum numbers and the dependence of P_I on the initial M_J. Inclusion of these effects will only change the results appreciably if there are widely varying Rabi frequencies and photo-ionisation cross sections for the different M_J. In the case of a constant $n(x,y,z)$ and a focused laser beam it is useful to write the number of ions as the concentration times an effective volume of ionisation. Thus, if V_I is the effective volume of ionisation, $\varepsilon(x,y,z) = 1$ and $n(x,y,z) = n_0$

$$V_I = \int_V dxdydz P_I(x,y,z).$$

Then, $N_I = n_0 V_I$.

In most applications of RIS an integration like that in equation (5.66) must be evaluated if a detailed analysis of saturation effects on the ionisation signal is to be made. We will now consider one of the simplest situations which is actually encountered in practice.

Let the situation be exactly as described in §5.5. The only feature to be added here is a radial power dependence for the unfocused laser beams such that

$$\Omega_0(\rho) = \Omega_0(0) \exp\left(-\rho^2/R_0^2\right)$$
$$\mathscr{F}_0(\rho) = \mathscr{F}_0(0) \exp\left(-2\rho^2/R_0^2\right) \tag{5.67}$$

The expression for P_I in equation (5.67) is now dependent on the distance from beam centre ρ, but not upon any other position coordinate. We take $\varepsilon(x,y,z)$ to be unity for a length of the laser beam L and zero elsewhere. Thus, if $n(x,y,z) = $ constant $= n_0$:

$$N_I = 2\pi n_0 L \int_0^\infty \rho d\rho \{1 - \exp[-\sigma_i\mathscr{F}_0(0)e^{-2\rho^2/R_0^2} Q(2|\Omega_0(0)|e^{-\rho^2/R_0^2}/|\delta|)]\}$$
$$= \pi R_0^2 LH[\sigma_i\mathscr{F}_0(0)\tau, |\delta|/(2|\Omega_0(0)|)] \tag{5.68}$$

where

$$H(x,y) =$$
$$\int_0^\infty dv(1 - \exp\{-xe^{-4v^2}[(\pi^{1/2})/8]/[y^2 + 0.392ye^{-v^2} + (e^{-2v^2}/2^{3/2})]\}). \tag{5.69}$$

In equation (5.69) we have used the rational approximation to Q. Figure 5.7 shows ionisation line shapes as a function of y, where $y = |\delta|/(2|\Omega_0(0)|)$ for various values of $x = \sigma_i\mathscr{F}_0(0)\tau$. This model is

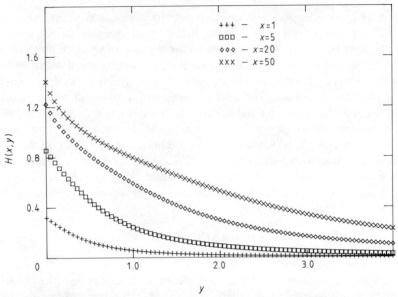

Figure 5.7 Plots of the ionisation line shape function $H(x,y)$ against y for various values of x.

discussed because it shows some of the undesirable effects which happen when the power is too high. The adiabatic theory also has the advantage that it holds for multimode lasers once the detuning is much larger than the band width. Consequently, many of the power-broadening effects which have been demonstrated also appear in a slightly modified form for broad band width lasers.

Strictly speaking the adiabatic approximation should not be used at line centre. However, even with broad band width lasers it is usually easy to pump the discrete–discrete transition as compared with the ionisation step. Consequently, it is common at line centre to have half of the un-ionised M_J sub-level population in the excited state and the other half in the ground state, an equilibrium occurring on a much faster time-scale than the ionisation. Almost all of the ionisation would come from regions where such an equilibrium exists and

$$P_{\mathrm{I}}(\rho) = 1 - \exp\left[-(\pi/8)^{1/2}\sigma_i\mathscr{F}_0(0)\tau e^{-2\rho^2/R_0^2}\right]. \tag{5.70}$$

Evaluating N_{I} with this expression for P_{I} and letting $v = \exp(-2\rho^2/R_0^2)$ we obtain

$$N_{\mathrm{I}} = (\pi/2)R_0^2 Ln_0\int_0^1 (dv/v)\{1 - \exp\left[-(\pi/8)^{1/2}\sigma_i\mathscr{F}_0(0)\tau v\right]\} \tag{5.71}$$

$$= (\pi/2)R_0^2 Ln_0 Ev[(\pi/8)^{1/2}\sigma_i\mathscr{F}_0(0)\tau].$$

The term $Ev(x)$ is given by

$$Ev(x) = \int_0^1 (dv/v)(1 - e^{-xv}) \qquad (5.72)$$

$$= \sum_{n=1}^{\infty} (-1)^{n+1} [x^n/n(n!)].$$

A graph of $Ev(x)$ is shown in figure 5.8.

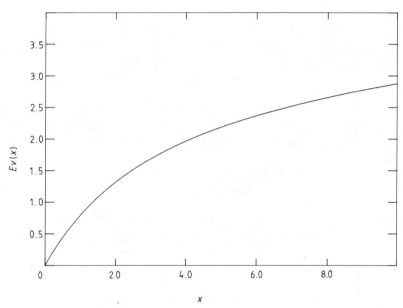

Figure 5.8 Plot of $Ev(x)$ against x. The term $Ev(x)$ is closely related to the well studied exponential integral.

Numerous examples of how to deal with the position dependence of the laser power density can be found in the literature (Payne *et al* 1981). In Chapter 9 some numerical values for effective volumes of ionisation will be given for some important cases involving RIS of noble gases.

References

Bayfield J E and Koch P M 1974 *Phys. Rev. Lett.* **33** 258
Bushaw B A, Cannon B D, Gerke G K and Whitaker T J 1987 in *Resonance Ionization Spectroscopy (Swansea) 1986* ed G S Hurst and C Grey Morgan (Inst. Phys. Conf. Ser. 84) pp 103–8

Choi C W and Payne M G 1977 Two-State and Two-State Plus Continuum Problems Associated with the Interaction of Intense Laser Pulses with Atoms *Oak Ridge National Laboratory Report* ORNL/ TM-5754

Edmonds A R 1960 *Angular Momentum in Quantum Mechanics* (Princeton, N J: Princeton University Press)

Feneuille S and Jacquinot P 1981 Atomic Rydberg States in *Advances in Atomic and Molecular Physics 17* ed Sir David Bates and B Bederson (Orlando, FL: Academic)

Gallas J A C, Leuchs G, Walther H and Figger H 1985 Rydberg Atoms: High-Resolution Spectroscopy and Radiation Interaction-Rydberg Molecules in *Advances in Atomic and Molecular Physics 20* ed Sir David Bates and B Bederson (Orlando, FL: Academic)

Grossman L W, Hurst G S, Payne M G and Allman S L 1977 *Chem. Phys. Lett.* **50** 70

Haroche S and Raimond J M 1985 Radiative Properties of Rydberg States in Resonant Cavities in *Advances in Atomic and Molecular Physics 20* ed Sir David Bates and B Bederson (Orlando, FL: Academic)

Hurst G S, Nayfeh M H and Young J P 1977 *Appl. Phys. Lett.* **30** 229

Hurst G S, Payne M G, Kramer S D and Young J P 1979 *Rev. Mod. Phys.* **51** 767

Hurst G S, Payne M G, Kramer S D, Chen C H, Phillips R C, Allman S L, Alton G D, Dabbs J W T, Willis R D and Lehmann B E 1985 *Rep. Prog. Phys.* **48** 1333–70

Kramer S D, Bemis C E Jr, Young J P and Hurst G S 1978 *Opt. Lett.* **3** 16

Merzbacher E 1970 in *Quantum Mechanics* (New York: Wiley)

Messiah A 1966 in *Quantum Mechanics* vols I and II (New York: Wiley)

Payne M G 1987 in *Resonance Ionization Spectroscopy (Swansea) 1986* ed G S Hurst and C Grey Morgan (Inst. Phys. Conf. Ser. 84) pp 59–66

Payne M G, Chen C H, Hurst G S and Foltz G W 1981 *Adv. At. Mol. Phys.* **17** 229

Payne M G, Hurst G S, Nayfeh M H, Judish J P, Chen C H, Wagner E B and Young J P 1975 *Phys. Rev. Lett.* **35** 1154

Schomburg H, Dobele H F and Ruckle B 1983 *Appl. Phys.* B **30** 131

Stebbings R G, Latimer C J, West W P, Dunning F B and Cook T B 1975 *Phys. Rev.* A **12** 1453

Vasilenko L S, Chebotaev V P and Shishaev A V 1970 *JETP Lett.* **12** 113

6

Chemical physics

6.1 Introduction

In the early stages of the development of RIS—as a sensitive method for counting individual atoms—new applications to chemical physics appeared to be attractive. In fact, as we have seen in Chapter 3, it was necessary to deal with the high reactivity of caesium atoms in order to demonstrate one-atom detection. Subsequently, it was shown (Grossman *et al* 1977a) that one laser (a source laser) could be used to photodissociate a chemically stable alkali halide molecule to produce the highly reactive alkali atom at a desired time and place, while a second laser could be used to detect the atoms. This opened up a new method for the study of photodissociation itself and for the study of mutual diffusion and chemical reaction of free atoms. These topics are discussed in this chapter. In Chapter 7 we discuss the extension of the method of controlling atomic populations into the examination of some basic assumptions of statistical mechanics.

6.2 Photodissociation of CsI

The concept in which one laser is used to liberate free atoms at $t = 0$ and a second laser is used to detect free atoms at $t > 0$ is illustrated in figure 6.1. Such an arrangement was first used by Grossman *et al* (1977a) to study photodissociation of CsI, and variations of the arrangement have been used to study the diffusion of atoms and their chemical reaction, and for the control of atomic populations in statistical studies.

In these experiments the CsI sample was heated to about 700 K, while the exterior of the reaction cell stayed near 300 K. Therefore, the concentration of CsI molecules varies with location in the cell and is quite low in the sensitive volume defined by the portions of the laser

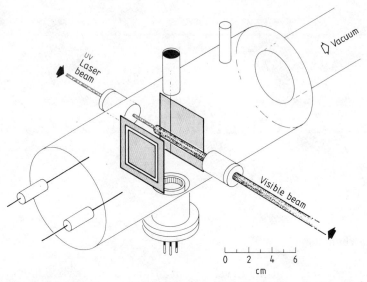

Figure 6.1 Experimental arrangement for the study of saturated photodissociation of alkali halide molecules. The pulsed UV laser is used to dissociate CsI molecules at time $t = 0$, and the pulsed visible laser is used to detect Cs atoms at $t > 0$.

beams between the parallel plates of the ionisation detector. This low concentration of CsI in a buffer gas (such as argon) was adequate only because of the high sensitivity of the RIS method.

A pulsed laser of the linear flashlamp variety was used to pump a cell containing kiton-red dye to produce a narrow beam of about 0.5 mm diameter. The beam was used to photodissociate CsI to spatially define a population of free caesium atoms at $t = 0$. A second pulsed laser (coaxial, lamp pumped dye laser) had a larger diameter (about 7 mm) and was made coaxial with the first narrow beam. Thus, the second pulsed laser could be used to detect those free atoms which were liberated on the axis of the detector beam at $t = 0$ and which remain in the detector volume at any arbitrary time $t > 0$. Further, the photon fluence (ϕ_D) associated with the detector laser was large enough to remove one electron from each of the liberated atoms still in the detector volume. A data acquisition system was used to record for each sequence the energy per pulse of the source laser, the energy per pulse of the detector laser and the magnitude of the ionisation signal.

The wavelength of the source laser was set at 317.5 nm near the CsI dissociation peak (Davidovits and Brodhead 1967). To detect the neutral caesium, the detector laser was set to produce photons at 459.3 nm, which promote $Cs(6^2S_{1/2})$ to $Cs(7^2P_1{}^2P_{1/2})$, and (as appropriate for two-photon RIS) a second photon of the same wavelength photo-ionised

Cs($7^2P_{1/2}$). By carrying out the experiment in a buffer gas such as argon at moderate pressure (e.g. 100 Torr), several desirable effects were produced. First, the CsI molecules were in thermal equilibrium near 300 K due to argon collisions. Also, photo-ionisation occurred from all the degenerate magnetic levels. Finally, with a buffer gas, caesium atom diffusion was of no consequence during the lifetime (FWHM) of the laser pulse, i.e. 1.5 μs for the source laser and 0.5 μs for the detector laser. Ionisation signals were studied as a function of the detector laser fluence, ϕ_D. As ϕ_D increased, the ionisation signal climbed gradually to a saturated value. See figure 6.2 for data at several buffer gas pressures.

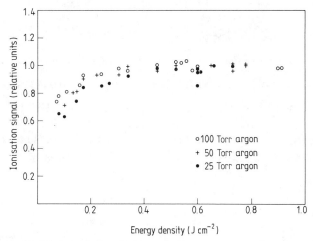

Figure 6.2 Measured signals due to Cs atoms as a function of the energy density of the detector laser and at a fixed energy density for the UV laser used to dissociate CsI.

With sufficient fluence, ϕ_D, to saturate the ionisation (i.e. to detect each free atom in the laser beam), studies were then made of the photodissociation process. Several significant observations were made on the production of neutral species. For instance, there was a gradual decline in the number of free atoms as the time between the source laser and detector laser was increased; but this variation was just what one expected from calculations of the rate of diffusion of the atoms out of the detection region. Special tests were made with very short time delays between the source and detector lasers; all of the atoms were dissociated in less than 0.5 μs after the source laser pulse. No ionisation signals due to the source laser alone were observed. Berkowitz (1969) observed ionisation with a photo-ionisation mass spectrometer only when the photon energy exceeded 7 eV.

Figure 6.3 shows the ionisation signal as a function of the number of photons in a single pulse of the source laser, both for an unfocused beam and for a beam which was focused with a 50 cm focal length lens. The focused beam signals continue to rise gradually because of a non-uniform source beam. To obtain the caesium photoproduction cross section, σ, the following analysis was made. Assuming a gaussian beam profile,

$$\phi(\rho) = \phi_0 \exp\left(-\rho^2/R^2\right) \tag{6.1}$$

where ϕ_0 is the fluence when the radius $\rho = 0$ and R is a constant. Since each atom is detected, the measured signal is proportional to n_1, the number of atoms dissociated per unit of length, given by

$$n_1 = N \int_0^\infty 2\pi\rho \; \mathrm{d}\rho[1 - \exp\left(-\sigma\phi_0 e^{-\rho^2/R^2}\right)] \tag{6.2}$$

where N is number density of the CsI molecules. It can be shown that

$$F(\sigma\phi_0) = n_1/N\pi R^2 = \gamma + \ln \sigma\phi_0 + E_1(\sigma\phi_0) \tag{6.3}$$

where E_1 is the exponential integral and γ is Euler's constant (0.577. . .). The ratio of the focused beam signal to the unfocused beam signal (see figure 6.3) is just $F(\sigma\phi_0)/\sigma\phi_0$, since in the limit $\sigma\phi_0 \to 0$, $F(\sigma\phi_0) = \sigma\phi_0$. For a given total number of photons (e.g. 2.5×10^{14}),

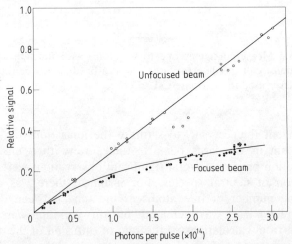

Figure 6.3 Signals due to Cs atoms as a function of the number of photons in a single pulse of the source laser. Each atom produced was detected with the RIS process. Data are shown for unfocused beams. The function $F(\sigma\phi_0)$, equation (6.3), is fitted to the experimental data and the curve is drawn through the focused data points.

one finds the the value of $\sigma\phi_0$ which makes $F(\sigma\phi_0)/\sigma\phi_0$ equal to the experimental ratio (0.41). The fluence ϕ_0 was determined experimentally by measuring the energy transmitted through a small aperture with a joule meter. In this way the value of 2.9×10^{-17} cm^2 was found for the caesium photoproduction cross section at 317.5 nm. Note that the actual value of N was not required to get an absolute cross section.

Figure 6.4 shows the cross section for the production of the caesium neutral atom from CsI as a function of wavelength. These results, found by Grossman *et al* (1977a), have a functional form which is similar to that for photo-absorption. Cross sections at the peak agree to within a few per cent with those of Davidovits and Brodhead (1967). The Grossman *et al* measurements were made at 320 K, while the photo-absorption data were taken at about 1000 K; thus, the reduction in vibrational populations which results from this temperature difference could account for the difference in widths. A knowledge of the vapour pressure of CsI was not required to obtain the photodissociation cross sections. In the Grossman technique, the number density of CsI molecules is obtained directly from the saturation curve obtained by plotting the number of caesium atoms per pulse against the laser energy per pulse, or it is obtained through fitting to equation (6.3).

Thus it was shown that all CsI molecules in a volume can be dissociated by using a photon fluence exceeding 3×10^{17} cm^{-2} in a single laser pulse of microsecond duration. When this fact is combined with the demonstrated fact that one atom can be detected when using an RIS scheme and a proportional counter, the capability for one-molecule detection is obvious.

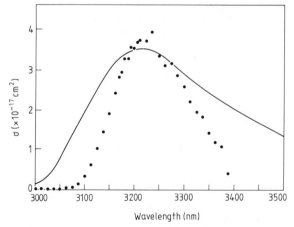

Figure 6.4 Cross section for the photodissociation of Cs from CsI as a function of wavelength.

Some clarifications of the photodissociation process in CsI were made with the RIS studies. Berry (1957) showed that in the alkali halide molecules one may expect to observe in some cases a band system and in other cases a narrow continuum in the photo-absorption spectrum. In the RIS studies a smooth continuum in the actual appearance of neutral atoms was observed; furthermore, these neutrals appear in a short time, i.e. in less than 0.5 μs after excitation. This implies a simple process in which photo-absorption occurs out of an ionic ground state to a non-ionic predissociation state, which dissociates into the neutral continuum state in a short time, perhaps much less than the measured upper limit of 0.5 μs. Because the predissociation state changes from a non-ionic to an ionic state at a rather large internuclear distance (about 2 nm), nuclear motion can no longer be considered adiabatic with respect to electronic motion; hence, an otherwise valid non-crossing rule is violated. These direct observations of prompt neutral atoms produced in a smooth photon energy continuum, as well as the observation that no Cs^+ or I^- ions are formed, are consistent with the simple and vivid picture of the alkali photodissociation process painted by Berry (1957).

6.3 Diffusion of caesium atoms in argon gas

Grossman *et al* (1977b) showed that the method depicted in figure 6.1 could also be used to study the diffusion of atoms through a gas. When measuring photodissociation, the time delay between the source laser and the detector laser is made so low that little diffusion occurs. However, to observe mutual diffusion of caesium atoms in the argon buffer gas, the population of caesium atoms in the detector beam can be recorded as a function of time delay. The measured fraction of atoms, $\gamma(t)$, for this simple geometry contains both the diffusion coefficient D and the rate of chemical reaction β.

Suppose a line source of atoms, λ, per unit length is created along an infinitely long line at time $t = 0$. When $t > 0$, the dissociated atoms spread by diffusion through an inert gas while reacting chemically (at rate β) with a reactive species. We further stipulate that the number density of the chemically active species is much less than that of the inert gas which determines the diffusion coefficient, D, for the alkali atoms. In other words, if n is the number density of the alkali atom,

$$\partial n/\partial t = D\nabla^2 n - \beta n. \tag{6.4}$$

The solution for an unbounded medium is

$$n(\rho, t) = (\lambda/4\pi Dt)\exp(-\rho^2/4Dt)e^{-\beta t} \tag{6.5}$$

where ρ is the radial distance from the line source.

If we define $\gamma(t)$ as the fraction of the number of ions contained in the cylinder of radius R, then

$$\gamma(t) = \lambda^{-1}\int_0^R 2\pi\rho d\rho \, n(\rho, t)$$

$$= [1 - \exp(-R^2/4Dt)]e^{-\beta t}. \tag{6.6}$$

Expression (6.6) is a slowly varying function of time with $\beta = 0$; for example, if $D = 2.5 \text{ cm}^2\text{s}^{-1}$ and $R = 1.0 \text{ cm}$, then $\gamma(t) = 0.63$ when $t = 0.1 \text{ s}$. Thus, atoms can be 'contained' for relatively long times so that chemical reaction can be measured even when β is relatively small.

The above idealisation is essentially met in the diagram (figure 6.1). The production of atoms and their detection occurs far from all walls, since the parallel-plate ionisation chamber collects electrons only from those atoms which were in a defined volume determined by the area of the detector laser beam and the length of the guarded collector plate. Thus, the assumption of an unbounded medium is entirely met.

Some initial experiments were performed on the diffusion of caesium atoms in argon. Referring to figure 6.1, the CsI sample was heated to 620 K, producing about 3×10^8 CsI molecules per cm^3 in the region of the laser beams, where the measured temperature was 325 K. The source laser photodissociated all of the molecules in a small volume of 10^{-2} cm^3 (area $= 2.5 \times 10^{-3} \text{ cm}^2$, length $= 4 \text{ cm}$)—thus producing about 3×10^6 caesium atoms. The detector laser, operated at 459.3 nm, ionised all of the caesium atoms by first exciting to the $\text{Cs}(7^2\text{P}_{1/2})$ level. With argon pressure at 100 Torr, the fraction $\gamma(t)$ was diffusion controlled, i.e. reactive gas impurities were at sufficiently low concentration so that $e^{-\beta t}$ was close to unity. At higher argon pressures it was difficult to keep impurity levels low enough so that the diffusion process would control the loss of atoms. Figure 6.5 shows a fit of equation (6.6)

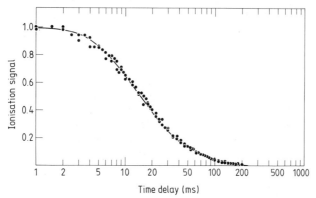

Figure 6.5 Relative Cs atom signal as a function of time in pure Ar. A comparison of experimental data is made with diffusion theory (full curve) at an Ar pressure of 50 Torr.

to the data with $\beta = 10\,\mathrm{s}^{-1}$ and $D = 1.8\,\mathrm{cm}^2\,\mathrm{s}^{-1}$ at 50 Torr—thus we have diffusion coefficients of $0.12\,\mathrm{cm}^2\,\mathrm{s}^{-1}$ at 1 atm (Franzen 1959) compared with $0.25\,\mathrm{cm}^2\,\mathrm{s}^{-1}$ for rubidium in argon and compared with $0.098\,\mathrm{cm}^2\,\mathrm{s}^{-1}$ for caesium in N_2 (Carabetta and Kaskan 1968).

6.4 Chemical reaction of caesium atoms with O_2 in the presence of an argon buffer gas

When small concentrations of O_2 were added to the argon buffer gas, Grossman *et al* (1977b) found that the decay curves, $\gamma(t)$, change to a simple exponential, as illustrated in figure 6.6. For simple interpretation of pulse height measurements it is important to avoid electron capture to O_2 (see Chapter 2). The O_2 molecule can capture thermal electrons to form O_2^- and electrons of a few eV can be removed by the formation of $O^- + O$. However, the problem has been treated in detail (Bortner and Hurst 1958), and it was shown that for the case of O_2 in argon there is a range of E/P where electron capture can be avoided.

The coaxial beam geometry is an excellent method for determining the rate of chemical reaction of a free atom with its environment. For pure argon, the $\gamma(t)$ is slow but goes over into a rapidly decaying

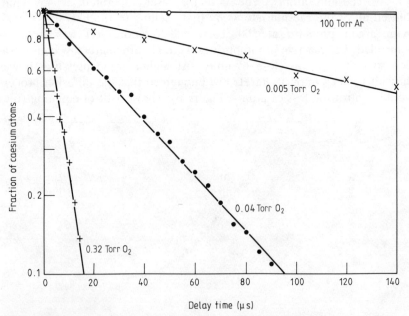

Figure 6.6 Relative number of Cs atoms surviving as a function of time for various partial pressures of O_2 in 100 Torr of Ar.

function that is exponential in time when traces of O_2 are added. From the slopes of these semilog plots, one can easily deduce β. It was found for the region $0 \leqslant P_{0_2} \leqslant 0.02$ Torr and $25 \leqslant P_{Ar} \leqslant 1200$ Torr that

$$\beta = 7000 \, P_{Ar} P_{0_2} \qquad (6.7)$$

where β has units of s^{-1} when the pressure units are in torr at 300 K. For $P_{0_2} > 0.5$ torr, equation (6.7) overestimates the observed rate, suggesting a somewhat complex reaction scheme. Basically, however, the following mechanism appears to reproduce the results:

$$Cs + O_2 \overset{k}{\rightleftarrows} (CsO_2)^{**} \qquad (6.8a)$$

$$(CsO_2)^{**} + Ar \overset{k_1}{\rightarrow} (CsO_2)^* + Ar \qquad (6.8b)$$

$$(CsO_2)^* + O_2 \overset{k_2}{\rightarrow} Cs + O_4 \qquad (6.8c)$$

$$(CsO_2)^* + Ar \overset{k_3}{\rightarrow} CsO_2 + Ar. \qquad (6.8d)$$

In these, $(CsO_2)^{**}$ is a highly excited vibrational state of the caesium superoxide molecule which will reverse to caesium plus O_2 unless an argon atom removes some energy to make $(CsO_2)^*$. However, caesium can be released (i.e. a back reaction can occur) due to collisions of $(CsO_2)^*$ with O_2 creating the O_4 molecule. Further relaxation of $(CsO_2)^*$ with an inert atom makes a stable (CsO_2) molecule. The O_4 molecule has been known for a long time (Herzberg 1950), both as an atmospheric and a laboratory species, and the CsO_4 molecule has been observed (Andrews *et al* 1973) in solid matrix samples at low temperatures.

The large three-body term, i.e. $7 \times 10^3 \, Torr^{-2} s^{-1}$, requires comment; it is about 10^3 times larger than that for the $Cs–O_2–N_2$ reaction (Carabetta and Kaskan 1968). However, the magnitude can be justified as follows. Assume $Cs–O_2$ come together with a cross section, σ_1, of $10^{-14} \, cm^2$ to form $(CsO_2)^*$—an intermediate which dissociates in time T (about 10^{-9} s). An energy-stabilising collision with argon, having an assumed cross section σ_2 of about $3 \times 10^{-16} \, cm^2$, competes with the dissociation. The large value of σ_1 is not unexpected; in fact, recent measurements (Maya and Davidovits 1973) of caesium with Br_2 yielded a cross section of $2 \times 10^{-14} \, cm^2$ and were explained with the 1940 theory of John Magee, now known as the 'harpooning model'. An electron from caesium could transfer out to harpoon an O_2 molecule, making CsO_2^{**} with a large cross section. The large (10^{-9} s) value for T is also reasonable (Eyring 1935) for a system of three atoms having a binding energy of a few eV. A value of 10^{-9} s for the lifetime of

$(NaO_2)^*$ was derived from rate measurements (Bauer and Evans 1937) as early as 1937.

The example above shows how the rate of reaction of free atoms with their chemical environment can be determined in a rather direct way, even when the free atoms are so reactive that normal chemistry studies are not feasible. With the RIS method we do not have to be concerned about corrosive reactions on the walls, because only a small number of free atoms are formed at a given time and these react before they find the wall. In the sense that reactive species never reach the walls of the apparatus, containerless chemistry is made possible in the laboratory.

6.5 Precision measurements of the diffusion of reactive atoms

The measurement of the coefficient for mutual diffusion of atoms diffusing through other atoms or molecules has always been difficult (Marrero and Mason 1973). It has not been possible to make the measurements in geometries where the diffusion equation can be rigorously solved. Furthermore, if one of the species (such as an alkali atom) is highly reactive with the medium or its impurities, additional problems can be encountered of both an experimental and analytical nature. In §6.3 we discussed a method in which a narrow laser beam produces atoms (by the photodissociation of a trace concentration of a molecule) at time $t = 0$ along the axis of an imaginary cylinder which can be swept at $t > 0$ with a larger diameter laser beam that detects the atoms which *have not diffused* out of the cylinder.

A much more precise measurement can be made of mutual diffusion coefficients by using two narrow laser beams which are parallel to each other at a distance ρ apart (Hurst *et al* 1978). One laser beam pulses on at $t = 0$ and during a short time, Δt, it produces atoms along a narrow line by photodissociation of a trace of a molecular gas. After time t the second laser beam pulses on for another short interval to detect the atoms which *have diffused into* the detector beam at distance ρ from the source beam. Diffusion processes can be studied in detail and precise results for D, the coefficient of mutual diffusion of two gaseous components, can be obtained. Again, in this case, atoms are created and detected in an infinite medium.

A schematic diagram of the method for precision measurements of the diffusion coefficient is shown in figure 6.7. A source of alkali halide molecules—in the present case CsI crystals—was heated to about 645 K to produce a concentration of CsI molecules of about 10^9 cm^{-3} in the region of the source laser (SL). A second pulsed laser, DL, detected caesium atoms in a very selective way by first promoting them to the $Cs(7^2P_{1/2})$ level so that another photon at 459.3 nm could photo-ionise

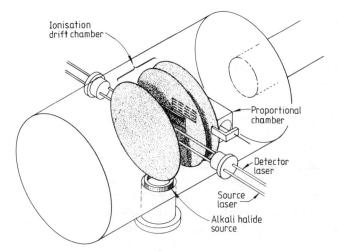

Ionisation
drift chamber

Proportional
chamber

Detector
laser

Source
laser

Alkali halide
source

Figure 6.7 Schematic diagram of experimental arrangement for studies of the diffusion of alkali atoms through other gases. An alkali halide is seeded into the gaseous medium which is then dissociated with a source laser (SL) to produce free alkali atoms which then diffuse into a detector laser (DL) beam. Electrons created by the RIS process occurring in the DL beam are drifted into a proportional counter for sensitive measurements. By varying the delay between SL and DL and by changing ρ, detailed studies of the diffusion of atoms in an unbounded medium can be made.

the excited species. Electrons produced in this way can be drifted by means of the ionisation drift chamber into the proportional counter for sensitive detection. This method avoids the contamination of the proportional counter surfaces with the CsI products and leads to stability and good reproducibility of the results. The distance ρ between the narrow laser beams could be changed over a wide range (by a translation of DL) using an optical stage equipped with a micrometer screw.

With the geometry just described, free atoms are dissociated and detected in a region of space completely decoupled from the walls of the apparatus. In fact, because of the high rate of reaction of the alkali atoms with even trace impurities, it is unlikely that the free atom ever contacts the wall. Under these conditions, the diffusion equation can be solved exactly.

Since we are stressing here the precise measurement of D, even with large β, it is convenient to note that if measurements are made at two separations, $\rho = \rho_1$ and ρ_2, where $\rho_2 > \rho_1$, we can write (see equation 6.5)

$$n(\rho_1, t)/n(\rho_2, t) = \exp\left[(\rho_2^2 - \rho_1^2)/4Dt\right]. \qquad (6.9)$$

Thus,

$$\ln[n(\rho_1, t)/n(\rho_2, t)] = [(\rho_2^2 - \rho_1^2)/4D](1/t). \tag{6.10}$$

Equation (6.10) expresses the fact that the slope of $\ln(n_1/n_2)$ plotted against $1/t$ is just $(\rho_2^2 - \rho_1^2)/4D$, independent of the chemical reaction rate, β! This is the basis of a precise determination of D, since the ρ values can be well defined for parallel laser beam geometries.

The data acquisition system schematised in figure 6.8 is consistent with the precision objectives of the above. Sets of signals (S,D,P) can be stored in a computer so that all information on each observation is kept. The signal S is proportional to the source laser energy per pulse, and the signal D applies similarly for the detector laser. Here, P is the pulse height of the proportional counter, giving the number of electrons which have drifted into the detector and providing accurate information

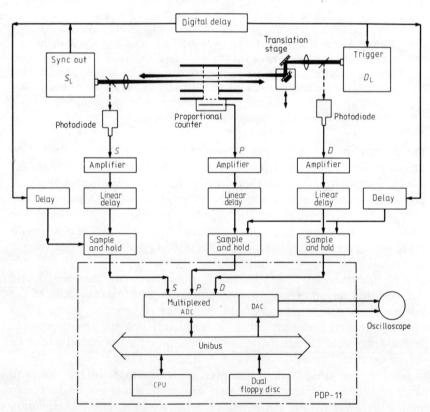

Figure 6.8 The signals S, D, and P associated with each observation are listed as sequential sets in a PDP-11 microcomputer. From these data a normalised quantity, $\mathscr{P}$, is generated as described in the text.

on n. When the data are retrieved, P can be normalised in two ways. In the Grossman data, P was divided by S since the number of atoms produced was known to be a linear function of the laser energy per pulse. Next, (P/S) was divided by F where $(P/S) = F(D)$ and represents a non-linear dependence of the number of atoms detected on the energy per pulse of the detector laser. In fact, (P/S) can saturate when the energy per pulse per unit of beam area exceeds $100\,\text{mJ}\,\text{cm}^{-2}$ for $Cs(7^2P_{1/2})$. The doubly normalised signals $P_{S,\,D}$ (i.e. P/SF) are then averaged over many trials to obtain $P_{S,\,D}$ ($\equiv \mathscr{P}$) for many values of t at each ρ. The ratios $\mathscr{P}_1/\mathscr{P}_2$ at $\rho = \rho_1$ and $\rho = \rho_2$ are then computed for each t and used in equation (6.10) for the ratios of the n values.

In figure 6.9 we show data for the diffusion of traces of caesium in P-10 (90% argon + 10% CH_4) counting gas at 50 Torr pressure. Plots are shown for the quantity for which $\rho_1 = 0.166\,\text{cm}$ and $\rho_2 = 0.315\,\text{cm}$. These ρ values were determined by accurately profiling the laser beams and using a $25\,\mu\text{m}$ pinhole where the only uncertainties are associated with the width, Δ, of the beams. It was found that

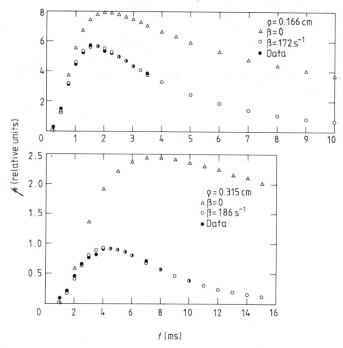

Figure 6.9 Pulse height data normalised with respect to S and D for two values of ρ are plotted as a function of delay time between SL and DL. Experimental data are compared with calculations using the 'best fit' for β and for $\beta = 0$.

$\Delta(\text{FWHM}) = 0.0068$ cm for SL and 0.0075 cm for DL. Figure 6.10 is a plot to test equation (6.10). Indeed the agreement is excellent; the chemistry completely cancels for the two ρ values if the time factor is kept common. From the slope of figure 6.10, $D = 3.30\ \text{cm}^2\,\text{s}^{-1}$; normalised to 760 Torr, it is $0.217\ \text{cm}^2\,\text{s}^{-1}$ at a temperature of 55° C. The self-consistence between this value for D and the β value derived from figure 6.9 was tested. With the above D and a simple least squares fitting procedure in which data was weighted by the square of its amplitude, $\beta(\rho = \rho_1) = 186\ \text{s}^{-1}$ and $\beta(\rho = \rho_2) = 172\ \text{s}^{-1}$—in good agreement. Finally, in figure 6.9 the fits to the complete data for these β values are plotted, and also, for comparison, what would be expected for both ρ values when $\beta = 0$. The value of β derived above is due to the presence of about 20 PPM of O_2 in the apparatus. Even when the medium is so reactive that severe distortion of the data is found at a given ρ, the technique involving the ratio $n(\rho_1,\ t)/n(\rho_2,\ t)$ gives accurate results for D. We note that, even though we have also obtained very consistent β values, this is not the strength of the present method. The coaxial beam technique is more appropriate for measuring β. The parallel beam geometry is far superior to the coaxial beam geometry for accurate measurement of diffusion coefficients.

Uncertainties in the absolute values of D are about $\pm 5\%$ due to uncertainty in the ρ values. With smaller β, the ρ values could be made large enough to reduce uncertainties in the absolute values to $\pm 1\%$ or less. Relative values were reproduced (Grossman *et al* 1977b) to somewhat better than $\pm 1\%$.

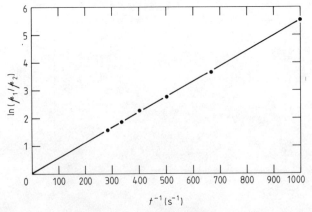

Figure 6.10 Plot of $\ln(\mathscr{P}_1/\mathscr{P}_2)$ against t^{-1}. The excellent agreement with theory implies that the diffusion coefficient can be accurately determined, even when the atoms are diffusing in a highly reactive medium.

The diffusion equation has been tested rather completely in both its spatial and temporal domains. We believe that this represents the first such rigorous test of the diffusion equation for an unbounded medium; other methods (Marrero and Mason 1973) have always required gas–solid interfaces at the source of atoms or at the detector of atoms.

6.6 Photodissociation of LiI

RIS methods could be applied to the alkali halides in general to obtain information on photodissociation of these simple diatomic molecules and to study diffusion and chemical reactions of the alkali atoms. To date, the only other molecule to be used extensively for these purposes is LiI.

A schematic diagram of the apparatus used by Kramer *et al* (1979) is shown in figure 6.11 and is a modification of the technique described for the study of CsI. The sample cell contained a heated LiI source and was filled with 30 Torr of argon. Ground state atomic lithium was produced by photodissociation of the LiI vapour by photons having a wavelength of 295 nm, which is at the peak of the cross section for photodissociation (Davidovits and Brodhead 1967). These photons were generated by intracavity doubling of a commercial Chromatix model CMX-4 dye laser designated as laser A in figure 6.11. The output was focused to a diameter of about 0.05 cm in the centre of the cell and it had a pulse width of about 1 μs. Lasers B and C, which were used to excite the

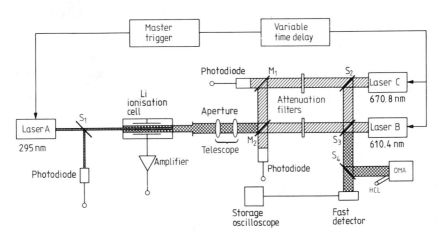

Figure 6.11 Schematic diagram of the experimental apparatus used to study photodissociation of LiI and to measure reaction rates of Li atoms. The term HCL stands for a Li hollow cathode lamp and OMA is an optical multichannel analyser used to determine the laser wavelengths.

2S–2P and 2P–3D transitions respectively (see figure 6.12), were grating-tuned, coaxial flashlamp pumped dye lasers. The lasers produced pulses that were asymmetric in time with a fast leading edge and a full width at half height of about 450 ns. The beams from both of these lasers were combined and then focused and apertured to a diameter of 0.42 cm in the detection cell. In the configuration used, the outputs from lasers B and C were coaxial with the beam generated by laser A. As determined by burn patterns on exposed film, laser C has a uniform intensity profile over the portion of the beam allowed to pass through the aperture. By measuring the total energy per pulse with a ballistic thermopile, it was determined that laser C produced a maximum fluence at 610.4 nm of $\phi(6104) = 0.19 \, \text{J cm}^{-2}$ with the cell geometry used. A fluence of $\phi(6708) = 1 \, \text{J cm}^{-2}$ was estimated for laser B.

In the experimental procedure, laser A was first fired into the cell to photodissociate LiI vapour. This produced a line source of free lithium atoms along the axis of the laser beam which was centred between the

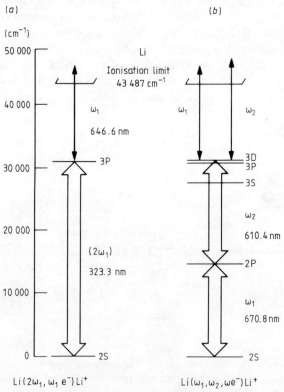

Figure 6.12 Two possible RIS schemes for Li. The one actually used is depicted in (*b*) where all levels below 3D are shown.

field plates of an ionisation chamber. There was a potential difference between the plates of 30 V and they were separated by about 4 cm. Two microseconds after the lithium was created, lasers B and C were fired simultaneously. Since laser B was tuned to 670.8 nm and laser C to 610.4 nm according to the scheme of figure 6.12, efficient resonant photo-ionisation occurs. The free charge generated by photo-ionisation, which was a direct measure of the number of lithium atoms produced, was detected by the field plates. For the maximum laser fluences, the measured signal corresponded to the ionisation of about 2×10^5 lithium atoms. When studying the saturation of photo-ionisation, the intensities of lasers B and C at the cell could be changed by the insertion of calibrated attenuating filters. From saturation curves for the RIS signal as a function of laser fluence, Kramer *et al* (1979) concluded that the three-step RIS process could be saturated with laser beams providing a fluence of $0.1 \, \mathrm{J \, cm^{-2}}$.

Photodissociation of LiI was studied by Lehmann *et al* (1980) using the method introduced by Grossman *et al* (1977a) for the study of CsI. For an unfocused ultraviolet (UV) laser beam, typically 2 mm in diameter, having an energy of 40 μJ per pulse, and a corresponding fluence of about 2×10^{15} photons per cm^2 per pulse, the number of dissociated molecules was a linear function of the number of photons per pulse (upper curve in figure 6.13). The relative cross section for photodissociation as a function of wavelength was determined by using the slopes of the various straight lines taken in the wavelength region from 270 to 312 nm. This region was covered by two different dyes: coumarin 522 below 290 nm and rhodamine 6G above 290 nm (with a small overlap region around 290 nm).

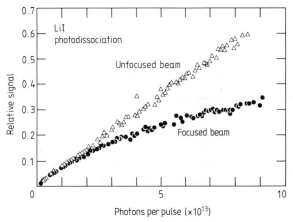

Figure 6.13 Relative number of detected Li atoms as a function of the number of photons in a single pulse of the UV laser that dissociates LiI. Data are shown for unfocused and focused beams.

By focusing the uv beam with a 25 cm focal length lens down to a diameter of 0.1–0.2 mm (corresponding to a fluence of the order of 10^{17} photons per cm^2 per pulse), partial saturation of the dissociation process could be achieved (lower curve in figure 6.13). Analysis of the saturation curve combined with determination of the actual beam profile within the collection region of the ionisation chamber yielded an absolute value for the photodissociation cross section in the vicinity of 300 nm. Figure 6.14 shows the absolute cross section for photodissociation between 270 and 312 nm measured at $T = 140°$ C. The broken line is the absorption cross section from Davidovits and Brodhead (1967) (at 745° C) with a peak value of $(1.4^+) \times 10^{-17}$ cm^2 at 294 nm. The solid line is a hand-made smooth fit through the data points.

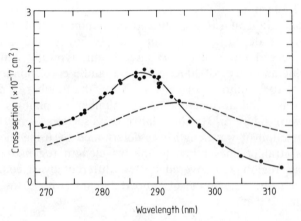

Figure 6.14 Cross section for the photodissociation of LiI as a function of wavelength at $T = 140°$ C. The broken line is the absorption cross section from Davidovits and Brodhead (1967) at $T = 745°$ C compared with the ris data of Lehmann *et al* (1980).

An absolute value for the cross section (at 300 nm) can be obtained from the two curves in figure 6.13 without knowing the number density of LiI molecules inside the ionisation chamber. The analysis to obtain the cross section was similar to that made for CsI (see §6.2), except that Lehmann *et al* (1980) actually measured the radial distribution of the laser beam used to dissociate LiI. This measured function, $h(\rho)$, is defined by

$$N_\mathrm{p} = \int_0^\infty 2\pi\rho\mathrm{d}\rho\phi(\rho) = 2\pi\phi_0\int_0^\infty \rho\mathrm{d}\rho h(\rho) \qquad (6.11)$$

= number of photons per pulse.

Thus, n_1, the number of dissociated molecules per unit of length is

$$n_1 = N \int_0^\infty 2\pi\rho d\rho [1 - \exp(-\sigma\phi_0 h(\rho))] \qquad (6.12)$$

if we assume a uniform density, N, of LiI molecules. If $x = \sigma\phi_0$ and $n_1/N = G(x)$, then

$$G(x) = \int_0^\infty 2\pi\rho \, d\rho [1 - \exp(-xh(\rho))]$$

for the focused beam; and for $x \ll 1$,

$$G_0(x) = xN_p/\phi_0$$

applies to the unfocused beam. The ratio $R(x) = G(x)/G_0(x)$ was calculated by numerical integration of measured beam profiles, and the cross section was found to fit the experimental ratio of the two curves in figure 6.13. It was not even necessary to actually measure the linear function $G_0(x)$ (upper curve in figure 6.13); its slope could be calculated from the slope of a fifth-order polynomial fit to the saturated curve (lower curve in figure 6.13) at low numbers of photons per pulse. Analysis yielded an absolute value of 0.8×10^{-17} cm^2 at 300 nm.

Among the alkali halides, LiI has some unique features. According to Berry's curve-crossing theory (Berry 1957), the first excited electronic state with the same symmetry as the Σ^+ ground state should show an avoided crossing at the first crossing point; therefore, LiI is expected to have a bound-state spectrum. Such a spectrum was not observed in the gas phase, and Berry suggested that the repulsive part of the upper curve is shifted to greater internuclear distances and, therefore, not accessible from the low-lying vibrational levels of the electronic ground state.

A bound-state spectrum has been observed by Oppenheimer and Berry (1971) in matrix spectra of LiI where matrix-induced changes in potential curves and Franck–Condon factors enable these transitions to be seen. In figure 6.15 this situation is schematically illustrated. The part of an upper potential curve that is accessible from the lower vibrational level of the electronic ground state had already been given by Davidovits and Brodhead (1967) and agrees well with a potential curve constructed from the photodissociation cross section in figure 6.15, except for a small shift of about 6.5 nm towards the shorter wavelengths.

Since Lehmann *et al* (1980) showed (by detecting neutral atoms of lithium) that this state dissociates, it has to be one with a different symmetry from the ionic ground state, and the first strong UV continuum in LiI is, therefore, due to a perpendicular ($\Pi \leftarrow \Sigma$) transition. In his first analysis, Berry (1957) assigned the strong continuum to a parallel transition ($\Sigma \leftarrow \Sigma$); but after Zare and Herschbach (1965) had shown in

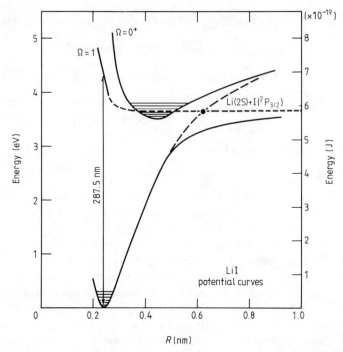

Figure 6.15 Schematic illustration of potential energy curves in LiI.

a charge-transfer model for the alkali halides that the transition strength depends on the degree of atomic and ionic mixing, this conclusion had to be questioned (Berry 1979, Oppenheimer and Berry 1971). The RIS result shows that the perpendicular transition is indeed favoured and therefore helps to clarify this question.

6.7 Chemical reactions of lithium atoms with O₂

Some studies of the chemical reaction of free atoms of lithium with O_2 in the presence of both helium and argon buffer gases were made by Kramer *et al* (1982). The schematic of the method is already described in figure 6.11. Once again the remarkable simplicity with which the reaction rate, β, is obtained from the slope of survival curves is shown in figure 6.16.

For lithium atom reactions with O_2, it was found that β depends on both the pressure of O_2 and the pressure of argon, see figure 6.17. Furthermore, the reaction rate depends on the type of inert buffer gas, M. Modelling of these results is therefore quite complex. It appears that the model used to describe the caesium data in §6.4 is not adequate for the lithium data. Many features are the same, however Kramer *et al* (1982) conclude that in addition to sequences like

$$Li + O_2 \rightarrow (LiO_2)^*$$

$$(LiO_2)^* + M \rightarrow LiO_2 + M$$

$$(LiO_2)^* + M \rightarrow Li + O_2 + M$$

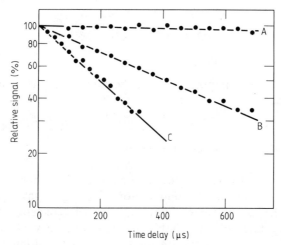

Figure 6.16 Typical decay curves taken for Li atoms in Ar–O_2 mixtures at low reaction rates. Curve A was taken in 30 Torr of pure Ar and demonstrates the effect of diffusion of Li out of the detector beam. Curve B was taken in 150 Torr of Ar that contained 51 PPM of O_2, and curve C was taken in 29 Torr of Ar that contained 1500 PPM of O_2.

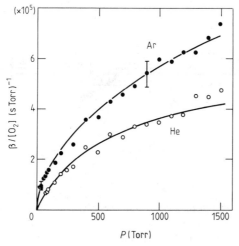

Figure 6.17 A plot of the averaged, measured reaction rate β divided by O_2 partial pressure against the inert gas pressure for the Li + O_2 + He and Li + O_2 + Ar reactions. The curves are the fits to the data described by Kramer *et al* (1982).

it is also necessary to include a sequence in which the bound complex (LiM)* is formed. Such models are frequently used (Johnston 1966) in gas phase reaction rate models. The sequence

$$Li + M \rightleftarrows LiM^*$$

$$(LiM)^* + M \rightarrow LiM + M$$

$$LiM + O_2 \rightarrow LiO_2 + M$$

$$LiM + M \rightarrow Li + M + M$$

appeared to be more important when the buffer gas, M, was argon as compared to helium.

6.8 Diffusion of lithium atoms in argon gas

Some recent work by Judish and Wunderlich (1987) has succeeded in measuring the diffusion of lithium atoms in argon gas by using an isothermal cell. As shown in figure 6.18, a new concept was used in which a source laser liberates lithium atoms along a well defined line and concentric detector lasers are used to detect the lithium atoms. A

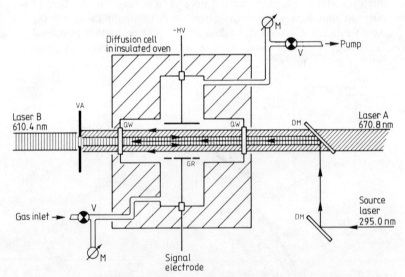

Figure 6.18 Experimental arrangement for the measurement of diffusion coefficients for Li in Ar using the compound coaxial geometry of Judish and Wunderlich (1987). Lasers A and B are the detector lasers. Lenses in the beam path of laser B and the source laser are not shown. The term VA represents a variable aperture; DM represents dielectric mirrors; M represents a pressure meter; V are valves; QW represents quartz windows; and GR is a guard ring.

variable aperture (VA) was used so that the diameter of laser B (which was 24 mJ per pulse and caused most of the ionisation signal since laser A was only 1.5 mJ per pulse) could be adjusted. In this way, the concentric geometry could be used for higher sensitivity, yet corrections due to chemical reactions could be made.

If $P(r)$ is the radial probability that a lithium atom is ionised in the RIS process, then the number of ions is given by

$$N(t) = (\lambda/2Dt)\exp(-\beta t)\int_0^r r\,dr\exp(-r^2/4Dt)P(r). \qquad (6.13)$$

Thus the ratio

$$R_{12}(t) = N_1(t)/N_2(t) \qquad (6.14)$$
$$= \left[\int_0^\infty r\,dr\exp(-r^2/4Dt)P_1(r)\right]\bigg/\left[\int_0^\infty r\,dr\exp(-r^2/4Dt)P_2(r)\right]$$

contains D but not β. However, unlike the case of parallel beams (§6.5), detailed characterisation of the laser beams and a knowledge of the photo-ionisation cross section of the 3D state in lithium are required.

Data for the ratio R_{12} are shown in figure 6.19 for argon pressures of

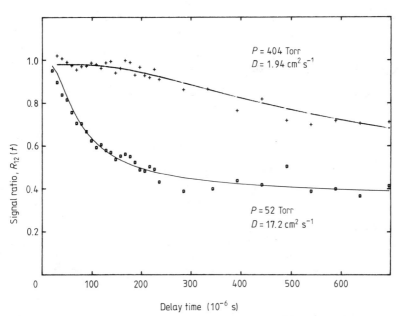

Figure 6.19 Signal ratios (for two detector laser diameters) against delay time in the compound coaxial geometry. The points represent experimental results; the curves are calculated from a fit of equation (6.14) to the experiment. The aperture diameters used to obtain the signal ratio are 0.158 and 0.276 cm.

52 and 404 Torr. Diffusion coefficients were obtained by fitting the data to equation (6.14). To understand the role of chemical reaction in these data better, a plot of the signal itself was made in figure 6.20 for two diameters of the detector laser. Thus, the best fit was found for $\beta = 1150\ \mathrm{s}^{-1}$, corresponding to less than 50 PPM of O_2 in the argon gas. In any case, this chemical rate does not appear in $R_{12}(t)$, consistent with the linear plot of D against P^{-1} in figure 6.21. For the pressure range from 52 to 517 Torr of argon, it was found that $PD = 920\ \mathrm{Torr\ cm^2\,s^{-1}}$.

Judish and Wunderlich (1987), to our knowledge, have made the first measurements of PD for lithium in a rare gas. Because they used an isothermal cell and a simple ionisation detector (parallel plate), it is possible to study temperature dependence of D and possibly to extract information on interaction potentials.

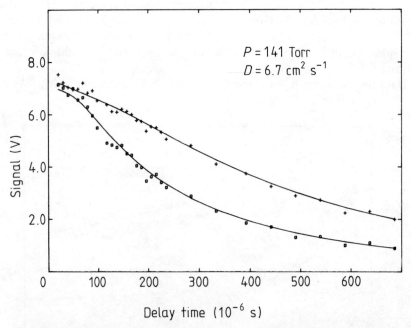

Figure 6.20 Signal against delay time for two different aperture settings of laser 2 in figure 6.19. The aperture diameters for the upper and lower curve are 0.276 and 0.106 cm, respectively. The points are experimental results; the curves are calculated from a fit of equation (6.13) to the experiment.

6.9 Concluding remarks

In this chapter we have discussed experimental arrangements in which RIS has been used to measure the diffusion coefficient and the rate of chemical reaction of alkali atoms in various gaseous environments.

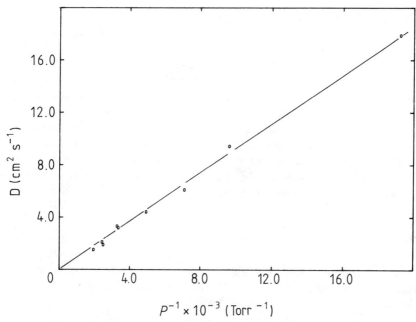

Figure 6.21 Diffusion coefficient for Li atoms in Ar gas against $1/P$, as measured in the compound coaxial geometry.

Three experimental geometries are compared schematically in figure 6.22. The simple coaxial geometry introduced by Grossman *et al* (1977a) is ideal for measurement of β but poor for D if β is large. The colinear geometry used by Hurst *et al* (1978) is excellent for D but poor for β. With care in characterising laser beam profiles and with known photo-ionisation cross sections, the compound coaxial geometry introduced by

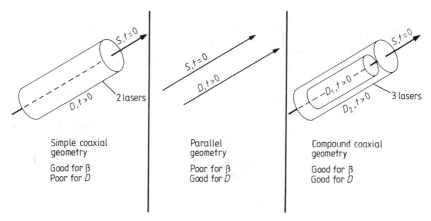

Figure 6.22 Comparison of geometries used to make diffusion coefficient and chemical reaction rate measurements using RIS.

Judish and Wunderlich is good for D and for β. Further, their method retains the high sensitivity of the simple coaxial geometry and allows the use of parallel-plate ionisation detectors, while the colinear geometry requires proportional counters or drift chambers.

Each of these geometries has a remarkable feature in common. Under normal conditions the medium is completely free of chemically reactive species—these are created only for a brief interval and even these small populations react to form stable compounds before they diffuse to the enclosure walls. Since one laser is used to create reactive atoms and another laser is used to detect them, the diffusion and the chemical reaction of free atoms can be studied in infinite media free from all surfaces such as enclosure walls.

References

Andrews L, Hsang Jenn-Tai and Trindle C 1973 *J. Phys. Chem.* **77** 1065
Bauer C E H and Evans A G 1937 *Trans. Faraday Soc.* **33** 158
Berkowitz J 1969 *J. Chem. Phys.* **50** 3503
Berry R S 1957 *J. Chem. Phys.* **27** 1288
——1979 in *Alkali-Halide Vapours* ed P Davidovits and D L McFadden (New York: Academic) Ch 3 p 93
Bortner T E and Hurst G S 1958 *Health Phys.* **1** 39
Carabetta R and Kaskan W E 1968 *J. Phys. Chem.* **72** 2483
Davidovits P and Brodhead D C 1967 *J. Chem. Phys.* **46** 2968
Eyring H 1935 *J. Chem. Phys.* **3** 107
Franzen W F 1959 *Phys. Rev.* **115** 850
Grossman L W, Hurst G S, Payne M G and Allman S L 1977a *Chem. Phys. Lett.* **50** 70
Grossman L W, Hurst G S, Kramer S D, Payne M G and Young J P 1977b *J. Chem. Phys.* **50** 207
Herzberg G 1950 *Molecular Spectra and Molecular Structure. I. Spectra of Diatomic Molecules* (Princeton: Van Nostrand) 2nd ed
Hurst G S, Allman S L, Payne M G and Whitaker T J 1978 *Chem. Phys. Lett.* **60** 160
Johnston H S 1966 *Gas Phase Reaction Rate Theory* (New York: Ronald) pp 253–262
Judish J P and Wunderlich R 1987 *J. Phys. B: At. Mol. Phys.* **20** 2317–25
Kramer S D, Young J P, Hurst G S and Payne M G 1979 *Optics Commun.* **30** 47
Kramer S D, Lehmann B E, Hurst G S, Payne M G and Young J P 1982 *J. Chem. Phys.* **76** 3614

Lehmann B E, Kramer S D, Allman S L, Hurst G S and Payne M G
    1980 *Chem. Phys. Lett.* **71** 91
Marrero T R and Mason E A 1973 *AIChE J.* **19** 498
Maya J and Davidovits P 1973 *J. Chem. Phys.* **59** 3143
Oppenheimer M and Berry R S 1971 *J. Chem. Phys.* **54** 5058
Zare R N and Herschbach D R 1965 *J. Mol. Spectrosc.* **15** 462

7

Statistical Mechanics

7.1 Introduction

We pointed out in Chapter 3 that the use of RIS with proportional counters is a very effective method for sensitive analyses of small numbers of atoms. In fact, the proportional counter is a nearly ideal detector for studies of small populations of atoms—since one atom can be detected in digital measurements and any number of atoms can be recorded when it is used as an analogue device. These facts were recognised at the very inception of one-atom detection (Hurst *et al* 1975, Hurst *et al* 1977a), and density fluctuations were first shown quantitatively by Hurst *et al* (1977b). In this chapter, we discuss how RIS is used to study density fluctuation for atoms and for molecules, and to examine other fluctuation phenomena associated with photo-ionisation events, dissociation of molecules, and collisions leading to line broadening. This chapter also describes how RIS made possible a new experimental method for determining the Fano factor and how it was used to experimentally test the ergodic hypothesis.

7.2 Density fluctuations in atomic populations

The method used to demonstrate one-atom detection (see Chapter 3) was also the first used to make electronic recordings of the density fluctuation of atomic populations. In this work (Hurst *et al* 1977b) a metallic caesium source was used (see figure 3.11) to provide a population of free atoms. Moderate heating of the source controlled the rate of evaporation. Furthermore, varying the distance from the source to the pulsed laser beam controlled the population of caesium atoms under study. After demonstrating one-atom sensitivity by using the proportional counter as a digital device, the source was arranged to provide an average population of less than 100 free atoms of caesium in the effective ionisation volume of the laser beam. By simply repeating the measurements and recording the pulse height distribution, fluctuations in atomic populations were directly observable.

A pulse height distribution corresponding to a low concentration of caesium atoms is shown in figure 7.1. In these experiments the laser sampled a small volume of space ($0.05\,cm^3$) and from every atom therein an electron was ejected and counted. For a range of counting gas pressures the time for diffusion of caesium atoms into the sensitive gas volume was much greater than the time width of the laser pulses and was much less than the time between these pulses. With these conditions, one may visualise the process of sampling as the successive emptying and refilling of a small volume surrounded by an infinite source of free atoms. By x-ray calibration it was found that the distribution in figure 7.1 peaks at 67 atoms and fluctuates considerably. Therefore, the fluctuation of atoms in a fixed volume of space was directly observed. Prior to the RIS method, these fluctuations were not directly observable but were deduced from such experimental observations as Brownian motion and the scattering of light. For an elementary review, see Present (1958).

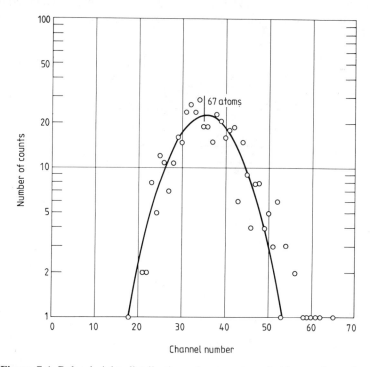

Figure 7.1 Pulse height distribution when most probable number of caesium atoms is 67.

7.3 Fluctuations in ionisation by swift particles: the Fano factor

When a swift charged particle (e.g. α-particle) interacts with a gas and creates ionisation, fluctuations occur in the number of ion pairs created per event. This is to be expected: however, the amount of fluctuation is not simply that of independent random events. This unusual situation in statistical phenomena was explained by Fano (1947) who showed that the usual standard deviation $\delta N = (\bar{N})^{1/2}$ is replaced with a quantity less than $(\bar{N})^{1/2}$. The now familiar expression is $\delta N = (F\bar{N})^{1/2}$, where F is the Fano factor and $F \leqslant 1$. In practice, this confers 'better than expected' energy resolution in ionisation detectors. Small Fano factors are desirable to improve the energy resolution of both gaseous and solid state radiation detectors.

The Fano factor has an interesting physical origin which can be understood in simple terms. Imagine an α-particle losing all of its energy (precisely E_0) in a gas which we represent as a simple atom with excited electronic states and an ionisation continuum, see figure 7.2. Each α-particle will excite many atoms to various discrete levels, having optical oscillator strengths f_j, and will ionise many atoms into the continuum with a spectrum of free electron energies ε. Clearly, there are fluctuations in ionisation since the energy E_0 can be expanded in a wide variety of ways. Suppose, for example, a given α-particle loses

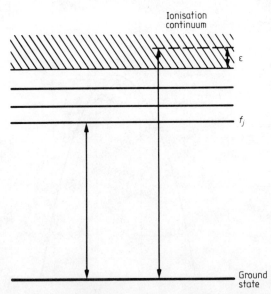

Figure 7.2 Origin of the Fano factor as explained in the text. When a charged particle loses all of its energy in a gas, excited electronic states and an ionisation continuum are involved in the energy losses.

more than the average amount of energy in the ionisation continuum but is compensated by less than the average energy loss in the discrete states to conserve energy precisely. To see how the fluctuations may be reduced by constraints built into the structure of the atom, imagine an unusual distribution of oscillator strengths. For instance, if in figure 7.2 all of the f_j values were zero and all of the oscillator strengths were concentrated into the continuum, not only would the ionisation yield, N, be larger but it would fluctuate much less. In fact, except for the spread in energies of the free electrons there would be no fluctuation of N, i.e. $F = 0$. This extreme example is of course unrealistic, but it illustrates that the distribution of oscillator strengths, different for each type of atom, determines the observed fluctuation. Thus, it is the constraint of the atom itself that reduces fluctuations and accounts for the Fano factor being less than 1.

We can now comment on the frequency distribution in figure 7.1 in a more quantitative way. In the proportional counter literature (see, for example, Campbell and Ledingham (1966)), the standard deviation, δP, of the mean pulse height, $\bar{P}$, is given by

$$(\delta P/\bar{P})^2 = (\delta N/\bar{N})^2 + (\delta A/\bar{A})^2/\bar{N} \tag{7.1}$$

where $\bar{N}$ and δN are, respectively, the mean and the standard deviation of the number of ion pairs and $\bar{A}$ and δA are, respectively, the mean and the standard deviation of the gas amplification. With swift charged particles, this equation would be used to evaluate fluctuations of ionisation for fixed energy losses; thus, δN is measured to deduce a Fano factor by using theoretical values for $(\delta A/\bar{A})$. In the early experiments on concentration fluctuations (Hurst *et al* 1977b), a rather different viewpoint was adopted. It was assumed that δN was the standard deviation of the concentration fluctuation for the free caesium atoms; thus, a measured $\delta P/\bar{P}$ could be used to estimate $(\delta A/\bar{A})$ from the experiment. It was concluded that the width of the frequency distribution (figure 7.1) was consistent with reasonable values of $(\delta A/\bar{A})$ and with a binomial distribution for δN. As a consequence, it was suggested that if frequency distributions are taken both for swift particles and for RIS of free atoms, a new method might be developed for measuring the Fano factor. This notion was advanced by Hurst *et al* (1978) to measure Fano factors for x-ray sources in P-10 gas.

Previously, radioactive sources (e.g. low-energy x-ray sources) or other sources of swift charged particles have been used to study both the magnitude and the fluctuation of the amplification of gas proportional counters (Curran *et al* 1949, Campbell and Ledingham 1966, Alkhazov *et al* 1967, Charles and Cooke 1968, Alkhazov 1970, Genz 1973, Breyer 1973, Sipila 1976). In contrast to this, the present method involves the production of free thermal electrons in a spatially well-defined laser beam at a known time. Furthermore, the mean number of electrons produced in the proportional counter can be 'dialled in' electronically, and the statistical fluctuation about the arbitrarily chosen mean number is described by the known Poisson function, which involves no Fano factor.

The concept of the experimental method is shown in figure 7.3 (Hurst *et al* 1978). Two laser beams parallel to each other at a separation ρ, and parallel to the counter wire, are pulsed into the proportional counter with an arbitrary time delay, τ, set between the lasers. With CsI crystals in the small furnace, a very low vapour pressure of CsI (e.g. 10^6 molecules per cm^3) can be created in the proportional counter otherwise filled with P-10 gas at a few hundred torr. Thus, the source laser set at 322 nm dissociates (Grossman *et al* 1977a) CsI into caesium plus iodine and the detector laser ionises caesium according to the RIS process. Briefly, in the detection process a photon at 455.5 nm excites the transition $Cs(6^2S_{1/2} \rightarrow 7^2P_{3/2})$ or, alternatively, photons at 459.3 nm can

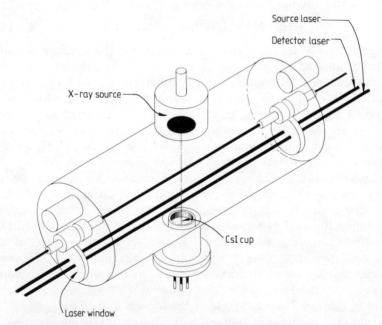

Figure 7.3 Schematic diagram of the proportional counter fluctuation experiment. A pulsed laser in the ultraviolet can be used to dissociate an alkali halide (e.g. CsI) vapour to provide a time-resolved source of atoms which diffuse into a detector beam. A pulsed laser (detector laser) in the visible region of the spectrum can be used to ionise caesium atoms in a resonant, two-step process. The electrons thus created are detected with a proportional counter.

be used to excite $Cs(7^2P_{1/2})$. In either case, a second photon interacts with one of the 7P levels, removing an electron from the excited state. This resonance ionisation process is quite selective in spite of modest collision broadening at high pressures of the counting gas.

On solving the diffusion equation for the parallel source–detector geometry in an infinite gaseous medium, one finds that the density of caesium atoms at the detector will go through a maximum in time and then decay slowly as the caseium atom cloud diffuses beyond the detector. Typically at a P-10 pressure of 100 Torr the density will be at its maximum value at 10 ms, but this depends on the concentration of impurities such as O_2, which at parts per billion level can cause caesium atoms to be converted to CsO_2 at a rate of about $100 \, s^{-1}$ (see Grossman *et al* (1977b)). Several parameters are available to control the number of electrons created, i.e. the CsI concentration, laser energies per pulse, the distance ρ and finally, for fine control, the delay time τ. In this way the average number $\bar{N}$ of electrons per pulse is under excellent control, and the various fluctuations associated with the counter can be measured as a function of $\bar{N}$. This experimental arrangement is suitable for a number of other measurements. Studies of the fluctuation of the density of atoms, collisional fluctuations, and photon–atom interaction fluctuations, as well as a precision method for the measurement of the diffusion coefficients, will be discussed below.

Figure 7.4 shows the data acquisition scheme and the electronic logic employed for the proportional counter fluctuation studies. Both lasers were commercial, linear, flashlamp-pumped dye lasers which produce about 1 mJ of photons tunable over wide ranges in the visible. Pulses could be repeated a few times per second. A time delay could be set between the source laser (SL) and the detector laser (DL) by using the digital delay generator. The SL is monitored with a photodiode and a beam splitter; it is stable enough so that a narrow (4% FWHM) window can be set on a single-channel analyser (SCA) without rejecting more than 50% of the laser shots. However, with the coumarin-2 dye, the DL is so unstable that control with a narrow window was not feasible. It is these output fluctuations which, unfortunately, dictate the kind of data acquisition which must be employed. The approach was the following. For the cases where signal S falls within the accepted range, the DL is fired and signals D and P are fed into a two-parameter multichannel analyser (MCA) where the function $N(P, D)$ is recorded. Electronic components such as preamplifiers, amplifiers, etc, are not described in detail in figure 7.4; the reader will be familiar with standard nuclear counting instrumentation.

Basic calibrations of the system were made at the $\bar{N} = 227$ and $\bar{N} = 100$ levels with x-ray sources ^{55}Fe and ^{37}Ar, respectively, and at the one-electron level by allowing ultraviolet photons from a mercury lamp

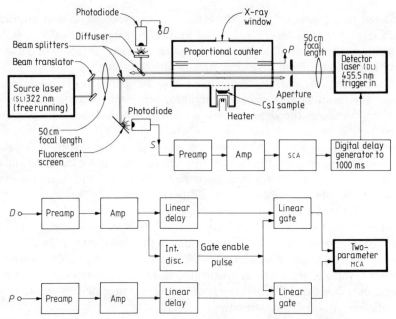

Figure 7.4 Data acquisition system for measuring the fluctuation of pulse heights in a proportional counter. Ionisation is created with the laser technique described in figure 7.3. The signals S and D are proportional to the energy per pulse of the source laser and detector laser, respectively, while the signal P is the proportional counter pulse height. (Int. disc. denotes integral discriminator.)

to release electrons one at a time from the counter walls. These data for the three calibrations are shown in figure 7.5.

Several pulse height spectra (i.e. plots giving the relative probability of observing various pulse heights) corresponding to various $\bar{N}$ in the range 4 to 20 are shown in figure 7.6. Since the values of D were large enough to partially saturate the RIS process, one sees that the RIS signals fluctuate due to fluctuation of atoms combined with the fluctuation of photon–atom interactions. It is normally assumed that these physical fluctuations are described with Poisson statistics, even when the observable events are the results of two or more processes. In spite of the fact that $\bar{N}$ was small enough to make observable the non-Gaussian tails, similar to what one expects for a Poisson distribution for small $\bar{N}$, we are not attempting here to test the statistics of atom density fluctuation since that test will be discussed below. In the latter case it is unnecessary to deconvolve the statistics of gas amplification from the statistics of atom density fluctuation.

It is appropriate to have somewhat larger values of $\bar{N}$, i.e. $\bar{N} > 25$, so that the data can be represented with Gaussian functions. Several of

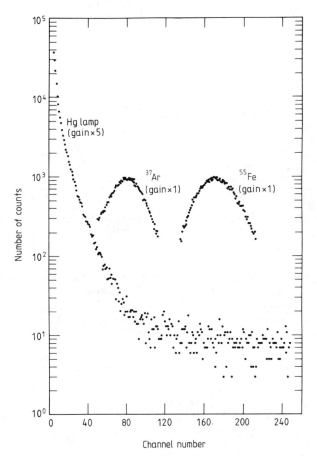

Figure 7.5 Pulse height spectra of the proportional counter for an Hg lamp source that produces one electron per pulse, an ^{37}Ar x-ray source at 2.6 keV and an ^{55}Fe x-ray source at 5.9 keV. The counter was filled with P-10 (90% Ar + 10% CH$_4$) at 100 Torr and operated at 1040 V.

these are plotted in figure 7.7 and compared to x-ray spectra with $\bar{N} = 100$ and $\bar{N} = 227$. At comparable values of $\bar{N}$, the spectra due to the laser interactions are clearly wider than those associated with the x-ray sources. This presentation vividly shows that the Fano process is operative. Without data analysis of any sort, one sees there is a Fano factor less than unity.

To analyse the RIS data and to compare it with the x-ray data, one uses

$$(\delta P/\bar{P})^2_L = (\delta N/\bar{N})^2_L + (\delta A/\bar{A})^2/\bar{N} + (\delta I)^2 \qquad (7.2)$$

where the term $(\delta N/\bar{N})^2_L$ will be just $1/\bar{N}$, assuming Poisson statistics for

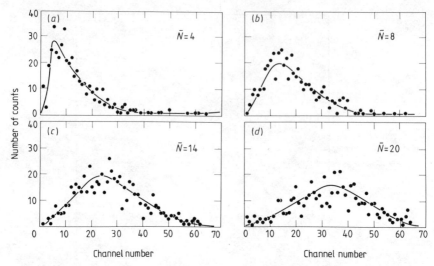

Figure 7.6 Pulse height spectra for a small number of electrons created by the laser in an RIS process. The mean numbers of electrons, $\bar{N}$, are approximately 4, 8, 14, and 20, respectively. Note the definite trend from a Gaussian to a Poisson distribution as $\bar{N}$ decreases. Solid lines through data serve as a visual aid only. The counter was operated at 1010 V.

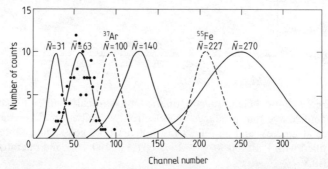

Figure 7.7 Pulse height spectra for the indicated $\bar{N}$ produced by laser ionisation of atoms in the RIS process. When the RIS distributions are compared with the more narrow x-ray distributions, the existence of a Fano factor is immediately apparent. The counter was operated at 950 V.

the fluctuation of the RIS signals. The term $(\delta I)^2$ represents any fluctuation which is independent of $\bar{N}$. For instance, fluctuation of the energy per pulse of the source laser can give rise to a term which is independent of $\bar{N}$. The term $(\delta A/\bar{A})^2$ is related to the single electron pulse height spectrum as follows:

$$(\delta A/\bar{A})^2 = [(\bar{\varepsilon^2}) - (\bar{\varepsilon})^2] \qquad (7.3a)$$

where

$$\overline{\varepsilon^m} = \int_0^\infty P(\varepsilon)\varepsilon^m d\varepsilon \qquad (7.3b)$$

and $P(\varepsilon)$ is the probability density function for pulse height ε due to a single electron. For x-ray sources we have, from equation (7.1),

$$(\delta P/\bar{P})_x^2 = \{F - 1 + [(\overline{\varepsilon^2})/(\bar{\varepsilon})^2]\}/\bar{N} \qquad (7.4a)$$

while for the RIS process,

$$(\delta P/\bar{P})_L^2 = (\delta I)^2 + [(\overline{\varepsilon^2})/(\bar{\varepsilon})^2]/\bar{N}. \qquad (7.4b)$$

When the RIS data of figure 7.7 are plotted to fit equation (7.4b), we see the results in figure 7.8. From the figure, $(\delta I)^2 = 0.015$ and $(\overline{\varepsilon^2})/(\bar{\varepsilon})^2 = 2.31$. From equation (7.4a) we find $F = 0.31$ and 0.21 for the ^{37}Ar and ^{55}Fe x-ray lines, respectively.

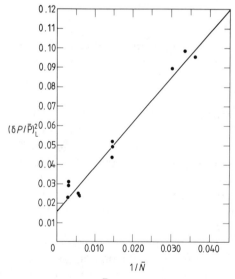

Figure 7.8 The quantity $(\delta P/\bar{P})_L^2$, i.e. the square of the standard deviation of the relative pulse height when electrons are produced with laser pulses, plotted against the reciprocal of the average number of electrons in a pulse. (Data based on figure 7.7.)

Previously the Fano factor was determined experimentally by measuring the pulse height fluctuation due to the complete absorption of ^{224}Ra α-particles in a pulse ionisation chamber. In this case the relative fluctuation was small due to the fact that $\bar{N}$ is of the order of 2×10^5 and it is difficult to separate the small fluctuation of ionisation from other fluctuations associated with the measurements. However, by using this method, Alkhazov *et al* (1967) were able to avoid the fluctuations associated with the gas amplification process that are encountered when a proportional counter is used. Prior to the present work there was no satisfactory way to measure independently the fluctuation of gas amplification. Our values for F for the two x-ray sources, compared with the value measured by Alkhazov *et al* (1967), for α-particles are shown in table 7.1. Also listed is the mean number $\bar{N}$ of electrons produced in a single pulse for each of the sources, where $\bar{N}$ was calculated by dividing the energy in eV by the W value (Melton *et al* 1954) for P-10 gas, i.e. $W = 26$ eV (see Chapter 1).

Table 7.1 Measured values of the Fano factor, F, for ^{37}Ar and ^{55}Fe x-ray sources in P-10 gas. Comparison is made with a measurement made for α-particles.

Source	$\bar{N}$	F	Reference
^{37}Ar(2.6 keV, x-ray)	100	0.31 ± 0.10	[†]
^{55}Fe(5.9 keV, x-ray)	227	0.21 ± 0.10	[†]
^{224}Ra(3.68 MeV, α-particle)	2.2×10^5	0.19	[‡]

[†]Hurst *et al* 1978.
[‡]Alkhazov *et al* 1967.

Fano factors can depend on the energy of the swift particle producing the ionisation. Therefore, in principle, the value for the 2.6 keV photoelectrons could be larger than the value for the 5.9 keV photoelectrons. Such a result is plausible if the 2.6 keV photoelectrons excite relatively more excited states (compared to the continuum) than do the 5.9 keV photoelectrons (see figure 7.2). The method described here gives a Fano factor for each source independently. However, we cannot conclude that the two values obtained are substantially different, for they lie within the range of experimental errors shown in table 7.1.

The technique for studying the fluctuation of proportional counters by using the RIS process allows one to determine the fluctuation of gas amplification under conditions where $\bar{N}$ can be arbitrarily selected and where the fluctuation about $\bar{N}$ can be assumed to be that of Poisson statistics. With this independent determination of $(\delta A / \bar{A})$, one can more accurately determine the Fano factor which enters into the statistics of the ionisation of gases by fast charged particles.

7.4 Fluctuations in atomic and molecular processes

Direct experimental observations on other fluctuation processes in atomic and molecular physics have been made with RIS methods by

Iturbe *et al* (1982). Figure 7.9 is a schematic diagram of the method used to generalise the statistical fluctuation studies to the following distinct atomic and molecular processes: (a) concentration of molecules; (b) yields of atoms in the photodissociation of diatomic molecules; (c) concentration of free atoms; and (d) the collision frequency of atoms leading to spectral line broadening. Only one of these, i.e. process (c), was previously studied. Further, Iturbe *et al* used the digital capability of the proportional counter for all of these measurements. This proved to be more quantitative and direct since the need to deconvolve pulse height spectra was eliminated. Analogue use of the proportional counter was essential to study the Fano factor (§7.3) but was inferior to the digital method when making quantitative statistical tests.

Referring to figure 7.9, note that the ionisation drift region and the proportional counter were filled with a gas at such pressures that the mean free path of atoms was short compared to the dimensions of the apparatus. A trace quantity of any alkali halide molecule can be seeded into the gaseous medium. A pulsed ultraviolet (UV) laser can be used to dissociate alkali halide molecules into constituent atoms in their ground state. This provides a source of alkali atoms which is well defined in

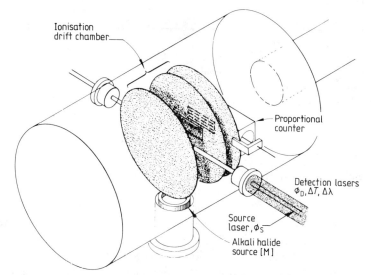

Figure 7.9 Schematic diagram of the method used to generalise statistical fluctuation studies. For example, LiI molecules can be evaporated from the cup and transported to the detection volume. A source laser dissociates the molecule into atoms. After a time delay, two detector lasers are fired simultaneously to excite and ionise the lithium atoms. Free electrons are drifted to a proportional counter having gas amplification greater than a value of 10^3. The detector signal gives the number of electrons (analogue response) or the presence or absence of one electron (digital response).

space at $t = 0$. After an appropriate diffusion time, $t > 0$, alkali atoms can be ionised with another laser in a state-selective process (RIS). Electrons thus produced can be drifted into a proportional counter where both digital and analogue information can be recorded.

The basic statistics of five distinct atomic phenomena can be measured simply by selection of parameters in one experimental arrangement. Let $[M]$ be the concentration of alkali halide molecules in the apparatus, ϕ_S the fluence delivered in one pulse of a 'source' laser which dissociates the molecule, ϕ_D the fluence delivered in one pulse of the 'detector' laser which excites and ionises the selected atom, ΔT the time delay between the source and detector lasers, and $\Delta\lambda$ the detuning of the detector laser away from a resonance line. As can be seen in table 7.2, a particular phenomenon can be selected for study simply by proper choice of the five experimental parameters. Each of the five phenomena can be carefully tested for random behaviour in time to see if Poisson statistics are applicable.

Table 7.2 Fluctuation phenomena and associated experimental parameters.

Physical phenomena which fluctuate	$[M]$	ϕ_S	ϕ_D	ΔT	$\Delta\lambda$
None—no observable fluctuation	Large	Large	Large	0	0
Molecular concentration	Small	Large	Large	0	0
Photodissociation yield	Large	Small	Large	0	0
Atomic concentration	Large	Large	Large	>0	0
Photo-ionisation yield	Large	Large	Small	0	0
Collision frequency	Large	Large	Large	0	>0

In the determination of fluctuations in the detection volume of a proportional counter by counting the electrons arriving at its wire, it is necessary to circumvent the fluctuations in the gas amplification process. Thus, when the number of electrons is small (for example, less than ten), it is preferable to make digital measurements instead of relying on the resolution of the analogue response of the counter. To ensure this, it is only necessary that conditions are maintained such that each time the laser is fired the probability of creating one electron is very low (e.g. less than or equivalent to 0.1) and that the counter is run at sufficient gain to detect all RIS electrons with unit efficiency. Then a computer-based data acquisition system can by used to record a list of all laser shots, together with an indication of those in which a free electron was created. The probability of one-electron detection, p, is simply the ratio of number of electron counts to the total number of shots.

In order to work with a suitable population of electrons, say $\bar{N}$, we only have to sum the number of detected atoms for a fixed number of shots, say n; thus, $\bar{N} = np$. For example, if the probability of detecting one electron is 0.1 and we sum 50 laser shots, $\bar{N}$ will be 5, and the fluctuations around this value will not depend on fluctuations of gas amplification. Physically, this procedure could be interpreted as the detection of the number of atoms in 50 identical systems, provided that the time between laser shots is long compared with the time for the decay of concentration fluctuations in the laser beam volume. This analysis tacitly assumes the system to be ergodic; hence, a confirmation of Poisson statistics in this experiment can be regarded as an indirect test of the ergodic hypothesis. In the next section we discuss an explicit test of the ergodic hypothesis.

An RIS technique for lithium atoms has been described in detail in Chapter 6. In the experiments of Iturbe *et al* (1982), a stainless steel chamber connected to a vacuum system (which could be evacuated to 10^{-7} Torr) was filled with P-10 counting gas to a pressure of approximately 200 Torr. To avoid impurity accumulation, the gas was kept flowing at 200 standard $cm^3\,min^{-1}$. A temperature-controlled electric oven heated a gold cup containing powdered anhydrous LiI (99.99% pure). A UV source from an intracavity, frequency-doubled Chromatix dye laser (model CMX-4, laser A in figure 7.10) was tuned to the LiI absorption peak at 290 nm, which is known to give lithium atoms in their ground state. With the laser focused down to a diameter of 0.1 cm, a line source of atoms was produced at $t = 0$ at the centre of the chamber. After several microseconds, two dye lasers (detector lasers) tuned to the transition frequencies for lithium detection were fired simultaneously. One of these was tuned to 670.8 nm, the 2S–2P transition (Chromatix CMX-4, laser B in figure 7.10) and another was tuned to 610.4 nm, the 2P–3D transition (Candela LFDL-1, laser C in figure 7.10). Both beams were combined and focused to 0.5 cm in the centre of the chamber. Atoms in this higher excited (3D) state are ionised by photons from either of the detector lasers. Simultaneity of the detector lasers is important because of the short lifetime of the lithium excited state which is of the order of tens of microseconds. The time delay between source and detector lasers allows any inadvertent, UV-created photoelectrons to be removed by the negatively charged ($V = 80$ V) field plate, but it is not long enough to allow the neutral atom to diffuse out of the detector volume.

The resonantly created electrons were drifted to a proportional counter by a negatively biased plate at -300 V. This plate was kept grounded until just before the detector lasers were fired in order to avoid dead times produced by photoelectrons that could have been directed through the field plate aperture into the proportional counter.

The electronics and data acquisition system are also shown in figure 7.10. An external clock, set at 5 Hz, masters the whole cycle from

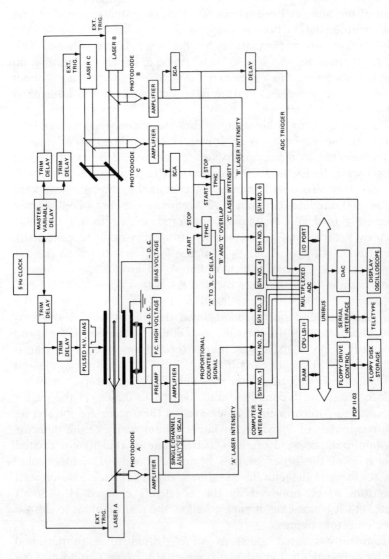

Figure 7.10 Electronics and data acquisition system for generalised fluctuation studies. A 5 Hz clock triggers the lasers after predetermined delays. Laser energies per pulse, time delays between laser shots and the ionisation signal are routed to different sample and hold circuits (S/H), digitised (ADC), and processed in a PDP-11 type computer.

dissociation to data storage. The clock triggers the source laser A and a delay triggers the detector lasers B and C. By means of beam splitters, photodiodes and amplifiers, the intensity signals of all three lasers are sampled and held at their peaks. Signals from the proportional counter are also amplified, sampled and held at their peak. Time delays between the source and detector lasers, and between the two detector lasers, are also converted into signals by means of converters from time to pulse height, and sampled and held. All signals were digitised with one multiplexed analog-to-digital converter (ADC), processed by a PDP-11 type computer and stored on floppy discs.

Ideally, the apparatus should not introduce any fluctuations of its own. In order to check this point, the 'no fluctuation experiment' was performed as seen in table 7.2. Once the system was in optimal condition for lithium detection, it was run for several hundred shots. Fluctuations in the source light intensity were compared with fluctuations in the signal intensity to confirm that no extraneous fluctuations were present. A series of experiments were carried out by Iturbe *et al* (1982) to test each of the last five phenomena listed in table 7.2. Brief comments on each follow.

7.4.1 Molecular concentration fluctuations

With a reading of 347 °C in the LiI source cup, the number of molecules in the source laser beam is quite large. At 192 °C, the probability of detecting one electron in the proportional counter, and therefore the probability of detecting one molecule, is only 0.0921 per detection volume per laser shot. By summing over 44 shots, the mean is 4.052; the distribution around this mean is given in figure 7.11, together with the Poisson distribution for the same mean. All the conditions listed in table 7.2 were met; therefore, we interpret the data as the probability that M molecules were in the volume of the source laser beam.

7.4.2. Photodissociation yield fluctuations

The energy per pulse of the UV laser was decreased by means of several neutral density filters and microscope slides; see table 7.2 for the other parameters. The probability of detecting one electron was 0.1509 per detection volume per shot. Summing over 27 shots, the mean is 4.074; the distribution of the number of photodissociated atoms around this value and the Poisson distribution with the same mean are given in figure 7.11. This is the frequency distribution for photodissociation of a large population of molecules into a small population of product atoms.

7.4.3 Atomic concentration fluctuations

After free lithium atoms are created in the detection volume, chemical reaction with impurities and diffusion occurs. The population of free

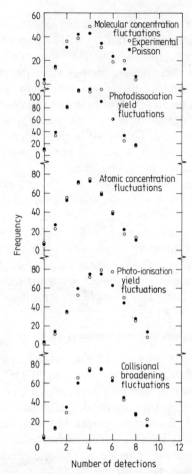

Figure 7.11 Distribution of fluctuations around the mean value of the number of molecules detected in a small volume, around the mean value of the photodissociation yield, around the mean value of the number of atoms detected, around the mean value of the photo-ionisation yield, and around the mean value of the collisional frequency.

lithium atoms in the detection volume will decline with time, and eventually it will drop to a level in which the probability of finding one atom will be very low. In the experiments it was seen that after 47.0 ms the probability was 0.098 per detection volume per shot. By summing 41 shots, the mean value is 4.018; the distribution around this value and the Poisson distribution of the same mean are given in figure 7.11. Since conditions of table 7.2 were met, Iturbe *et al* interpreted figure 7.11 as the probability that A atoms were in a small volume.

Atomic beam experiments (Valikin *et al* 1979) have also shown the existence of fluctuations in the number of atoms in a detection volume, although the data were not obtained in such a way that a detailed comparison with the Poisson distribution could be made.

7.4.4 Photo-ionisation yield fluctuations

Saturation of the three-photon process for the resonance ionisation of lithium requires that all the lithium atoms be excited and ionised during the pulse duration of the detector lasers. If the fluence of either of the detector lasers is decreased, fluctuation in excitation and/or ionisation will become apparent. The 610.4 nm laser (laser C, figure 7.10) was attenuated with several neutral density filters by a factor of almost 10^6, decreasing the energy to 0.009 μJ per pulse. The probability of detecting one electron was 0.1664 per detection volume per shot. For 30 shots the mean was 4.992; the distribution around this mean, together with the Poisson distribution with the same mean, is given in figure 7.11. This corresponds then (see table 7.2) to the probability that lithium atoms were ionised when a large population of atoms and photons interacted.

7.4.5 Collisional broadening fluctuations

The first laser used in the detection of lithium was detuned from 670.8 nm to 661.4 nm, making the probability of detecting one electron 0.1564 per detection volume per shot. For 32 shots, the mean number of atoms detected was 5.005; the distribution around this value and the Poisson distribution are given in figure 7.11 for a gas pressure of 200 Torr. This plot gives the probability that binary collisions were occurring during an observation.

The agreement between the five experimental fluctuations and the respective Poisson distributions is good. The Poisson distribution points are always within one standard deviation of the experimental points. Fluctuations from the mean values of physical quantities for large numbers of observations are known to follow Gaussian probability distributions with the maximum centred on the value corresponding to the mean value. With small populations, however, the probability distribution is Poisson.

The application of one-atom detection techniques has made possible the determination of the experimental probability distributions of fluctuations for the cases of atomic and molecular concentrations. The shapes of these distributions are Poisson, as expected from the molecular theory of gases. Furthermore, fluctuations in the photodissociation yield, photo-ionisation of atoms and collision frequency can also be described with the Poisson distribution. We should not leave the impression that all fluctuation phenomena are random; for example, the number of secondary electrons produced in ionisation tracks is one important exception. In this case, the more narrow frequency distributions can be used to deduce a Fano factor (see §7.3).

7.5 The ergodic hypothesis: an Einstein 'gedanken' experiment

In the next section we will show how the RIS method was used (Iturbe *et al* 1983) to test the ergodic hypothesis in context with a system of freely diffused atoms. Iturbe *et al* (see §7.6) performed an actual experiment which was first outlined as a *gedanken* (thought) experiment by Einstein. For an exposition of the *gedanken* experiment, see Furth (1956); and for a penetrating discussion of Einstein's views on the ergodic hypothesis, see Pais (1982).

An excellent introduction to the ergodic hypothesis may be found in Uhlenbeck and Ford (1963) and in Margenau and Murphy (1943). Ergodic theory was introduced by Boltzman, generalised by Gibbs and formalised by Birkhoff. The state of any system described by classical mechanics can be represented by a point moving in phase space (Γ space). Gibbs visualised the motion of many points representing all possible initial states of the classical system as the ensemble fluid. With the Liouville theorem, the medium can be shown to be incompressible. This mechanical model would appear inappropriate for describing the irreversible behaviour of macroscopic systems. It is recalled, in fact, that the Poincaré theorem predicts quasiperiodic motion with no tendency to equilibrate (Uhlenbeck and Ford 1963). However, Boltzman resolved the conflict by showing that the equilibrium state is merely the 'most likely' state of the system. In this purely statistical view, any non-equilibrium distribution goes quickly to a stable equilibrium. Boltzman's method of calculating distribution functions involved the six-dimensional phase space of individual molecules i.e. complexions or microstates (fine graining), while Gibbs introduced a more abstract subspace in his coarse-graining concept. For either method of calculation, there is considerable difficulty in understanding how these distributions can be compared with experimental observations.

The discussion of Pais (in which he stresses that Boltzman introduced two independent definitions of thermodynamic probability) gets to the heart of the ergodic hypothesis. In the first definition, Boltzman prescribes that a system be observed for a long time, τ, and if it is found to be in a state S_i for a time τ_i, then in the limit $\tau \to \infty$, τ_i/τ is the probability of the thermodynamic state S_i. In the second definition of probability, Boltzman calculated the probability w of the distribution specified by $n_1, n_2 \ldots$ by

$$w = N!/\prod_i n_i!$$

and assumed this to be the thermodynamic probability of the system. Gibbs' method of calculation using the coarse-grained probability W does not change the essence of the difficulty. Why should a calculated distribution involving these permutations be identical with the probabilities determined from time-averaging over actual observations? The ergodic hypothesis asserts this equivalence, but a general proof has been lacking. It is logical that the 'time spent' definition would be proportional to the 'volume in Γ space', yet this logic has not succumbed to mathematics.

The ergodic hypothesis comes from equating physically meaningful time averages $\langle F \rangle$, with calculated ensemble averages, $\bar{F}$. In spite of good agreement between expected and observed values in a variety of physical situations, attempts to justify the equality between both averages have led to a whole branch in mathematical physics. Some monographs (Farquhar 1964) and review articles (Lebowitz and Penrose 1963) have appeared on ergodicity, and several texts on statistical mechanics (Ehrenfest and Ehrenfest 1911, ter Haar 1954, 1955, Khinchin 1949) have good discussions of this subject.

Sinai (1967, 1970) has rigorously proved that the physically interesting hard-sphere gas is ergodic, and therefore $\bar{F} = \langle F \rangle$. On the other hand, a system of coupled anharmonic oscillators is not ergodic (Henon and Heiles 1974, Walker and Ford 1969).

Einstein preferred the first definition of Boltzman to his abstract second definition. To eliminate the abstract, Einstein visualised a *gedanken* experiment designed to tell whether a system is ergodic. We proceed to describe this thought experiment in some detail, since it was carried out in the laboratory (Iturbe *et al* 1983) almost exactly as suggested by Einstein (see Furth 1956).

We follow an idea which originated in the work of Einstein on Brownian motion (Furth 1956): see figure 7.12. Einstein and Furth considered the time-dependent solution $n(\rho, t)$ of the diffusion equation

$$\partial n(\rho, t)/\partial t = D\nabla^2 n(\rho, t)$$

for the boundary conditions that atoms are released from a plane source at $t = 0$ and detected on a parallel-plate detector at the distance ρ. It was argued that a system is ergodic if the solution of the diffusion equation $n(\rho, t)$ can be verified with two independent methods which were called 'space summation' and 'time summation'. In the space summation method one visualises the release of a large number of atoms at $t = 0$, and on each trial one measures a good approximation to $n(\rho, t_i)$ where t_i is a particular delay time. Some averaging over trials is permitted, consistent with Einstein's use of 'virtual summation'. For a time summation method, suppose the number of atoms released is so

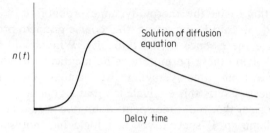

$n(t)$

Solution of diffusion equation

Delay time

(1) Do 'space summation' with $\bar{N} \gg 1$, by 'virtual summation' compare with $n(t)$

(2) Do 'time summation' with $\bar{N} \ll 1$

Compare the two cases: $n(t)_{(1)} = n(t)_{(2)} \Rightarrow$ Ergodic system

Figure 7.12 Outline of the Einstein–Furth *gedanken* experiment for testing the ergodic hypothesis for freely diffusing particles.

small that the probability that even one atom will be in the detector at time t_i is much less than 1. After many shots, probabilities can be added over the many trials and compared (with suitable normalisation) to the space-summation results. Tests can be made of the entire time domain $n(\rho, t)$ using the two methods. If the two results agree at all t, the system is ergodic.

At first glance it appears that the solution of the differential equation for the diffusion of free atoms is not connected with the movement of a point through Γ space. However, the diffusion of atoms is a physical example of non-equilibrium phenomena in general. Gibbs showed that if a system is prepared initially in a non-equilibrium state, its return to equilibrium can be visualised as a process in which a probability distribution (taken around a singular point in phase space) spreads out into a thin thread that eventually permeates all of phase space uniformly. Whether the thread actually fills all of phase space is not proven; the assertion that it does is an expression of the ergodic hypothesis.

Einstein's *gedanken* experiment for a system of freely diffusing atoms regarded the physical system to be tested as a large number of atoms mutually diffusing through another gas. Its testing would be done in two ways—one by actual measurement of the concentration of large numbers of atoms at one instant of time, another by measuring the small (much less than one) probability of an atom being present by time averaging over many trials. The first of these corresponds to the permutation of a large number of atoms which Einstein labelled space summation, while the second is the time summation preferred by Einstein. If the two methods are in agreement with each other, then the particular system tested is ergodic. Note that either experiment is a rigorous test of the diffusion equation, but both experiments are required to test the ergodic hypothesis.

7.6 An experimental test of the ergodic hypothesis

Resonance ionisation spectroscopy techniques offer the possibility of directly carrying out the Einstein–Furth gedanken experiment to test the ergodic hypothesis. It is simple, in principle, to do the prescribed diffusion experiment on free atoms, except for an insignificant difference in geometry. With laser techniques, it is more convenient to use a linear array of atoms and a linear detector, rather than a plane source and a plane detector. Otherwise, the Iturbe *et al* (1983) procedure follows Einstein in detail (see figure 7.12).

Imagine a parallel-plate ionisation chamber which can drift electrons into an attached proportional counter which is in a common enclosure filled with a good counting gas such as P-10 at a pressure of approximately 200 Torr. Such an arrangement permits electron collection from a known volume and can be used to detect a single electron (as a digital device) or many electrons at the same time (as an analogue device). A first laser (source laser) is tuned to 290 nm and fired into the apparatus between the parallel plates of the ionisation chamber to dissociate LiI molecules seeded into the gas. Thus, at a time defined as $t = 0$, lithium atoms are released in their ground state; and for $t > 0$, lithium atoms are freely diffusing from the line source. At a time $t = t_1$, two coaxially arranged detector lasers are simultaneously fired to accomplish saturated resonance ionisation of all lithium atoms in their path. One is tuned to 670.8 nm (2S–2P transition), and the other to 610.4 nm (2P–3D transition). After two-step excitation a photon from the same pulse of either of the lasers ionises the lithium. The electrons are pushed by an electric field toward a proportional counter where a signal is produced whose amplitude is proportional to the number of electrons and thus to the number of lithium atoms. Pulse height calibration can be made with an x-ray source (^{55}Fe in our case) which creates an average of 227 electrons per pulse (Hurst *et al* 1978).

To make a space-summation measurement, several hundred atoms are ionised with each shot, and an analogue recording is made of the number of electrons reaching the counter. An average over several sets of laser pulses is allowed to carry out virtual summation, recommended by Einstein and Furth, to obtain a closer approximation to the diffusion curve. By changing the delay time between the firing of the source laser and the simultaneous firing of the two detector lasers, the entire diffusion process can be explored in its time domain.

The procedure for the time summation is as follows. A well-calibrated UV filter is placed in the source laser path, decreasing the number of dissociated molecules to a point where the detector lasers 'see' zero atoms most of the time. On the rare occasions when an electron is liberated, the proportional counter, operating essentially as a Geiger–Müller detector with one-electron sensitivity, will give a digital signal which is a sure indication that an atom has been detected. Under these conditions, the probability that two atoms are detected at the same time is negligible. If the laser shots are repeated several hundred times, the probability that an atom will reach the detection volume at a fixed diffusion time can be determined simply as the ratio of detected electrons to the total number of laser shots. In this way, a probability is obtained (by the time-summation method) to represent one point on the time–diffusion curve $n(\rho, t)$. By repeating experiments at other time delays between source and detector lasers (diffusion times), one can again explore via these digital measurements the entire time domain of the diffusion process.

The actual details of the apparatus are the same as those previously described for fluctuation experiments. A stainless steel chamber, connected to a vacuum system, is filled with P-10 gas. In the bottom a temperature-controlled oven heats a gold crucible filled with LiI. Quartz windows allow the passage of source and detector laser beams. The optics outside the chamber allow beam translation, enabling the distance between both beams to be easily measurable by means of an array of small photodiodes with a resolution of 0.025 mm per photodiode. A beryllium window allows the penetration of the external x-ray calibration source.

The dual capacity of proportional counters to work both as digital and analogue devices is worthy of additional consideration. The free electrons from the selectively photo-ionised lithium atoms are drifted towards the window of the proportional counter and then towards a central stainless steel wire which is positively charged. The diameter is small enough (0.005 cm) to produce an avalanche (i.e. as one electron is accelerated near the wire it produces secondary electrons). An electrical signal is induced mainly by the positive ions driven away from the wire. Under carefully controlled conditions, the signal will be proportional to the number of initial electrons; thus, it provides analogue information. When the positive wire potential is increased, the Geiger–Müller counting region is approached where the signal is independent of the number of initial electrons; thus, under these conditions the detector can also give good digital information. A simple trial-and-error process can be used to determine the optimum voltages for both analogue (1000 V) and digital (1320 V) measurements at a particular gas pressure.

The electronics and the data acquisition system were essentially the same as those used for fluctuation experiments. Mirrors on translation stages were used to achieve parallel-beam geometry inside the chamber, and long focal length lenses were used to make the source and detector volumes as thin as possible, thereby decreasing the uncertainty in the distance between beams. To carry out the digital experiments, the source laser intensity was reduced by placing a calibrated UV filter in front of the source laser. Saturation conditions were checked to be sure that all of the atoms that reached the detection volume were photoionised.

By controlling the LiI oven temperature and the uv beam energy per pulse, a population was prepared of, say, N_0 atoms, of which N were detected at a particular time delay between source and detector laser at a fixed distance. When the uv filter, which is known to have an attenuation factor of f, was inserted in the uv beam, the number of lithium atoms dissociated was N_0/f since all laser energies per pulse were kept in the region where the LiI dissociation is a linear function of the number of photons per pulse. With $N \ll f$, the ratio N/f is just the probability that an atom will be detected if the system is ergodic.

Figure 7.13 shows the experimental results obtained for both analogue and digital measurements taken at several delay (diffusion) times and at one particular separation of the source laser from the detector laser (i.e. $\rho = 4.56$ mm). The analogue data are the average of 1000 shots and represent approximately 600 atoms per pulse at the peak time. Measurements of the filter attenuation factor gave $f = 3100$ at 296 nm, accurate to approximately $\pm 5\%$. A 'probability' scale to the right of figure 7.13 was established simply by dividing the scale on the left by 3100. The digital measurements, made after inserting the filter, were plotted on

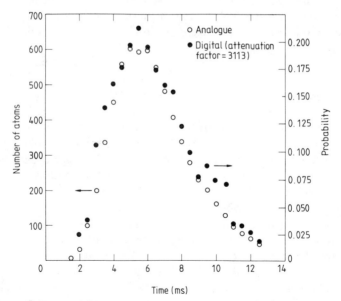

Figure 7.13 Comparison between time-summation and space-summation measurements on an absolute scale. (Comparison made with $\rho = 0.456$ cm and $D = 0.586$ cm^2 s^{-1}.)

this scale on an absolute basis for the several delay times. Each data point represents approximately 3000 shots and thus approximately 600 atoms counted at the peak time. Agreement between the digital and analogue measurements is well within the ±5% range allowed by the uncertainty in the filter attenuation.

It is important to characterise the chemical environment associated with the ergodic test. Due to the high reactivity of lithium atoms, even minute concentrations of impurities can interfere with the precise determination of the diffusion coefficient. However, chemical effects can be eliminated by making the diffusion measurements at two different distances, as has already been shown. The diffusion equation with a chemical reaction occurring at a rate β for this geometry, in which both the line source and the line detector are parallel and situated far from any walls, was given in Chapter 6.

From diffusion measurements made at two different distances, ρ_1 and ρ_2, Iturbe *et al* (1983) determined both D and β. By plotting $\ln(n(\rho_1, t)/n(\rho_2, t))$ against $1/t$, D could be determined from the slope. A self-consistent β for the two distances was then determined by fitting experimental data to a solution of the diffusion equation. In these experiments the diffusion coefficient was $0.586 \, \text{cm}^2 \, \text{s}^{-1}$, normalised to 1 atm and measured at 143 °C. The reaction rate β was kept at approximately the same level during the ergodic experiment. Controlled chemical reaction at a constant level actually has a significant advantage in these statistical experiments. All of the free atoms combine chemically between shots; thus, new ensembles of atoms can be prepared simply by firing the dissociation laser.

7.7 Further comments on the ergodic hypothesis

Perhaps the best way to interpret Einstein's suggestion of a test of the ergodic hypothesis by doing a diffusion experiment is the following. In a time-resolved diffusion experiment, the atoms which are established in a non-equilibrium concentration at $t = 0$ can be regarded as 'test atoms' to probe the state of a system of atoms presumed to be in thermal equilibrium. The test atoms can be deployed in two basic ways to bring out 'space summation' and 'time summation' features of the test of our equilibrium system of atoms. Thus, suppose a sufficient number of test atoms are deployed at $t = 0$ so that at any arbitrary time, $t > 0$, the system of atoms tested is found to be in such a state that the concentration $n(x, t_1)$ is measured at the instant of time t_1. This is a space-summation test and not a time-summation test, since each test atom included in $n(x, t_1)$ had to be near the plane at x at time t_1. On the other hand, if only one test atom is deployed at time $t = 0$, the state of the system, specifying $n(x, t)$, can only be measured after a large number of test atoms have been deployed in many tests, all starting at $t = 0$. Obviously, a 'time summation' is now involved since no single deployment of atoms can give enough information to specify $n(x, t)$. If the system is in equilibrium it does not evolve with time; hence, changing the time of deployment of an atom to test the system has no effect. However, according to Einstein and Furth, the ergodic assumption is required to equate the 'space summation' and the 'time summation' observations.

References

Alkhazov G D 1970 *Nucl. Instr. Meth.* **89** 155
Alkhazov G D, Komar A P and Voreb'ev A A 1967 *Nucl. Instr. Meth.* **48** 1
Breyer B 1973 *Nucl. Instr. Meth.* **112** 91
Campbell J L and Ledingham K W D 1966 *Br. J. Appl. Phys.* **17** 769
Charles M W and Cooke B A 1968 *Nucl. Instr. Meth.* **61** 31
Curran S C, Cockroft A L and Angus J 1949 *Phil. Mag.* **40** 929
Ehrenfest P and Ehrenfest T 1911 in *Encyklopaedie der Mathematischen Wissenschaften* vol. 4 (Leipzig: Teubner) article 32 (1959 Engl. Transl. *The Conceptual Foundation of the Statistical Approach in Mechanics* (Ithaca, NY: Cornell University Press))
Fano U 1947 *Phys. Rev.* **72** 26
Farquhar I E 1964 *Ergodic Theory in Statistical Mechanics* (New York: Interscience)
Furth R (ed) 1956 *Investigation on the Theory of the Brownian Movement* (New York: Dover)
Genz H 1973 *Nucl. Instr. Meth.* **112** 83
Grossman L W, Hurst G S, Payne M G and Allman S L 1977a *Chem. Phys. Lett.* **50** 70
Grossman L W, Hurst G S, Kramer S D, Payne M G and Young J P 1977b *Chem. Phys. Lett.* **50** 207
ter Haar D 1954 *Elements of Statistical Mechanics* (New York: Rinehart)
——1955 *Rev. Mod. Phys.* **27** 289
Henon M and Heiles C 1974 *Astron. J.* **69** 73
Hurst G S, Payne M G, Nayfeh M H, Judish J P and Wagner E B 1975 *Phys. Rev. Lett.* **35** 82
Hurst G S, Nayfeh M H and Young J P 1977a *Appl. Phys. Lett.* **30** 229
——1977b *Phys. Rev.* A **15** 2283
Hurst G S, Allman S L, Payne M G, Marshall K A and SooHoo K L 1978 *Nucl. Instr. Meth.* **155** 203

Iturbe J, Allman S L, Hurst G S and Payne M G 1982 *Chem. Phys. Lett.* **93** 460
——1983 *Chem. Phys. Lett.* **94** 505
Khinchin A I 1949 *Mathematical Foundations of Statistical Mechanics* (New York: Dover)
Lebowitz L and Penrose O 1963 *Phys. Today* (February) p 23
Margenau H and Murphy G M 1943 *The Mathematics of Physics and Chemistry* (New York: Van Nostrand)
Melton C E, Hurst G S and Bortner T E 1954 *Phys. Rev.* **96** 643
Pais A *Subtle is the Lord: The Science and the Life of Albert Einstein* 1982 (Oxford; Clarendon: New York; Oxford University Press)
Present R D 1958 *Kinetic Theory of Gases* (New York: McGraw-Hill) pp 157–77
Sinai Ya G 1967 in *Statistical Mechanics, Foundations, and Applications* ed T A Bak (New York: Benjamin)
——1970 *Russian Math. Rev.* **25** 137
Sipila H 1976 *Nucl. Instr. Meth.* **133** 251
Uhlenbeck G E and Ford G W 1963 *Lectures in Statistical Mechanics* (Providence, RI: American Mathematical Society) Ch. 1
Valikin V I, Bekov G I, Letokhov V S and Mishin V I 1979 in *Proc. 6th Int. Conf. on Atomic Physics* (New York: Plenum)
Walker G M and Ford J 1969 *Phys. Rev.* **188** 417

8

Elemental analyses of solids and related applications of RIS

8.1 Introduction

The rest of this book emphasises the use of RIS for the development of analytical methods capable of detecting small numbers of atoms. In this chapter we discuss the analyses of solids, especially the sensitive determination of low levels of impurities in the sample. Here we explore the possible use of RIS to contribute to the field of elemental analysis by improving the selectivity and the sensitivity of the methods.

Elemental analysis with RIS requires that the atom is ionised in a free state, since the laser schemes depend on the known spectroscopy associated with atoms which are nearly isolated. Thus, any approach to the elemental analyses of solids must provide a way to 'atomise' the sample. In this way, the inherent features of RIS—Z selectivity and high efficiency—are retained.

There are many well known methods for the atomisation of a solid sample. Thermal evaporation by simply heating a sample is the best known. In some cases a liquid sample containing solids to be analysed is aspirated into a flame. Flames have been quite successfully used in laser-enhaced ionisation work; see, for example, the reviews of this subject by Travis *et al* (1982) and Travis (1982). Ionisation backgrounds can be reduced by selective photon absorption processes to enhance the ionisation from a selected element. Electrical discharge is another method, but there are major problems due to high-density ionisation that would be a background to the resonance ionisation.

It is also possible to focus laser light on a solid and produce atoms by laser ablation. This method too suffers from background ionisation. Even strong plasmas can complicate the RIS analysis. Sputtering of solids with energetic ion beams is a highly developed field and has now been used extensively as atomisation for RIS. Both of these methods will be discussed further in this chapter.

Essentially, all of the RIS methods now under development for the analyses of solids utilise a combination of lasers and mass spectrometers (Beekman *et al* 1980), and the entire field could be called resonance ionisation mass spectrometry (RIMS). A combination of Z selection using RIS and A selection with a mass spectrometer was recognised at the beginning of the RIS work at ORNL but was discussed more explicitly in later articles by Beekman *et al* (1980), Chen *et al* (1980), and Hurst *et al* (1980). The many advantages of this Z and A selectivity will be explored in this chapter. Although very different in its objective, an early proposal to combine laser ionisation and mass spectroscopy was made by Ambartzumian and Letokhov (1972) and further discussed by Letokhov (1976). These, however, dealt with improved characterisation and detection of complex molecules. See the text by Letokhov (1987) for a complete discussion of the early USSR work.

Actually, some of the earliest work on a RIMS system involved detection of noble gases and is discussed in Chapter 10. However, the acronym RIMS usually applies to the analyses of solids. Therefore, RIMS always involves at least four steps: (a) atomisation of the solid to liberate neutral atoms; (b) resonance ionisation; (c) mass analyses of positive ions; and (d) sensitive detection of the positive ions. In any case, the primary objective of RIMS is to provide more sensitivity and greater selectivity in the analysis of impurities in a solid. The use of a mass spectrometer is a key factor in selectivity since it reduces background due to non-selective multiphoton ionisation. Viewed from the perspective of mass spectrometry, the use of resonance ionisation sources in a mass spectrometer decreases interference due to molecular ions and provides isobaric resolution as well.

8.2 Laser ablation methods (LARIS)

One of the earliest applications of RIS to solids analyses was demonstrated by Mayo *et al* (1982) at the National Bureau of Standards, using proportional counters as detectors. In the arrangement shown in figure 8.1 (Mayo 1984) a pulsed laser $(0.6\,\mu s)$ was used to generate about $10^7\,\mathrm{W\,cm^{-2}}$ on the silicon target, which formed a crater of $10^{-8}\,\mathrm{cm^3}$. In the 5×10^{14} silicon atoms ejected into the P-10 counting gas, Mayo found about 10^3 atoms of sodium, or about 10^{11} sodium atoms per $\mathrm{cm^3}$—a concentration less than 0.01 PPB. This very impressive work has perhaps not been pursued to its full potential because of basic problems associated with laser ionisation (plasmas) at the target, and impurity problems inherent in gas-filled enclosures.

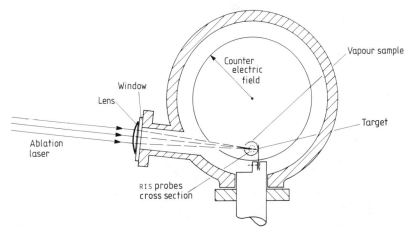

Figure 8.1 LARIS apparatus devised at the National Bureau of Standards in which laser ablation releases atoms from a solid sample situated in a proportional counter. Courtesy of S Mayo (from Mayo 1984).

Beekman *et al* (1980) used a *Q*-switched Nd:glass laser to vaporise atoms from a solid target, followed with a nitrogen pumped dye laser for RIS of potassium atoms at a single wavelength of 404.4 nm. With the Nd:glass laser, at a peak power of 20 MW in 30 ns pulses, 10^7 W cm^{-2} was delivered to a 10^{-3} cm^2 area of the target. Under these conditions, the ratio of neutrals to ions should be about 100. Following the RIS process, the ions were detected with a channeltron. In figure 8.2 the ionisation signal is plotted as a function of delay time between the ablation laser and the RIS laser. The peak at 50 μs corresponds to the most probable arrival time of neutral atoms released 2.5 cm from the RIS laser beam. Shorter distances to increase the solid angle, and hence detection efficiency, were not feasible because of the large ionisation background associated with the ablation laser. Using a quadrupole mass analyser, Beekman *et al* (1980) measured the ^{39}K/^{41}K ratio, finding 13.6 compared to the accepted value of 13.5. Thus, a RIMS system was used to resolve isotopes of potassium atoms released from a solid target.

An extension of the above work was made by Beekman and Callcott (1984) to measure both the excitation temperature and the kinetic temperature of samarium atoms released from a solid by laser ablation. For this work a Nd:YAG laser producing 250 mJ pulses in 9 ns was focused to a spot of 0.02 cm diameter. This power density (10^{11} W cm^{-2}) can vaporise any solid but, unfortunately, produces an ionisation background that interferes with the RIS signals. At 10^9 W cm^{-2} this background is much smaller, but the neutral yield is skewed toward the more volatile elements.

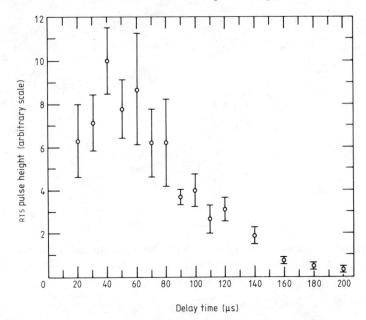

Figure 8.2 RIS signal strength (arbitrary units) against delay time of ionising laser. Courtesy of D W Beekman (from Beekman *et al* 1980)

Beekman and Callcott (1984) used the RIS schemes shown in figure 8.3 to obtain the excitation temperature. The necessary wavelengths λ_1 and λ_2 were generated by pumping two dye lasers with an excimer laser. By measuring the relative ionisation signals for the various ground levels shown and by using the effective degeneracy appropriate to a linearly polarised laser beam, they calculated the excitation temperature from a Boltzmann equation. From the measured time of arrival of neutral samarium atoms to the RIS beam, it was found under typical conditions that the kinetic temperature was of the order of 1300 K compared to an excitation temperature of 1600 K. The significantly higher excitation temperature is an indication of a non-equilibrium and was attributed to recombination and relaxation processes.

Laser ablation has also been investigated by Nogar *et al* (1985) and Apel *et al* (1987), and anomalous effective temperatures were found. For 10^8 W cm^{-2} (from a Q-switched pulse of a Nd:YAG laser) on tantalum, they found a 'hydrodynamic temperature' of 8000 K, a 'kinetic temperature' of only 400 K, and an 'electronic temperature' around 2000 K. Apel *et al* found that the technique does increase the probability (compared to CW heating of a sample) that an atom leaving the surface will be ionised in a pulsed RIS beam. These ionisation probabilities approach 10%, a most useful result when analysing small samples.

Laser ablation has a great appeal as an atomiser for elemental

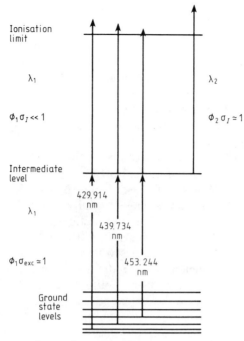

Figure 8.3 RIS scheme for excitation temperature measurement of Sm vapour. Here λ is the photon wavelength, ϕ is the photon flux (photons per cm²), σ is the transition cross section, and $\phi\sigma$ is the transition probability. Courtesy of D W Beekman and T A Callcott (from Beekman and Callcott 1984).

analyses of small samples. Injection of laser pulses through windows of the analysis chamber is very simple and would lead to good duty cycles when using pulsed lasers for resonance ionisation. However, the high ionisation density associated with the laser–surface interaction prevents the achievement of high sensitivity in many cases. Other systems of analysis depend on the formation of ions in the laser ablation process. For a comprehensive review of the use of lasers as non-selective ionisation sources for mass spectrometers, see Conzemius and Capellen (1980). In this application, the yield of ions per atoms eroded is in the range 10^{-5} to 10^{-2}.

8.3 RIMS using pulsed lasers

8.3.1 General comments

Most of the early studies of RIS were carried out with pulsed lasers. The fact that early CW dye lasers were limited in power and wavelength region and are expensive probably accounts for much of the continued popularity of the simpler, broad band width, pulsed dye laser. However, aside from history and simplicity of operation, pulsed dye lasers do have real advantages for use with RIMS. The first important advantage of the pulsed laser is high peak power, which makes possible the efficient use of non-linear processes for excitation and for the extension of the wavelength region over which tunable light can be generated. Consequently, nearly all of the elements are amenable to RIS with pulsed lasers, while only about half of the elements can be ionised effectively with continuous wave lasers. The second advantage is related to the fact that when the pulsed laser is combined with a pulsed atomisation method which can be turned on and off in a time less than the average flight time of an atom across the laser beam, the fraction of the released atoms which are ionised can be close to unity. We will emphasise some of the advantages of CW lasers in a later section.

We restrict our discussion in this section to the use of RIMS for solids analysis. Several other types of RIMS with which the authors have been involved have been singled out for discussion in separate sections or chapters; while others have been omitted due to lack of space. In particular, the RIMS scheme developed at Oak Ridge for the detection of ^{81}Kr is discussed in Chapter 10. The possibility of the isotopically selective detection of small molecules has been omitted, but a discussion of an example of this type of RIMS can be found in a review paper by Payne *et al* (1981).

Since the basic idea of RIMS involves the introduction of the sample into laser beams as neutral atoms, with the RIS-produced ions then being mass analysed, it is appropriate to note that the preparation of samples and the choice of atomisation methods often differ from those used in conventional mass spectroscopy where ions are desired in the absence of a laser beam. Several pulsed atomisation schemes for RIMS have been used with success (Young *et al* 1979, Beekman *et al* 1980, Winograd *et al* 1982, Parks *et al* 1983a), but the most widely used atomisation method (Donahue *et al* 1982, Miller *et al* 1982, Fassett *et al* 1983) continues to be an offshoot of thermal vaporisation which has been used for many years in conventional thermal ionisation mass spectroscopy. The main advantage of this atomiser is that it can draw effectively on a wealth of experience which has been accumulated on the preparation of samples. With a CW thermal atomiser the advantages of pulsed lasers are less significant due to duty cycle effects. The fraction of the atoms ionised by a pulsed laser is given roughly by

$$F_i \simeq |\bar{N}_s d/\bar{v}| F_g F_s \qquad (8.1)$$

where F_i is the fraction of the spectroscopically selected atoms ionised, N_s is the number of laser shots per second, d is the diameter of the laser beam over which laser ionisation is assumed to be saturated, $\bar{v}$ is the mean speed of the released atoms, F_g is a geometrical factor representing the fraction of the atoms which leave the source travelling in a direction so that they will pass through the laser beam, and F_s is the fraction of the selected atoms which are atomised in the state which will be selectively ionised. The factor $N_s d/\bar{v}$ is the probability that an atom released at a random time in a direction so that it will pass through the laser beam will be in the laser beam when the laser is fired. With thermal atomisation a typical $\bar{v}$ is 10^5 cm s^{-1} and with a commercial laser a beam diameter of a few mm can usually be used. If the sample is located in a very small area of a heated metal strip the product of $F_s F_g$ will usually be greater than 0.1. Consequently,

$$F_i \geq 3 \times 10^{-7} N_s. \tag{8.2}$$

We see that with a Nd:YAG system, $F_i \simeq 10^{-5}$ is a respectable ionised fraction. If some special tricks are used for the ionisation step this number could reach $F_i \simeq 10^{-2}$ for a dye laser system pumped by a copper vapour laser with $N_s \simeq 6 \times 10^3$ s^{-1}. The ionisation step might, for instance, involve pumping two resonant transitions to reach a Rydberg state with $n \simeq 15$, which could be ionised effectively with a cw CO_2 laser (Nebenzahl and Levin 1973), or it might make use of a narrow auto-ionising resonance (James *et al* 1976, Solarz *et al* 1976) which can enhance the photo-ionisation rate by a factor of several hundred. The efficient utilisation of vaporised atoms makes possible measurements on samples of very small size.

Many workers intentionally choose dye lasers with band widths which are large compared with both the Doppler width and any isotope shifts or hyperfine splittings. The most desirable laser of this type would have a continuous spectrum of frequencies, as opposed to having multiple longitudinal modes which are separated by $1/2L$ wavenumbers (L is the length of the oscillator cavity in cm). Some of the early commercial dye lasers with flashlamp pumping probably came rather close to meeting the continuous spectrum criterion. This type of laser, while poor for many applications, can be combined with a mass spectrometer for the purpose of measuring isotope ratios. In the simplest version of these measurements it is assumed that the laser provides nearly equal ionisation probabilities for all isotopes of an element in the limit where transitions from all initial degenerate states are strongly saturated.

When the pulsed dye laser has a pulse length of a few nanoseconds and a continuous energy spectrum, a relatively simple rate analysis can be applied in which the rate equations for different degenerate sub-levels are not coupled appreciably by spontaneous emission. This is in contrast to the case of cw laser excitation, where the time of interaction of the atoms with the laser beam is very long compared with the natural lifetimes of the excited states and there are large redistributions of the populations among magnetic substates and low-lying metastable or hyperfine states. At power densities such that the Rabi frequencies are small compared with the laser band width the line shape for one-photon resonant, two-photon ionisation will be close to that of the laser near line centre, but with Lorentzian wings. At power densities such that the instantaneous Rabi frequency considerably exceeds the laser band width, the entire line shape becomes Lorentzian with a FWHM close to twice the mean Rabi frequency. The power-broadened widths can be rather different for different initial M_J. With the one-photon resonant, two-photon ionisation scheme, the ionisation rate only becomes comparable to the Rabi frequency at very high power densities such that $\Omega_R \simeq 10^7 I^{1/2} \leqslant \sigma_i \mathscr{F} \simeq 10I$, where I is the power density in W cm^{-2} and a fairly typical Rabi frequency, Ω_R, and photo-ionisation cross section, σ_i, have been assumed. Correspondingly, in RIS studies using this simple scheme one almost never sees increased line widths due to high ionisation rates, or asymetric lines due to AC Stark shifts. On the other hand, increased line widths due to power broadening are common when the same laser is used for both excitation and ionisation. The Z selectivity of the laser ionisation scheme is greatly improved by observing a few simple rules.

(i) Use separate lasers for the ionisation and excitation steps so that power broadening of the resonance transitions can be avoided.

(ii) If possible employ two resonance steps, using IR light, such as the fundamental of the Nd:YAG for the ionisation step.

(iii) Choose the power density for both of the discrete–discrete steps so that the Rabi frequencies are less than the laser band widths.

When the IR is the only intense light many photons are required to cause the MPI of atoms of another element. The two resonance steps also make near resonances with transitions in another element (or molecule) less likely.

We consider the possibility of accidental ionisation of an atom of another element under conditions where the selected species would be ionised with a probability near unity. An estimate of the probability of accidental MPI can be obtained from the following formula for n-photon ionisation by some combination of the lasers used in the RIS scheme:

$$P_{\text{MPI}} \simeq \tau(\alpha)^{2n-4} \prod_{i=1}^{n-1} |\Omega_R(i)/\bar{\Delta}_i|^2 \bar{\sigma}_I \mathscr{F}. \tag{8.3}$$

The above relationship does not include duty cycle effects, but is intended to provide a simple way of making a crude estimate of the probability of ionisation of atoms of another element which happen to be in the laser beam at the time it is fired. Equation (8.3) is based on the use of time-dependent perturbation theory to write an n-photon MPI probability, but with the resonant denominators (which occur $n - 1$ times) all replaced by mean detunings $\bar{\Delta}_i$ to simulate a mean detuning from atomic resonances after the absorption of different numbers of photons. After the replacement of the $n - 1$ resonant denominators by constants, closure is invoked to give a matrix element of $(\hat{D} \cdot E/2\hbar)^{n-1}$. This is estimated as a product of Rabi frequencies which are taken to be of the order of $\Omega_R(i) \simeq 10^8(I_i)^{1/2}$, where I_i are the power densities of the laser beams in W cm^{-2}. The fact that a high order closure matrix element is usually very much larger than a one-photon matrix element raised to a power equal to that high order is taken into account by the factor α^{2n-4}, where $\alpha \simeq 10$ is a reasonable value for $n \geq 2$. The last step into the ionisation continuum has a form similar to a photo-ionisation cross section and this similarity has been used for an order of magnitude estimate of the term in question. The $\mathscr{F}$ is the photon flux for the laser which provides the final photon for the MPI process. The photo-ionisation cross section for the nearest resonance before ionisation provides a reasonable educated guess for $\bar{\sigma}_I$. The pulse shape has been taken as rectangular with width τ and amplitude fluctuations of the laser have been ignored. If there are multiple colours used in the RIS scheme, then there will be different combinations of photon absorptions which lead to MPI, and each can be estimated individually from the above formula. It is important to realise that the estimate could be in error by several orders of magnitude.

As an example of an application of equation (8.3), consider a situation where a single colour is being used for an RIS process, but another species of atom can also be ionised by two-photon MPI. To estimate the MPI probability we write

$$P_{\text{MPI}} \simeq |\Omega_R/\bar{\Delta}|^2 \sigma_i \mathscr{F} \tau$$

$$\simeq 10^{-15} I^2 \tau$$

where we have assumed that the photons have an energy of about 4 eV, the effective photo-ionisation cross section, $\bar{\sigma}_I$, was taken to be 10^{-18} cm^2, Ω_R was taken to be $10^8(I)^{1/2}$ (with I in W cm^{-2}), and the nearest one-photon resonance was assumed to be nearly 2 eV (so that $\bar{\Delta} \simeq 3 \times 10^{15}$ s^{-1}) from resonance. With $I \simeq 10^8$ W cm^{-2} the fraction of the other atoms ionised with $\tau = 10^{-8}$ s is approximately 10^{-7}. Around 10^{12} W cm^{-2} is required in such a situation for almost all atoms which can be ionised by two photons to become ions. A comparison of estimates based on this formula with experimental values has been made for the case of the MPI of alkali metals (Hurst *et al* 1979). A detailed review of MPI has been written by Lambropoulos (1976).

Even though many applications of RIMS can be carried out with broad band width lasers, there are others where one wants to enhance the isotopic selectivity achievable with the mass spectrometer by carrying out isotopically selective RIS with narrow band width lasers. A slight modification of equation (8.3) can be used to estimate the isotopic selectivity which can be achieved. The probability of accidentally ionising another isotope when narrow band width pulsed lasers are used can be obtained by evaluating the perturbation theory expression for the ionisation probability. In this case each resonant step in the selected isotope is a near-resonance for the other isotopes. Thus, instead of using a mean detuning for each resonant denominator in evaluating the perturbation theory expression, one notes that there is a dominant resonant term for each step of the MPI process. Thus, there is a well defined set of detunings and dipole matrix elements for each near-resonant step and a clearly defined photo-ionisation cross section for the last step. The Rabi frequencies Ω_1 and Ω_2 are closely related to the ones involved in ionising the selected isotope (differing only by possible angular momentum considerations). The Δ_i are related to isotope shifts and (or) hyperfine splittings, and they are known. For instance, if the detunings are large compared with either the Doppler shifts or the laser band width and a doubly resonant three-photon ionisation scheme is being used, then

$$P_{\text{MPI}} \simeq |(\Omega_1/2\Delta_1)(\Omega_2/2\Delta_2)|^2 \sigma_i \mathscr{F}\tau. \tag{8.4}$$

With a narrow band width laser the one-photon Rabi frequencies should be chosen to be nearly equal for the two resonances, and they should be just large enough to either produce several Rabi flops during the pulse or to power-broaden the transition beyond Doppler shifts. If the atoms are heavy and the energy of the neutrals is relatively low we might have $\Omega_1 = \Omega_2 \simeq 4 \times 10^9 \text{ s}^{-1}$, with $\Delta_1 \simeq \Delta_2 \simeq 10^{11} \text{ s}^{-1}$. If $\sigma_i \mathscr{F}\tau \simeq 2$ we find $P_{\text{MPI}} \simeq 3 \times 10^{-7}$. When only one resonant step is used for the efficient ionisation of the selected isotope an MPI probability for the other isotopes of approximately 1×10^{-3} results for the same parameters. Obviously, the second resonance makes a large difference. In practice, the presence of clusters of the selected element, or weakly bound dimers with another matrix material, or an impurity, could greatly reduce the isotopic selectivity of an RIS scheme. If one settles for 20% ionisation of the selected species at beam centre, the Rabi frequency can be reduced and the selectivity is increased. The reduction in power density and the use of two resonance steps also help greatly in reducing the ionisation of molecular species. It is important to point out that such a large difference in the absorption spectrum of isotopes is only found in either very light elements or in heavy elements. For instance, the shifts in the inert gases Ne, Ar and Kr are typically two orders of magnitude smaller.

An important variation on the isotopically selective scheme described here involves the use of two-photon Doppler-free excitation (Lucatorto *et al* 1984). In this case there is no Doppler width to overcome in order to ionise a large fraction of the selected isotope. With longer laser pulses (i.e. approximately 50 ns) this excitation scheme permits efficient isotopically selective detection of lighter elements (even for pulsed sources having a large energy spread). With Doppler-free excitation, the two-photon Rabi frequency only needs to exceed the natural level width, the reciprocal time of passage through the laser beam and the Fourier-transform-limited band width of the laser in order to yield a high probability of ionisation. In many applications where the Doppler width is much larger than any of these quantities, the ratio of the Rabi frequency to the detuning is much smaller for the other isotopes, thereby making the single resonance step selectivity much greater than it would be for efficient one-photon excitation. Even though the hyperfine splitting in Kr and Xe is small, an isotopic selectivity for two-photon, Doppler-free excitation of about a factor of 100 has been demonstrated (Whitaker and Bushaw 1981, Bushaw and Whitaker 1981). The earliest combined use of Doppler-free, two-photon excitation and ionisation was carried out in a thermionic detector (Harvey and Stoicheff 1977, Niemax and Weber 1978). The latter devices have proven to be very sensitive for trace analysis (Niemax *et al* 1987).

8.3.2 *Application of RIMS to the removal of isobaric interferences*

In a number of applications of conventional thermal vaporisation mass spectroscopy one encounters situations where the measurement of isotope ratios for one element is interfered with due to the detection of isotopes of another element which have the same mass numbers as one or more of the isotopes of the element under study. This problem is a very natural one for RIMS since in most cases the element of interest can be ionised very effectively, while RIS discriminates strongly against making ions of other elements. The yield of ions from thermal ionisers is very low for almost all elements except alkali atoms, thereby permitting a situation in which most of the evaporated material from a thermal source is neutral and the dominant production of ions is due to laser ionisation. Time analysis of the ion detection and the effective use of pulsed electric fields before each laser pulse permits one to very effectively discriminate against any ions that do arise thermally. The earliest applications of RIMS with pulsed lasers to the isobaric interference problem were carried out by Donahue, Young, and Smith (Donahue *et al* 1982). In this study isobaric interferences which caused difficulty in measuring isotope ratios for Nd were avoided by using Z selective ionisation of this element. This situation was chosen because of the importance of these measurements to reactor fuel burn-up. Interferences due to isotopes of the neighbouring elements cerium and samarium made it impossible to measure neodymium isotope ratios with conventional ion sources. In another study (Donahue and Young 1983) these workers used the same method to determine the isotope ratios for uranium and plutonium. These two elements overlap in mass at atomic number 238, and plutonium overlaps with its decay product americium at mass number 241.

8.3.3 Application of RIMS to isotopic ratios in osmium and rhenium

The ingrowth of ^{187}Os from the decay of ^{187}Re (half-life 4.35×10^{10} years) has long been of interest as a possible 'clock' for the resolution of a number of unanswered questions related to the chemical evolution of the earth and solar system. Secondary ion mass spectroscopy (SIMS) has been the primary technique for the isotopic analysis of Os/Re for many years (Allegre and Luck 1980). However, it remains to be seen if SIMS, or any of the conventional mass spectroscopic techniques, will have the selectivity and sensitivity to determine the less than one part per billion concentration of Os and Re in geological samples.

Recently, workers at the National Bureau of Standards (NBS) (Walker and Fassett 1986) have made use of efficient chemical separation of Os and Re from the matrix in order to obtain picogram quantities of Os/Re which were used with a pulse-heated thermal source that was pulsed synchronously with a dye laser. The resulting RIS ions were mass analysed in order to obtain results which were calibrated by isotope dilution mass spectroscopy. The 192/190 and 187/186 isotope ratios were determined to 1.3% and 3.2% accuracy while working with subnanogram samples. This work is currently being applied to the analysis of real geological materials from a komatiite flow in the Munro Township Abitibi Belt, Ontario (Walker *et al* 1987). The crystallisation age of the flow was found to be 2.726×10^9 years, in excellent agreement with measurements based on other isotopic systems. The particular application was one in which the Re and Os were present at levels of the order of 1 PPB. The logical extensions of this work could provide a solution to one of the most important problems that has been attacked with the RIMS technique.

8.3.4 RIMS studies at the university of Mainz

Several very impressive studies have been carried out recently by scientists from the University of Mainz (Rimke *et al* 1987, Bollen *et al* 1987). In one set of studies these workers have used a three-photon ionisation scheme in which the first two resonance transitions are to bound states, but the third is also resonant with a relatively narrow auto-ionising resonance, as shown in figure 8.4. With such an ionisation scheme a copper vapour laser operating at a repetition rate of 6.5 kHz, average power of 30 W, and a pulse length of 30 ns can pump three dye lasers with conversion efficiencies between 10 and 25%. In the case of Gd and Tc, narrow auto-ionising resonances were found which permitted the saturation of the ionisation step with photon fluences of greater than or equal to 10^{15} cm^{-2}. With the scheme described here and with dye laser band widths of approximately 0.15 cm^{-1} it is plausible that the ionisation signal could be near saturation with a 1 cm beam diameter and less than 0.5 mJ per pulse output for the dye laser used for the ionising step. With this ionisation scheme and the high repetition rate, the detection efficiency is impressive. For both Gd and Tc the detection limit was 10^6–10^7 atoms. A less complicated ionisation scheme was used on plutonium and it was shown that 10^8 atoms could be detected

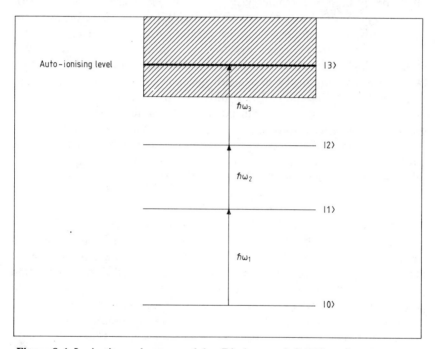

Figure 8.4 Ionisation scheme used by Rimke *et al* (1987), using three dye lasers. The first two dye lasers pump two sequential resonance steps, with the third dye laser used to ionise the element by pumping a third resonance transition to a narrow auto-ionising level. The photo-ionisation cross section is frequently enhanced by a factor of several hundred by making use of a narrow auto-ionising resonance to enhance the photo-ionisation cross section. Also, the ionisation scheme is made even more selective.

(Peuser *et al* 1985). The use of an auto-ionising state in the detection of Pu might result in a detection limit of 10^6 (Rimke *et al* 1987).

It is likely that a careful study of auto-ionising resonances in most heavy elements having more than one optically active electron will result in the identification of narrow auto-ionising resonances which can be used to enhance the photo-ionisation cross section for some excited states by orders of magnitude. Several other examples of the use of auto-ionising resonances can be found in the literature. (Solarz *et al* 1976, James *et al* 1976, Carlson *et al* 1976, Bradley *et al* 1976).

8.3.5 RIMS using two-photon, Doppler-free excitation

Workers at the NBS have used two-photon, Doppler-free three-photon ionisation in several recent studies (Lucatorto *et al* 1984, Clark 1983). They have suggested that this technique could be useful in the detection of such interesting tracers and 'clocks' as ^{10}Be, ^{14}C, ^{26}Al, ^{36}Cl and ^{129}I. High-energy mass spectrometry has already demonstrated the detection of abundances of the order of 10^{-16} for ^{14}C and ^{36}Cl. However, the technique is two orders of magnitude less sensitive for ^{10}Be.

Most of the above cases involve the ionisation of elements with relatively high ionisation potentials and sizeable isotope shifts. Thus, two-photon excitation eliminates the necessity of generating very short wavelengths and simultaneously avoids the large line widths which occur in low Z atoms with most pulsed atomisation schemes. The isotopic selectivity is easily estimated by using time-dependent perturbation theory to estimate the ionisation probability of one of the other isotopes under conditions where the ionisation probability of an atom of the selected isotope is near unity. We have

$$P_{\text{MPI}} \simeq |\Omega^{(2)}/2\Delta|^2 \sigma_i \mathscr{F} \tau. \tag{8.5}$$

Above, Δ is the isotope shift, $\Omega^{(2)}$ is the two-photon Rabi frequency for the transition, $\mathscr{F}$ is the flux of the dominant laser used for the ionisation step, τ is the pulse length and σ_i is the photo-ionisation cross section of the excited state. In order for the two-photon resonance to be saturated (or nearly so) the Rabi frequency must be large compared with τ^{-1}, $\bar{v}/d$ and γ, where γ is the spontaneous decay rate of the excited state. That is, the time of interaction must be large enough for a sizeable portion of a Rabi flop to occur, and the time for the laser to change the state populations must be fast compared with spontaneous decay. In the case of ^{14}C the value of Δ is approximately 3×10^{10} s^{-1}. With a pulse length of $\tau \simeq 3 \times 10^{-8}$ s, a two-photon Rabi frequency of $\Omega^{(2)} \simeq 10^8$ s^{-1} is needed for effective ionisation. We assume that both the time of passage through the laser beams and the natural width are less than 10^8 s^{-1}. This is generally the case. Taking $\sigma_i \mathscr{F} \tau \simeq 2$, we find $P_{\text{MPI}} \simeq 5 \times 10^{-6}$. Having a laser band width a few times larger than the Fourier transform limit would require an even larger peak Rabi frequency, and the value of P_{MPI} would be increased further.

With transform-limited pulses of length 30–60 ns an even larger discrimination against other isotopes may be possible in the detection of ^{10}Be, where the isotope shift is even larger. In most cases a power density of $10^7 \, W \, cm^{-2}$ is needed to produce a two-photon Rabi frequency of $10^8 \, s^{-1}$. This is a fairly large two-photon Rabi frequency in a situation where there are no one-photon resonance enhancements (see §9.7). The two-photon, Doppler-free excitation method will also be useful in some applications for low ionisation potential elements. In this case the two-photon Rabi frequency can often have a one-photon resonance enhancement which easily yields a two-photon Rabi frequency large enough for the resonance transition to be saturated at $10^5 \, W \, cm^{-2}$.

The NBS team (Moore *et al* 1985) has studied the ionisation of carbon using two-photon excitation, three-photon ionisation. The band width was not small enough to investigate the anticipated isotopic selectivity, but it was demonstrated that atomic carbon in the vapour phase can be detected at densities as low as $10^7 \, cm^{-3}$. The authors indicate that they have demonstrated the feasibility of the RIMS of carbon with unprepared carbon samples.

More recent studies at NBS (Wen *et al* 1987) have combined thermal atomisation with two-photon, Doppler-free excitation using laser light of a band width which is almost Fourier-transform-limited (band width $\simeq 150 \, MHz$) in order to carry out isotopically selective detection of beryllium. The initial studies have been carried out with the counterpropagating beams having the same frequency. It is found that the Doppler pedestal limits the discrimination against ^{9}Be to be about a factor of 100 in the detection of ^{10}Be. Estimates indicate that if slightly different frequencies are used for the counterpropagating beams (to eliminate the Doppler pedestal) the discrimination will become a factor of several thousand. The sample size used in the study was 100 μg of $BeCl_2$ which had been enriched to a 0.1% concentration of ^{10}Be. The study is currently being generalised to make use of laser ablation. If this form of pulsed vaporisation can be perfected it should make possible studies with samples which are orders of magnitude smaller.

8.4 RIMS using continuous wave lasers

8.4.1 Introduction

The importance of CW dye lasers in RIMS changed dramatically about 1978 with the commercial availability of the ring dye lasers pumped by argon ion and krypton ion lasers. Relatively soon after their introduction it became possible to purchase a dye laser which could provide over

100 mW of CW output at all wavelengths between 420 and 960 nm. With frequency doubling, the output is greater than 10 mW at all wavelengths between 275 and 380 nm, so that high power output was available nearly continuously between 268 and 1000 nm. The band width of the commercial single mode ring dye laser is smaller than the natural line width for most excited states.

To realise the significance of these lasers, consider the Rabi frequency for a strong atomic transition when a 1 mm diameter laser beam is used. The power density is greater than 1 W cm^{-2} at all wavelengths between 275 and 960 nm, so that with a strong transition lying in this wavelength region, $\Omega_R \simeq 10^8$ s^{-1}. If the time of passage of an atom through the laser beam is approximately 10^{-6} s and the spontaneous decay rate of the excited state is less than 10^8 s^{-1}, the transition will be strongly saturated for those atoms having small components of velocity parallel to the laser beam. In fact, when the laser is tuned to the unshifted resonance, power broadening will lead to saturation for all atoms with parallel components of velocity such that the Doppler shift is less than 10^8 s^{-1} in angular frequency units. For a typical, low ionisation potential (IP $\lesssim 8$ eV) atom having a mass greater than 100 AMU, and a vaporisation energy of approximately 0.25 eV, the Doppler width will be less than 10^{10} s^{-1} in angular frequency units. As a consequence of these considerations, about 2% of the atoms having the smallest velocities parallel to the laser beam are effectively excited by the laser. Only the atoms with small components of velocity parallel to the laser beam develop large amplitudes for being in the first excited state. This is crucial to understanding what happens when a second dye laser is tuned to the unshifted resonance between the first excited state and a second excited state. Note that due to the small values of the parallel component of velocity a second dye laser providing a Rabi frequency of 10^8 s^{-1} for the second transition can pump the second excited state with little additional loss due to the Doppler effect. Suppose that the second dye laser is tuned through the resonance, and that a third photon from one of the dye lasers or a third laser produces an ionisation signal. The line width in three-photon ionisation will be observed to be much smaller than the Doppler width.

To expand the above discussion into an effective RIS scheme we choose the excitation energies in the two-step resonant excitation so that the second excited state can be ionised by a high-power CW diode laser tuned between the second excited state and a narrow auto-ionising resonance, as shown in figure 8.4. A 1 W diode laser operating in the 800 nm region has a power density of 100 W cm^{-2} when telescoped to a 1 mm beam, and in the time of passage through the beam an atom will be exposed to a photon fluence of 4×10^{14} cm^{-2}. With an auto-ionising cross section of 10^{-15} cm^2 and the double resonance excitation described in the previous paragraph, nearly 1% of the atoms passing through the three 1 mm laser beams are ionised. As diode lasers continue to improve one or more of the dye lasers might eventually be replaceable by diode lasers. The potential of the diode laser in analytical techniques has been discussed by Niemax *et al* (1987).

In the future it will not be necessary for the auto-ionising laser beam to have a wavelength near 800 nm. An alternative way of achieving a high ionised fraction with cw lasers (Bushaw *et al* 1987, Nebenzahl and Levin 1973) is to choose the second resonance to have $n^* \geqslant 15$ so that the ionisation step can be carried out with a cw CO_2 laser. With a careful choice of the $n^* \simeq 15$ state the photo-ionisation cross section with CO_2 light can exceed 10^{-16} cm^2. The combination of the large cross section and the low photon energy reduces the power density requirements for saturated ionisation during the time of passage through the beam. For example, approximately 200 W cm^{-2} is adequate for cw CO_2 lasers. Since even a 500 W CO_2 laser costs less than about £20 000, the hard step is the saturation of the transition to the $n^* \simeq 15$ state.

One of the ionisation schemes described above involves three resonance steps and the other employs two resonances. Even when the isotope shifts and hyperfine splittings are smaller than the Doppler width, the second resonance step can usually be used to select a particular isotope of an element. In the first resonance excitation, atoms of the other isotopes which have large components of velocity parallel to the laser beam could be resonantly excited, but in the second step they are Doppler-shifted out of resonance. With either of the schemes described above there is excellent discrimination against clusters and molecules.

Nearly all elements with ionisation potentials less than 8 eV can be ionised by one of the above schemes. This makes nearly 50% of all elements available for RIS with cw lasers. By making use of auto-ionising states there are even a few elements with ionisation potentials above 8 eV which can be ionised. The limit is finally imposed by the condition that there be an excited state that can be reached with $\lambda \geqslant 268$ nm. The above considerations of ionisation efficiency and selectivity may make cw-based RIMS the technique of choice for some types of applications by specialised users. As examples of important problems where the above techniques could be useful, we note that Os, Re and Tc should all be detectable, and the cw laser technique is ideal for use with thermal atomisers.

The cost of setting up a two-dye-laser, cw system is higher than the cost of a pulsed system. Also, the required expertise in laser physics, spectroscopy and optics is considerably higher than with broad band width dye lasers. Obviously, when a narrow band width laser is used one must be very familiar with hyperfine structure, isotope shifts and other effects which affect the spectroscopic selectivity and ionisation efficiency. For instance, the time of interaction with the laser beam is generally much longer than the lifetime of the first excited state and the combination of pumping of a hyperfine transition and spontaneous emission leads to spectacular redistributions of the atomic population between magnetic substates and hyperfine levels. The redistribution occurs because the excitation with polarised light has different selection rules than does spontaneous emission. Also, the spontaneous emission may occur at wavelengths other than that of the laser. These effects must be understood since they can decrease RIS efficiencies. The effects we have just described are called optical pumping effects. Optical pumping studies which combined excitation with polarised light sources and electron spin resonance were very popular 20 years ago as a means of measuring hyperfine structure (Kastler 1950, Happer 1969). More recently, optical pumping has been used to orient nuclei, thereby modifying the angular distributions of energetic particles emitted in the subsequent nuclear decay (Jacquinot and Klapisch 1979). We strongly suggest that those interested in using the techniques described above should devote a large portion of their effort to the study of literature on optical pumping and high-resolution spectroscopy.

8.4.2 RIMS studies at Los Alamos National Laboratory

Some of the earliest RIMS studies were carried out at Los Alamos National Laboratory (LANL) (Miller *et al* 1982). Much of this work has been devoted to the resolution of isobaric interferences, in which RIS excitation was carried out with broad band width CW dye lasers and the ionisation was due to an argon ion laser beam. The isotopic selectivity was due entirely to a mass spectrometer. In this situation we can write a rough approximation to the fraction of the selected vaporised atoms which are ionised:

$$F_i \simeq F_g F_s F_e (\sigma_i \mathcal{F} d / \bar{v})$$

where F_g is the fraction of the atoms which pass through the beam in a region where they will be transmitted through the mass spectrometer, F_s is the fraction of the selected atoms which are vaporised in the spectroscopically selected initial state, F_e is the average fraction of the selected atoms which are excited while they are in the laser beam, σ_i is the photo-ionisation cross section of the excited state, $\mathcal{F}$ is the photon flux due to the argon ion laser, and $d/\bar{v}$ is the mean time of passage of the selected atoms through the laser beam. This relation neglects losses in ionisation efficiency due to spontaneous decay to other states. Typically, with 5 W of energy from the argon ion laser in a 1 mm beam we have $\sigma_i \mathcal{F}(d/\bar{v}) \simeq 10^{-4}$–$10^{-2}$. The other factors ordinarily reduce the fraction by another two or three orders of magnitude. Thus, we estimate an ionisation efficiency between 10^{-7} and 10^{-4}.

One of the more impressive studies at LANL (Miller and Nogar 1983) involved the measurement of the ^{173}Lu$/^{175}$Lu isotope ratio while working with a sample containing only 10^8 atoms of ^{173}Lu. More recent studies of this same system have been made with a narrow band width cw dye laser (Miller *et al* 1985). In the latter study the hyperfine structure was measured, and signals were easily measured for ^{174}Lu and ^{173}Lu with the total amount of these rare isotopes being 2×10^{-10} and 3×10^{-11} g. One of the very impressive features of this study is that accurate isotope ratios were measured in a situation where one of the abundant isotopes was nearly 10^6 times as abundant as the rare isotopes ^{173}Lu and ^{174}Lu.

The LANL group has also used pulsed lasers in RIMS. The most extensive study of this type has been devoted to the detection of Tc in connection with a proposed solar neutrino experiment. See Chapter 13 for other uses of RIS in solar neutrino experiments.

8.4.3 Double resonance cw RIS of barium

In a very impressive series of studies (Bushaw *et al* 1985, 1987) a group at the Pacific Northwest Laboratory (PNL) has used two single-frequency, cw dye lasers to carry out doubly resonant three-photon ionisation of barium in an atomic beam. The second resonance step in the ionisation scheme was to a 12d level of Ba which could be ionised by CO_2 laser light. On introducing 1.7 W from a CO_2 laser, the ionisation signal was observed to be increased by a factor of 30. The absolute ionisation efficiency was measured to be 6% with a modest CO_2 laser power density of 100 W cm^{-2}. This is certainly the highest ionisation efficiency yet observed with commercial cw dye lasers. Since the atomic beam was collimated, the Doppler shifts were smaller than in experiments with ordinary thermal atomisers. However, since the hyperfine splittings in Ba are not particularly large, the 10^5 selectivity observed in the study is very impressive. This group has published several other papers (Whitaker 1986, Whitaker *et al* 1987) documenting a large number of effects which affect the experimental results when single-mode dye lasers are used.

8.5 Atomisation by ion sputtering

8.5.1 General comments on ion sputtering

In a sputter-source technique being developed at Atom Sciences Inc. pulsed atomisation is achieved by making use of a pulsed ion beam to sputter atoms of the sample into the laser beams. The pulsed ions, having energies of several keV, typically result in the sputtering of several target atoms for each incident ion, with the selected atoms being ionised by properly synchronised laser pulses. Since we believe that this technique of sputter-initiated resonance ionisation spectroscopy (SIRIS) is promising, we will now discuss ion sputtering as a method of atom-isation.

When heavy atoms having kinetic energies less than 30 keV move through a solid material, their mean charge is much less than the atomic number. In fact, many such atoms spend a large fraction of their stopping time as neutrals. In effect, collision times are so long at these low energies that there are only small Fourier components of the interaction which can cause appreciable ionisation or excitation. When two low-energy neutral atoms collide there is little interaction between the pair until the electronic clouds begin to overlap. Once overlap occurs there is a strong repulsion which increases nearly exponentially as the intranuclear separation decreases. While deviations from hard sphere collisions are important, the secondary collisions have many features which can be qualitatively understood in terms of a hard sphere model. These almost hard sphere collisions between atoms of similar mass lead to large deflections and to energy losses of the order of

$$\Delta E_{max} \simeq 4M_1 M_2 E_1/(M_1 + M_2)^2.$$

Here M_1 is the mass of the energetic particle, M_2 is the mass of the target material, and E_1 is the energy of M_1. In a solid the hard core radii almost overlap; thus if a fast atom or ion penetrates a solid, an energy loss and a correspondingly large momentum change occurs with a mean free path which is not much larger than the internuclear separa-tion. The resulting path of an energetic atom is very complicated due to the fact that each energy loss collision results in a sizeable change in its direction of motion. The distance travelled before the direction of motion is completely randomised is only a few atomic separations if $M_1 \simeq M_2$, but is considerably larger if $M_1 \gg M_2$.

Consider what happens to the atoms of the solid when an energetic particle of mass M_1 passes through the vacuum–solid interface into the solid. Within a few atomic layers of the surface the incident particle undergoes several collisions in which an appreciable fraction of its energy is converted into kinetic energy of atoms of the solid (the mean energy loss in hard sphere collisions is $\Delta E_{max}/2$). Each of the latter target atoms either escapes from the solid or undergoes collisions with other target atoms in which sizeable portions of the energy they received is imparted to other target atoms. The typical final result of this collisional cascade process is that within a period of time less than

10^{-12} s one or more target atoms can pass through the solid–vacuum interface with an energy larger than the surface binding energy, so that they escape. A picture which is similar to the one described above for amorphous solids has been formulated mathematically by Sigmund (1969). A somewhat simpler description which is in the same spirit as that of Sigmund can be found in a paper by Thompson (1980).

Some of the main results of the model could be simulated on a macroscopic scale by imagining a volume of superballs (i.e. balls with coefficients of restitution near one and nearly frictionless surfaces) in a box, with superballs of a different mass being dropped from a height h into the box. If the ball-air interface is level in the box the interface is a surface on which the falling projectile balls are incident. The yield of 'sputtered' particles for a given surface binding energy corresponds to the mean number of balls which rise a distance greater than h_e above the surface for each projectile ball which is incident. The analogue of the mass dependence of sputter yields is simulated by the ratio of masses of the target balls to projectile balls, the dependence on the projectile energy is simulated by changes in h, and the dependence on the surface binding energy is simulated by the choice of h_e. If readers imagine the details of describing the results of this mechanical model they will understand many of the essential points of the models for predicting the sputter yield and the energy distribution of sputtered particles. We will now describe some of the results of these models which have been quite successful in describing many features of heavy-ion sputtering from amorphous solids.

One of the predictions of the Sigmund theory is that the fraction of the sputtered atoms having energy E to $E + \mathrm{d}E$ is

$$P(E)\mathrm{d}E \simeq C E \mathrm{d}E/(E + U)^{n+1}$$

where U is the surface binding energy, and a least square fit to data frequently yields a value of $n \simeq 2$. The choice $n = 2$ corresponds to the hard sphere model for the atom–atom interaction potential. The peak in the energy distribution is at $E_{\max} = U/n$. Since U is often of the order of 4 eV, a typical most probable energy is around 2 eV. The energy distribution has a long tail towards high energy which drops off as $1/E^2$. As a consequence of this slowly decreasing tail there can be 10% of the escaping particles with energies more than ten times larger than the most probable energy.

Within the hard sphere model we can write an expression for the yield of sputtered particles per unit solid angle at θ per unit energy at E as

$$\mathrm{d}^2 S/\mathrm{d}\Omega \mathrm{d}E = ED(\mathrm{d}E_1/\mathrm{d}x)\cos\theta/8\pi(E + U)^3\cos\theta'.$$

In this equation $\mathrm{d}E_1/\mathrm{d}x$ is the nuclear part of the stopping power for the incident ions with energy E_1, θ' is the angle of incidence of the ions and

D is the mean distance between atoms in the solid. Both θ and θ' are measured relative to the normal to the surface. This expression contains the energy distribution of the sputtered particles and, when integrated over exit angles and energies, also the sputter yield:

$$S = D(dE_1/dx)/4U \cos(\theta').$$

The latter expression has an extremely simple interpretation as the energy deposited in passing through the surface layer divided by four times the energy required for an atom to escape the surface binding. What is most important is the amount of energy deposited very near the surface where it can be effectively spread among other surface layer atoms, resulting in their escape. Indeed, a high percentage of all sputtered particles comes from within the first few atomic layers adjacent to the surface. For angles which are close to grazing incidence the incident ions are strongly reflected and the above relation for the sputter yield fails. A very crude estimate of the nuclear part of the stopping power (usually an over-estimate) is obtained by dividing the average energy loss for a hard sphere collision by twice the mean spacing between atoms. In this crude approximation

$$dE_1/dx \simeq M_1 M_2 E_1/D(M_1 + M_2)^2.$$

The latter expression is a poor estimate except at relatively low energies. It is most useful for purposes of pointing out that sputter yields are highest when the mass of the ions is nearly equal to the mass of the target atoms and can be relatively low when the mass ratio is either too large or too small. The simple relations given here are not particularly accurate, but they predict correct trends and describe a surprising amount of data reasonably well.

Figure 8.5 shows the number of sputtered atoms per incident Ar^+ ion as a function of incident ion energy for Si and Ge targets. The yields are for normal incidence in each case. For energies less than 100 eV the yield is less than 0.1 for each target. In the case of Si the yield is around two for energies between 5 and 40 keV. With Ge the yield climbs to around five for energies between 10 and 50 keV. Table 8.1 shows ion yields for a large number of target materials when they are sputtered by 10 and 50 keV Ar^+ ions. We have placed a great deal of emphasis on sputtering by Ar^+ because it is a favourite for use with SIRIS.

A comprehensive set of experiments on energy distributions of sputtered neutrals and of the angular distribution of sputtered neutrals has been carried out by Winograd's group at Pennsylvania State University (Baxter *et al* 1986). With normally incident ions it was found empirically that $d^2S/d\Omega dE$ is better represented by a relationship of the form

$$d^2S/d\Omega dE = [CE \cos \theta/(E + U)^4](E \cos^2\theta + U).$$

For small θ this agrees with the hard sphere version of the Sigmund theory. However, the angular distribution for high-energy sputtered particles is best fitted by a $\cos^3\theta$ angular distribution. This was verified

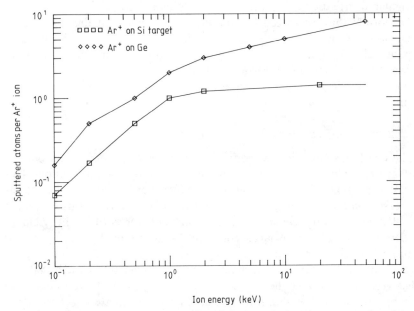

Figure 8.5 Graph of sputter yields as a function of Ar$^+$ ion energy for the targets germanium and silicon. The data were based on Andersen and Bay (1981).

Table 8.1 Sputtering yield of neutral particles for Ar$^+$ ions (at 10 and 50 keV) in various materials†.

Material	Yield	
	10 keV	50 keV
Carbon	0.7	0.8
Aluminium	4	3
Silicon	1.5	1.5
Iron, stainless steel	5	5
Nickel	5	6
Copper	7	7
Germanium	6	7
Silver	11	15
Cadmium	28	35
Tungsten	45	60
Platinum	7	10
Gold	10	15
Uranium	9	12

†Data from Andersen and Bay (1981).

for 5 keV Ar$^+$ ions normally incident on both In and Rh. Jackson (1975) has argued that partial blocking of the motion of an atom in the surface plane due to the neighbouring surface atoms tends to make the angular distribution of sputtered neutrals more strongly peaked toward the normal than predicted by the analytical theory. In the same study the above form of the energy distribution was shown to fit the data quite well. The energy distribution was found to depend on the angle of escape of the sputtered particle, as predicted by the above equation. The slowly decreasing high-energy tail is still of the $1/E^2$ functional form.

8.5.2 Matrix effects on sputter atomisation

The nearly instantaneous vaporisation of atoms following an ion pulse is a very appealing feature of the sputtering method of vaporisation. This makes possible the ionisation of a large percentage of the atoms released on a particular pulse. Another positive feature of this technique is that with a very clean metal or semiconductor surface the yield of neutrals is usually very large compared with the number of sputtered ions. The ion-to-neutral ratio depends on the sample, but typical numbers are 10^{-4}–10^{-2}. This mechanism for atomisation is such that one has great control over the positioning and intensity of the ion beam and there are no highly non-linear features to the sputtering process to complicate the interpretation of the sputter yield, or to cause large pulse-to-pulse fluctuations. Thus, there are a great many good features for this method of atomisation.

One of the less desirable features of an ion-sputter atomiser is that the energy distribution of the atoms has a most probable value which is rather high (approximately 2 eV), with a very long, slowly decreasing tail towards the high-energy part of the spectrum. This means that Doppler effects are large and there is a very large spread of energies, which decreases the resolution and the transmission of most mass spectrometers. The technique also shares some other problems with most other atomisation methods. For instance, the presence of surface contamination is expected to have several kinds of effects, as listed below.

(1) Since most of the sputter yield comes from the first one or two atomic layers, a deposit of CO or other surface contaminants may cause sizeable changes in sputter yields. The absorbed molecules replace the bulk material in the first few layers. Consequently, it is probably the impurity which is sputtered efficiently. To some degree the impurities serve as a cage for the bulk material.

(2) A layer of oxides or other chemical layer (even one containing the dominant bulk material) can result in a large yield of sputtered

molecules and large decreases in the yield of neutral atoms. This is particularly true when the bulk material is a very heavy element and the surface compound involves light atoms such as H or O, with the molecular binding being comparable to or larger than the surface binding energy. In such cases the heavy atom can get a great deal of kinetic energy without moving very fast compared with the velocity of the light atom in its vibrational motion. The energy imparted to the heavy particle can then overcome the surface binding energy without breaking the chemical bond.

(3) In cases where there is a surface layer of a chemical compound the molecular bonds are sometimes broken by the sputtering process, but the molecule may tend to dissociate into ions instead of neutrals. Even with the physical absorption of some impurities there can be charge exchange, or effects on the effective work function of the material which increases the yield of ions relative to neutrals. In particular, the presence of oxide layers frequently increases the yield of ions by orders of magnitudes.

The factors which affect the relative yield of ions and neutrals, as well as the fraction of the material released as molecules or clusters, have been studied by Winograd's group (Kimock *et al* 1987). For instance, it was found that the yield of indium atoms decreased by a factor of six when the surface was oxidised. During this chemisorption the yield of the secondary ions, In^+, increased by a factor of 200. Questions about the increase in the yield of molecules relative to atoms could not be answered completely due to the large internal energy of the molecules, and the resulting low efficiency with which the neutral molecular yield could be detected. Consequently, it is not clear whether the decrease in the yield of neutral atoms was mostly compensated for by the amount of the bulk material sputtered in the form of molecules, or if the amount of bulk material sputtered was decreased by a factor of six. The matrix effects are smaller on the yield of neutrals than for secondary ions, but they are large for both in a dirty system, or for a sample with a complex composition.

Christie (Christie and Goeringer 1987) documented a number of effects due to impurities on the sputter-initiated RIMS of U and U_3O_8. In effect, they find that oxide layers make the SIRIS detection of uranium atoms nearly impossible. Very similar changes in the relative yields of ions, molecules and neutral atoms due to surface contamination are also seen for the case of laser ablation.

8.5.3 Requirements for the ion beams

The ion beam that is used in the sputter-induced atomisation process must be extremely free of the impurities of interest. This requirement is based on the fact that many of the incident ions penetrate the sample to some depth and become a part of the sample. As the sputtering process continues the constituents of the ion beam build up in concentration until an equilibrium is reached where the sputtering away of the ion-beam constituents in the target just balances the implantation. The equilibrium fraction of ion-beam constituents in the target varies with target composition and with the ions used, but it can be 30%, or more, by atom numbers. Clearly, if one wanted to look for Fe at a level of one part in 10^{10}, it would be disastrous for there to be more that one part in 10^{10} of Fe^+ in the sputtering ion beam. The problem of making extremely clean ion beams which can be pulsed and delivered to the target without contamination is non-trivial and will require continued attention. It is possible that the best way to get very clean pulses of ions is to carry out RIS on a clean atomic beam with a high-repetition-rate pulsed dye laser, with the resulting ions being accelerated towards the target by a very open arrangement of ion optics.

8.6 Elemental analyses of solids using SIRIS

The basic concept of an RIS-based method for the analysis of impurity atoms in a solid is shown in figure 8.6 (Parks *et al* 1983a). Here we take advantage of the well known characteristics of ion sputtering as de-

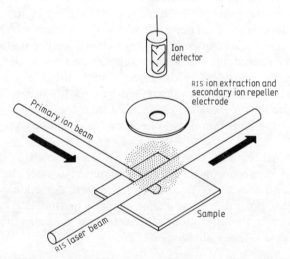

Figure 8.6 Sputter-initiated resonance ionisation spectroscopy (SIRIS). A diagram showing the basic concept in which atoms are sputtered from a solid using ion beams and selectively ionised using RIS. Courtesy of J E Parks (from Parks *et al* 1983a).

scribed in the previous section. In principle, the sputtering of neutral atoms from a solid should be much less matrix dependent than the sputtering of ions, since surface chemistry is much reduced for the neutral species. Furthermore, as discussed, the yield of neutrals due to the impact of energetic ions is much greater (by a factor of 100 or more in most cases) than that of ions. For both of these reasons, in sputter-initiated RIS, or SIRIS, the secondary ions (which constitute the signal in SIMS analyses) are rejected prior to efficient and selective ionisation of the neutrals in a laser beam. Furthermore, it is convenient to pulse ion beams onto surfaces, thus solving the problem of overlap of the atomisation source and a pulse laser for resonance ionisation.

Estimates of the sensitivity of a SIRIS method are simple to make for the geometry illustrated in figure 8.6. Suppose a 10 keV Ar^+ beam is incident on a solid in a square wave pulse of 1 mA amplitude and 2 μs duration. This pulse of 10^{13} Ar^+ ions would sputter approximately 10^{13} neutral atoms from a typical solid. If a mean energy of 10 eV is assumed, 100 AMU atoms would travel 3 mm from the surface in 1 μs. Overlap with a pulsed laser beam is excellent, and, assuming an ionisation efficiency of 100%, conceivably 10% of the sputter atoms could be ionised. Thus, if the laser is tuned for RIS of an impurity atom at a concentration of 10^{-12}, one atom could be detected for each laser pulse. This idealisation has not been achieved for a number of practical reasons, and the above is intended only for illustration of the SIRIS principle. For instance, it is known that some of the sputter neutral atoms are in excited states. Furthermore, as already discussed, there are matrix effects which appear important for cases like uranium atoms (Christie and Goeringer 1987).

Figure 8.7 shows schematically the SIRIS system developed for commercial uses by Atom Sciences Inc. (ASI) of Oak Ridge, Tennessee. Additional information on the various technical problems overcome and

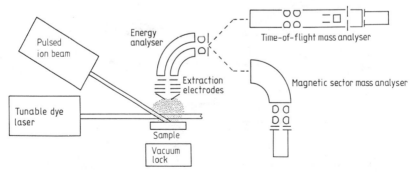

Figure 8.7 Schematic diagram of the SIRIS apparatus. Courtesy of J E Parks (from Parks *et al* 1987).

a chronology of the improvement in performance is contained in Hurst *et al* (1984), Parks *et al* (1983a,b, 1984a,b, 1985a,b), and Parks (1986). Basically, as shown in figure 8.7, the ions produced are mass analysed and then particle counted. Two options are now available (magnetic sector and time-of-flight) for the mass analyses (Parks *et al* 1987).

Another version of the SIRIS technique has been developed at Argonne National Laboratory by Pellin and co-workers (Pellin *et al* 1984, 1986, Young *et al* 1987). Their method utilises a time-of-flight mass spectrometer combined with a laser for RIS where special attention has been given to the ion extraction region (see figure 8.8). They achieve less than 2 PPB sensitivity in some cases. An impressive example

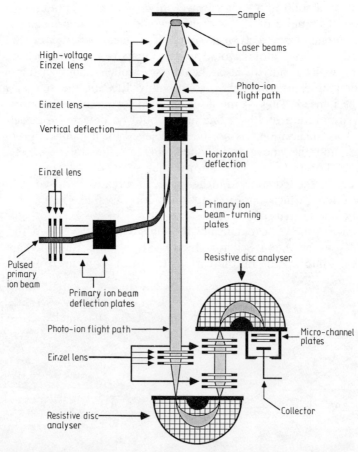

Figure 8.8 Schematic diagram of a surface analyser using RIS, developed at Argonne National Laboratory. Courtesy of M J Pellin (from Young *et al* 1987).

of their analysis capability is shown in figure 8.9 for a depth profile of implanted iron in silicon.

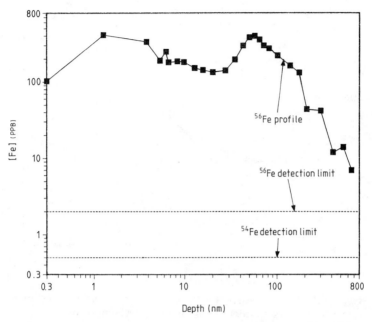

Figure 8.9 Depth profile for ^{56}Fe implanted in silicon, using the apparatus of figure 8.8. The dose is 60 keV Fe$^+$ with 10^{11} atoms per cm^2. Courtesy of M J Pellin (from Young *et al* 1987).

8.6.1 Analyses of impurities in semiconducting materials

One of the motivations for the development of the SIRIS apparatus was the analysis of impurities in electronics grade materials such as silicon and gallium arsenide for the semiconductor industry (Parks *et al* 1983a). A sample result is shown in figure 8.10 for boron in silicon (Parks *et al* 1985a). Here we see a sensitivity approaching 10^{-9} and a correlation plot with some values obtained at Tekronix. Also shown is boron in an NBS steel sample. The absence of any appreciable matrix effect when comparing boron atoms in silicon and steel is noted. We do not imply that matrix effects are never seen in SIRIS. For example, severe effects of the chemical environment have been noted in uranium analyses (Parks *et al* 1985a, Christie and Goeringer 1987).

8.6.2 Depth profiling with SIRIS

In the semiconductor industry and in the fabrication of composite materials, depth analysis is quite important. With SIRIS, both a beam

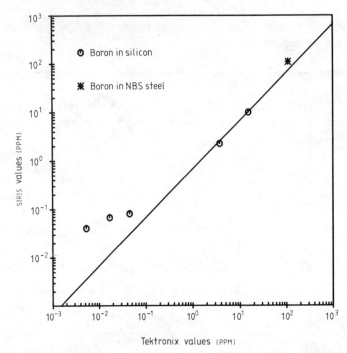

Figure 8.10 Correlation plot showing SIRIS values against resistivity values for boron concentrations in silicon. Courtesy of J E Parks (from Parks *et al* 1985a).

raster and depth profile capability have been provided. In silicon, for instance, depths can be penetrated at a rate of 0.065 μm per second (Parks *et al* 1983a). A sample of depth profiling in a composite material is shown in figure 8.11 for the case of silicon impurities in GaAs. Good resolution of boundaries is seen, implying the absence of matrix effect with SIRIS. We are not suggesting that the present SIRIS capability is adequate for the new material structures where layer thickness approaches one atom. Mixing of atoms due to recoiling atoms would blur the boundaries. These effects can be reduced by using low-mass ions such as H^+ or He^+ at low energies, rather than Ar^+ at 10 to 20 keV.

8.6.3 Medical applications

Another example of SIRIS capability is taken from medical research (Moore *et al* 1987). Moore *et al* explored the application of two forms of the RIS analysis technology to medicine and biology and conclude that both RIMS and SIRIS should play significant roles. Trace element analysis is known to be important in a variety of biological and medical

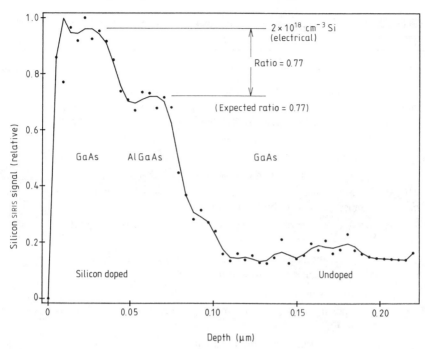

Figure 8.11 A sample of depth profiling in a composite material. Courtesy of J E Parks (Parks *et al* 1988).

applications, such as illustrated in table 8.2 (Moore *et al* 1987). These 15 elements are essential to animals, and most of them are difficult to measure at the concentrations found in biological media. In addition, many other elements at very small concentrations can play significant roles in nutrition, toxicity and biological dysfunctions.

A specific example to illustrate the use of the SIRIS technique in the medical field can be drawn from paediatric studies (Lorch *et al* 1987). The elements copper, molybdenum and vanadium are thought to be important to the growth of an infant. For premature babies, the goal is an analysis capability for trace elements that requires no more than 100 mg or about 100 μl of blood. Molybdenum in human serum is found at about 1 ng ml^{-1}, thus about 0.1 ng in the blood sample. Presently, SIRIS sensitivity is a few picogrammes for molybdenum and can be extended to the femtogramme range, while the RIMS technique can be extended to the picogramme range (Moore *et al* 1987). In either case, practical limitations are introduced due to trace elements in typical reagents used to prepare the samples for either of the RIS analysis methods. Analysis of copper in human serum is an example of the demonstrated application of SIRIS to paediatrics (Lorch *et al* 1987). Isotope dilution was used as an internal standard, and accuracies of

Table 8.2 Trace element analyses important in a variety of biological and medical applications†.

Essential element	Associated metabolic disorders/functions
Zn	Sickle cell disease, liver disease, gastrointestinal disorders, impaired wound healing, genetic disorders (acrodermatitis enteropathica)
Cu	Wilson's disease, Menkes disease, anaemia
Cr	Diabetes mellitus, cardiovascular disease, impaired glucose tolerance, elevated serum cholesterol
Se	Keshan disease (Se-responsive cardiomyopathy), atherosclerosis, muscular dystrophy, cystic fibrosis
Mn	Skeletal abnormalities, ultrastructural abnormalities, blood cholesterol level
Mo	Enzymatic reactions, severe bifrontal headache, night blindness, nausea, lethargy, disorientation, coma
Co	Part of vitamin B-12, interacts with iron
I	Hyperthyroidism, cretanism (essentially demonstrated for animals only)
Ni	Depressed haematocrit, ultrastructural liver abnormality
As	Depressed birth weight, impaired fertility, elevated haematocrits
Si	Aberrant connective tissue and bone metabolism, atherosclerosis, hypertension, aging process
V	Cardiovascular disease, renal disease, kwashiorkor
Cd,Pb,Sn	Growth factor . . unknown

†Courtesy of L J Moore (Moore *et al* 1987).

$\pm 10\%$ were achieved with 80 to 200 μl samples. Figure 8.12 compares data for the analysis of copper in blood serum, using SIRIS with reference samples analysed by atomic absorption spectroscopy. Experimental data suggested that sample sizes less than 1 μl could be processed, even at levels of parts per million or even parts per billion. These are the normal levels of essential metal nutrients found in human serum.

8.6.4 Exploration of natural resources

Another promising SIRIS application is provided by the search for natural resources. Industrial and other uses of rare materials are increasing due to the more technically advanced processes which require only minute quantities. For instance, platinum is used extensively for catalytic converters in automobiles, yet only 2000 tons of the scarce metal have been mined through history compared to 100 000 tons of gold.

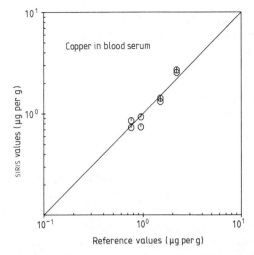

Figure 8.12 A plot of the copper concentration in blood, determined by the SIRIS method. Reference data is from measurements of larger samples using atomic absorption spectrometry. Courtesy of L J Moore (from Lorch *et al* 1987).

One of the missions of the RIS research group at Tsinghua University (Beijing) is to develop a SIRIS system for the exploration of natural resources in the Xinjiang Province of China (Chen *et al* 1987). The detection of ppb concentrations of precious metals such as gold, platinum, and silver would open up new vistas for geological exploration. These techniques require low-level analyses since the exploration could involve sampling from water streams which carry geological samples at low concentration (Chen *et al* 1987).

8.7 Comparison of RIS with accelerator mass spectroscopy (AMS)

We comment briefly on the accelerator mass spectrometer (AMS) method for the elemental analyses of samples. The AMS technique, in which tandem accelerators are used in ingenious ways to detect small numbers of atoms, was originated at roughly the same time as was RIS. An excellent review of this field can be found in the proceedings of a discussion meeting on 'Ultra-high Sensitive Mass Spectrometry with Accelerators' of The Royal Society in London. In an overview article, Litherland (1987) gives some of the history, the principles and the current status of AMS. In contrast to RIS, the AMS method has not made use of lasers but relies primarily on highly developed tandem accelerators which became available for AMS analyses applicable to important dating applications using ^{14}C. Basically, the AMS analyser utilises a combination of energy, mass and charge analysis of individual particles.

Particular advantage is taken of the fact that negative ions can be formed only in selected elements, and this leads to a way of reducing isobaric interferences. In common with other forms of mass spectrometers—as we have discussed with RIS methods—isobars, as well as molecular ions, interfere with the detection of a particular ion mass of interest, and these interferences are addressed with AMS.

Spectacular results have been obtained on ^{14}C dating for archaeology, anthropology and the environmental sciences (Hedges and Gowlett 1986). For instance, it is now possible to measure ^{14}C abundances as low as one atom in 10^{15} atoms of ^{12}C, and this permits dating of samples up to about 50 000 years BP. This is truly remarkable in view of the fact that the half-life of ^{14}C is only about 5700 years. In comparison, β-decay counting techniques are limited to about 30 000 BP unless very large quantities of carbon can be recovered from kilogramme samples of natural materials. One strength of the AMS technique is the relatively small (0.5 to 5 mg) sample of carbon needed for a ^{14}C analysis (Hedges and Gowlett 1986). The AMS technique has produced impressive results not only on ^{14}C but also on ^{10}Be for environmental research (Brown 1987, Oeschger 1987, Raisbeck and Yiou 1987) and on ^{23}Al and ^{36}Cl for other applications.

At present, AMS and RIS are complementary techniques with some common and some contrasting features (Hurst 1987). Table 8.3 summa-

Table 8.3 A comparison of AMS with RIS as discussed at the AMS conference of The Royal Society of London.

Problem to solve	Solution	
	AMS	RIS
Isobaric interference	Negative ions: (e.g. N$^-$ is negligible compared to C$^-$) separate ^{14}C from ^{14}N	Inherent in process
Molecular interferences	Ion stripping at high energy	Inherent in process
Sensitivity	Inherent, C$^-$ yield is large, e.g. 10%	Inherent, sputter yield of neutrals with SIRIS is 1–10
Isotopic interferences	High resolution MS	High resolution MS; additional can be provided with high resolution RIS
General	Special capability is required for each element of interest	RIS works for nearly all elements

rises these features. It is hoped that the best properties of AMS and RIS can be combined, as expressed in the discussions of The Royal Society meeting. In this way, it should be possible to extend the two new methods of atom counting into applications not addressable by either method alone.

8.8 On-line RIMS in nuclear physics

One of the most elegant applications of RIMS has been made by H J Kluge and his associates at the University of Mainz and at CERN for the study of nuclear properties of short-lived isotopes. Further, the Resonance Ionisation Spectroscopy 86 symposium paper (Bollen *et al* 1987) gives an excellent overview of the impact which laser spectroscopy is making on nuclear physics facilities, having on-line isotope separators at Daresbury, GSI/Darmstadt, ISOLDE/CERN, Leningrad, TRISTAN/ Brookhaven, and at UNISOR/Oak Ridge.

The basic idea of these experiments is to deduce nuclear properties from measured hyperfine structure (HFS) and isotope shifts (IS). The Bollen *et al* experiments (see figure 8.13) represent the first use of RIMS

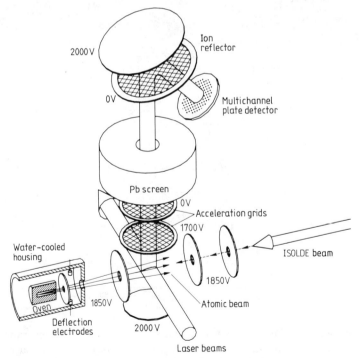

Figure 8.13 Set-up for on-line resonance ionisation mass spectrometry (RIMS) on short-lived Au isotopes. Courtesy of H J Kluge (from Bollen *et al* 1987).

to determine these properties. The ISOLDE beam delivered short-lived mercury isotopes to an atomic-beam oven, where these atoms decayed by electron capture to isotopes of gold. After appropriate accumulation times, the furnace then produced a beam of short-lived gold isotopes. The RIS process was used to ionise gold atoms using a three-step scheme starting with $6s^2S_{1/2} \rightarrow 6p^2P_{1/2}$ at about 268 nm, using a laser of about 0.4 GHz band width. Some results of high-resolution RIS on gold are shown in figure 8.14. Nuclear magnetic moments and the changes of mean square charge radii, $\delta \langle r^2 \rangle$, were deduced from the HFS splitting

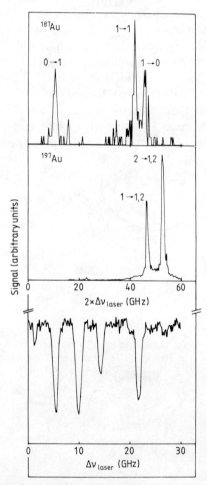

Figure 8.14 Photo-ion yield as a function of the laser frequency of the first optical transition (D_1) for ^{187}Au (top), simultaneously measured signals of the resonance fluorescence of stable ^{197}Au in an atomic beam (middle) and of the absorption spectrum of iodine in a cell (bottom). Courtesy of H J Kluge (from Bollen *et al* 1987).

and the IS of the D_1 line. Figure 8.15 is a plot of deduced $\delta\langle r^2\rangle$ for gold isotopes compared to values for mercury isotopes (Ulm *et al* 1986). Important inputs for nuclear models are derived from the drastic changes occurring in $\delta\langle r^2\rangle$ as a function of neutron number.

These first results on the use of RIMS to obtain definitive information on the nucleus are already impressive. New work is underway to improve the sensitivity by increasing the laser duty cycle and to apply the on-line RIMS techniques to a number of challenging problems in nuclear physics (Bollen *et al* 1987).

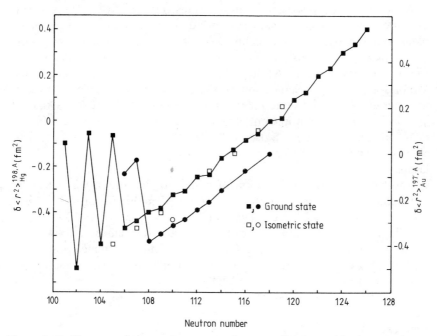

Figure 8.15 Changes of the mean square charge radii of Au (dots) and of Hg (squares) (Ulm *et al* 1986) isotopes. The isotopes ¹⁹⁸Hg and ¹⁹⁷Au are used as references. Courtesy of H J Kluge (from Bollen *et al* 1987).

8.9 Some additional applications of RIMS

We have emphasised in this chapter the use of RIS for the analysis of solids using either the RIMS or the SIRIS techniques. Unfortunately, space does not permit us to discuss many other novel and important applications of resonance ionisation. For instance, the application of both the understanding and the detection of molecules is rapidly developing. Hessler and Glab (1987) reported on three-step ionisation schemes for the detection of molecular hydrogen or any of its isotopic varients—with adequate discrimination in the laser itself so that a mass spectrometer is not needed. The combination of resonance ionisation with photoelectron spectroscopy was used (Sander *et al* 1987) to fully resolve the rotational spectra in the $(NO^+)X \leftarrow (NO)A$ process. Detailed studies of clusters is leading to a better understanding of condensation phenomena (Castleman *et al* 1987).

Xylene isomer analysis (Blease *et al* 1987) and large involatile molecular characterisation (Boesl *et al* 1987) are examples of the use of resonance ionisation with more complex molecules. Another impressive example is the work of Benedetti *et al* (1987) on the amide groups.

While we have discussed almost exclusively the use of resonance ionisation for sensitive analyses or detection, other groups have pioneered the use of laser techniques for the separation of materials. The books of Radziemski *et al* (1987) and Letokhov (1987) describe the history of this subject. At the 1986 symposium on RIS, the Atomic Vapor Laser Isotope Separation (AVLIS) project was reviewed (Comaskey *et al* 1987), and some recent applications were discussed. Crane *et al* (1987) described isotopic enrichment of ^{196}Hg to improve the efficiency of fluorescent lights. Also with mercury, Dyer (1987) described studies of nuclear isomers aimed at the development of gamma-ray lasers.

Another impressive application of resonance ionisation was made by Ledingham *et al* (1987) for the calibration of multiwire drift chambers used in high-energy physics. The simulation of charged particle tracks with laser ionisation (both resonance and non-resonance) is now common in particle physics (Sandweiss 1987). The resonance ionisation studies of Ledingham *et al* identified phenol and toluene as major sources of laser ionisation in these detectors.

References

Allegre C J and Luck J M 1980 *Earth Planet. Sci. Lett.* **48** 148

Ambartzumian R V and Letokhov V S 1972 *Appl. Opt.* **11** 354

Andersen H H and Bay H L 1981 in *Sputtering by Particle Bombardment I.—Physical Sputtering of Single Element Solids* ed Rainer Behrisch *Topics in Applied Physics* vol. 47 (Berlin, Heidelberg, New York: Springer) pp 145–218

Apel E C, Nogar N S, Miller C M and Estler R C 1987 in *Resonance Ionization Spectroscopy 1986* ed G S Hurst and C Grey Morgan (*Inst. Phys. Conf. Ser. 84*) pp 179–82

Baxter J P, Singh J, Schick G A, Kobrin P H and Winograd N 1986 *Nucl. Instrum. Methods in Phys. Res.* **B8** 345

Beekman D W, Callcott T A, Kramer S D, Arakawa E T, Hurst G S and Nussbaum E 1980 *Int. J. Mass Spectrom. Ion Phys.* **34** 89–97

Beekman D W and Callcott T A 1984 in *Resonance Ionization Spectroscopy 1984* ed G S Hurst and M G Payne (Inst. Phys. Conf. Ser. 71) pp 143–50

Benedetti E, Borsella E and Bruzzese R 1987 in *Resonance Ionization Spectroscopy 1986* ed G S Hurst and C Grey Morgan (Inst. Phys. Conf. Ser. 84) pp 229–34

Blease T G, Donovan R J, Langridge-Smith P R R, Ridley T and Wilkinson J P T 1987 in *Resonance Ionization Spectroscopy 1986* ed G S Hurst and C Grey Morgan (Inst. Phys. Conf. Ser. 84) pp 217–22

Boesl U, Grotemeyer J, Walter K and Schlag E W 1987 in *Resonance Ionization Spectroscopy 1986* ed G S Hurst and C Grey Morgan (Inst. Phys. Conf. Ser. 84) pp 223–8

Bollen G, Dohn A, Kluge H-J, Kroner U and Wallmeroth K 1987 in *Resonance Ionization Spectroscopy 1986* ed G S Hurst and C Grey Morgan (Inst. Phys. Conf. Ser. 84) pp 295–304

Bradley D J, Dudan C H, Ewart P and Purdie A F 1976 *Phys. Rev.* A **13** 1416

Brown L 1987 *Phil. Trans. R. Soc.* A **323**, 75–86

Bushaw B A, Cannon B D, Gerke G K and Whitaker T J 1987 in *Resonance Ionization Spectroscopy 1986* ed G S Hurst and C Grey Morgan (Inst. Phys. Conf. Ser. 84) pp 103–8

Bushaw B A and Whitaker T J 1981 *J. Chem. Phys.* **74** 6519

Bushaw B A, Whitaker T J, Cannon B D and Warner R A 1985 *J. Opt. Soc. Am.* B **2** 1547 (See also Cannon B D, Bushaw B A and Whitaker T J 1985 *J. Opt. Soc. Am.* B **2** 1542

Carlson L R, Paisner J A, Worden E F, Johnson S A, May C A and Solarz R W 1976 *J. Opt. Soc. Am.* **66** 846

Castleman A W Jr, Dao P D, Morgan S and Keesee R G 1987 in *Resonance Ionization Spectroscopy 1986* ed G S Hurst and C Grey Morgan (Inst. Phys. Conf. Ser. 84) pp 209–17

Chen C H, Hurst G S and Payne M G 1980 *Chem. Phys. Lett.* **75** 473–7

Chen D Y, Xiao G Y and Wen K L 1987 in *Resonance Ionization Spectroscopy 1986* ed G S Hurst and C Grey Morgan (Inst. Phys. Conf. Ser. 84) pp 175–8

Christie W H and Goeringer D E 1987 in *Resonance Ionization Spectroscopy 1986* ed G S Hurst and C Grey Morgan (Inst. Phys. Conf. Ser. 84) pp 169–74

Clark C W 1983 *Opt. Lett.* **8** 572

Clark C W, Fassett J D, Lucatorto T B and Moore L J 1984 in *Resonance Ionization Spectroscopy 1984* ed G S Hurst and M G Payne (Inst. Phys. Conf. Ser. 71) pp 107–17

Comaskey B J, Crane J K, Erbert G V, Haymam C A, Johnson M A, Morris J R, Paisner J A, Solarz R W and Worden E F 1987 in *Resonance Ionization Spectroscopy 1986* ed G S Hurst and C Grey Morgan (Inst. Phys. Conf. Ser. 84) pp 245–9

Conzemius R J and Capellen 1980 *Int. J. Mass Spectrom. Ion Phys.* **34** 197–271

Crane J K, Erbert G V, Paisner J A, Chen H L, Chiba Z, Beeler R G, Combs R and Mostek S D 1987 in *Resonance Ionization Spectroscopy 1986* ed G S Hurst and C Grey Morgan (Inst. Phys. Conf. Ser. 84) pp 251–4

Donohue D L, Young J P and Smith D H 1982 *Int. J. Mass. Spectrom. Ion Phys.* **43** 293

Donohue D L and Young J P 1983 *Anal. Chem.* **55** 378–9

Dyer P 1987 in *Resonance Ionization Specroscopy 1986* ed G S Hurst and C Grey Morgan (Inst. Phys. Conf. Ser. 84) pp 257–62

Fassett J, Travis J, Moore L and Lytle F 1983 *Anal. Chem.* **55** 765

Happer W 1969 Optical Pumping Theory *Summer Institute of Theoretical Physics, University of Colorado* vol. XI-C (New York: Gordon and Breach)

Harvey K C and Stoicheff B P 1977 *Phys. Rev. Lett.* **38** 537

Hedges R E M and Gowlett J A J 1986 *Sci. Amer.* **254**(1) 82–9

Hessler J P and Glab W L 1987 in *Resonance Ionization Spectroscopy 1986* ed G S Hurst and C Grey Morgan (Inst. Phys. Conf. Ser. 84) pp 183–7

Hurst G S 1987 *Phil. Trans. R. Soc.* A **323** 155–70

Hurst G S, Parks J E and Schmitt 1984 *US Patent Specification* 4442354

Hurst G S, Payne M G, Kramer S D and Chen C H 1980 *Phys. Today* **33**(9) 24

Hurst G S, Payne M G, Kramer S D and Young J P 1979 *Rev. Mod. Phys.* **51** 767–819

Jackson D P 1975 *Can. J. Phys.* **53** 1513

Jacquinot P and Klapisch R 1979 *Rep. Prog. Phys.* **42** 773

James G S, Itzkan I, Pike C T, Levy R H and Levin L 1976 *IEEE J. Quant. Electron.* **QE-12** 111

Kastler A 1950 *J. Phys. Radium* **11** 155

Lambropoulos P 1976 *Adv. At. Mol. Phys.* **12** (New York: Academic) 87

Ledingham K W D, Cahill J W, Drysdale S L T, Raine C, Smith K M, Smyth M H C, Stewart D T and Towrie M 1987 in *Resonance Ionization Spectroscopy 1986* ed G S Hurst and C Grey Morgan (Inst. Phys. Conf. Ser. 84) pp 289–94

Letokhov V S 1976 in *Tunable Lasers and Applications* ed A Mooradian, T Jarger and P Stokseth (Berlin: Springer) pp 122–39

——1987 *Laser Photoionization Spectroscopy* (Orlando, Florida: Academic)

Litherland A E 1987 *Phil. Trans. R. Soc.* A **323** 5–21

Lorch V, Moore L J, Parks J E and Taylor E H 1987 to be published

Lucatorto T B, Clark C W and Moore L J 1984 *Opt. Commun.* **48** 406

Mayo S 1984 in *Resonance Ionization Spectroscopy 1984* ed G S Hurst and M G Payne (Inst. Phys. Conf. Ser. 71) pp 335–6

Mayo S, Lucatorto T B and Luther G G 1982 *Anal. Chem.* **54** 553–6

Miller C M, Engleman R and Keller R A 1985 *J. Opt. Soc. Am.* B **2** 1503

Miller C M and Nogar N S 1983 *Anal. Chem.* **55** 1606

Miller C M, Nogar N S, Gancarz A J and Shields W R 1982 *Anal. Chem.* **54** 2377

Moore L J, Fassett J D, Travis J C and Lucatorto T B 1985 *J. Opt. Soc. Am.* B **2** 1561

Moore L J, Parks J E, Taylor E H, Beekman D W and Spaar M T 1987 *Resonance Ionization Spectroscopy 1986* ed G S Hurst and C Grey Morgan (Inst. Phys. Conf. Ser. 84) pp 239–44

Nebenzahl I and Levin M 1973 *Chem. Abstr.* **79** No 152148

Niemax K, Lawrenz J and Obrebski A 1987 in *Resonance Ionization Spectroscopy 1986* ed G S Hurst and C Grey Morgan (Inst. Phys. Conf. Ser. 84) pp 45–50

Niemax K and Weber K H 1978 *J. Phys. B: At. Mol. Phys.* **11** L267

Nogar N S, Estler R C and Miller C M 1985 *Anal. Chem.* **57** 2441

Oeschger H, Beer J and Andreé M 1987 *Phil. Trans. R. Soc.* A **323** 45–56

Parks J E 1986 *Optics News* **12**(10) 22–7, 40

Parks J E, Beekman D W, Moore L J, Schmitt, H W, Spaar M T and Taylor E H 1987 in *Resonance Ionization Spectroscopy 1986* ed G S Hurst and C Grey Morgan (Inst. Phys. Conf. Ser. 84) pp 157–62

Parks J E, Beekman D W, Schmitt H W, and Spaar M T 1985b in *Applied Materials Characterization* ed W Katz and P Williams (Pittsburgh: Materials Research Society) **48** pp 309–17

Parks J E, Beekman D W, Schmitt H W and Taylor E H 1985a *Nucl. Instrum. Methods* **B10/11** 280–4

Parks J E, Schmitt H W, Hurst G S and Fairbank W M Jr 1983a *Thin Solid Films* **108** 69–78

——1983b in Laser-based Ultrasensitive Spectroscopy and Detection V ed R A Keller *Proc. SPIE* **426** 32–9

——1984a in *Analytical Spectroscopy* ed W S Lyon (Amsterdam: Elsevier) pp 149–54

——1984b in *Resonance Ionization Spectroscopy 1984* ed G S Hurst and M H Payne (Inst. Phys. Conf. Ser. 71) pp 167–74

Parks J E, Spaar M T and Crossman P J 1988 Analysis studies of semiconductors and electro-optic materials using sputter initiated resonance ionisation spectroscopy (SIRIS) *Proc. SIMS-VI (Sixth Int. Conf. on Secondary Ionisation Mass Spectrometry) (Versailles, France)*

September 1987 (Chichester: Wiley)

Payne M G, Chen C H, Hurst G S and Foltz G M 1981 *Adv. At. Mol. Phys.* **17** 229

Pellin M J, Young C E, Calaway W F and Gruen D M 1984 *Surf. Sci.* **144** 619

——1986 *Nucl. Intrum. Methods* B **13** 653

Peuser P, Herrmann G, Rimke H, Sattelberger P, Trautman N, Ruster W, Ames F, Bonn J, Kronert U and Otten E W 1985 *Appl. Phys.* B **38** 249

Radziemski L J, Solarz R W and Paisner J A 1987 *Laser Spectroscopy and Its Applications* (New York: Marcel Dekker)

Raisbeck G M and Yiou F 1987 *Phil. Trans. R. Soc.* **323** 101–2

Rimke H, Peuser P, Sattelberger P, Trautman N, Herrmann G, Ruster W, Ames F, Kluge H J and Otten E W 1987 in *Resonance Ionization Spectroscopy 1986* ed G S Hurst and C Grey Morgan (Inst. Phys. Conf. Ser. 84) pp 235–8

Sander M, Chewter L A and Muller-Dethlefs K 1987 in *Resonance Ionization Spectroscopy 1986* ed G S Hurst and C Grey Morgan (Inst. Phys. Conf. Ser. 84) pp 189–94

Sandweiss J 1987 *private communication* (See Sandweiss J 1978 *Phys. Today* **31** (10) 40–5 for an article by Sandweiss on drift chambers)

Sigmund P 1969 *Phys. Rev.* **184** 383 (See also Sigmund P in *Sputtering by Particle Bombardment I.—Physical Sputtering of Single Element Solids* ed R Behrisch *Topics in Applied Physics* vol 47 (Berlin, Heidelberg, New York: Springer) pp 9–71

Solarz R W, May C A, Carlson L R, Warden E F, Johnson S A and Paisner J A 1976 *Phys. Rev.* A **14** 1129

Thompson M W 1980 *Phys. Rep.* **69** 335 (See also Thompson M W 1968 *Phil. Mag.* **18** 377)

Travis J C 1982 *J. Chem. Ed.* **59** 909–14

Travis J C, Turk G C and Green R B 1982 *Anal. Chem.* **54** 1006A–18A

Ulm G *et al* 1986 *Z. Phys.* A**325** pp 247–59

Walker R J and Fassett J D 1986 *Anal. Chem.* **58** 2923

Walker R J, Shirey S B and Stecher O 1987 *Earth Planet Sci. Lett.* in press

Wen J, Travis J C, Lucatorto T B, Johnson B C and Clark C W 1987 *Phys. Rev.* A in press

Whitaker T J 1986 *Lasers and Applications* **5**(8) 67

Whitaker T J and Bushaw B A 1981 *Chem. Phys. Lett.* **79** 506

Whitaker T J, Cannon B D, Gerke G K and Bushaw B A 1987 in *Resonance Ionization Spectroscopy 1986* ed G S Hurst and C Grey Morgan (Inst. Phys. Conf. Ser. 84) pp 27–32

Winograd N, Baxter J P and Kimock F M 1982 *Chem. Phys. Lett.* **88** 581

Young J P, Hurst G S, Kramer S D and Payne M G 1979 *Anal. Chem.* **51** 1050A

Young C E, Pellin M J, Calway W F, Jorgensen B, Schweitzer E L and Gruen D M 1987 in *Resonance Ionization Spectroscopy 1986* ed G S Hurst and C Grey Morgan (Inst. Phys. Conf. Ser. 84) pp 163–8

9

Non-linear optics: applications to resonance ionisation spectroscopy

9.1 Introduction

There are several reasons for including material on non-linear optics in a book on resonance ionisation spectroscopy. The first is the frequent need for tunable radiation in the VUV or IR regions of the electromagnetic spectrum for use in laser ionisation schemes. Non-linear processes in gaseous media provide convenient ways to generate both tunable VUV and IR radiation. The second reason for the importance of this material is that it points out a wide variety of processes that become important when laser ionisation is attempted at high gas phase concentrations.

We will not attempt a complete discussion of non-linear optics; in fact, the discussion will concentrate on a few non-linear processes carried out very near resonances in alkali vapours or inert gases. Consequently, there will be no treatment of the effects of symmetry on non-linear susceptibility tensors. For more information on this subject see a book by Levenson (1982), or the classic treatise on non-linear optics by Bloembergen (1965).

Our approach to non-linear optics will begin with an attempt to show clearly how the medium develops a polarisability (i.e. dipole moment per unit volume) at harmonics of the laser frequencies, as well as at sum and difference frequencies. We will also see how the amplitude of these dipoles increases non-linearly with the laser power density, and how they can be increased by making use of resonance enhancements. The demonstration of the existence of polarisabilities at new frequencies is based on the straightforward evaluation of higher order time-dependent perturbation terms due to the coupling between the laser fields and the atoms of the gas. Having established the existence of a source term for the generation of new frequencies, we will demonstrate the dominant roles played by the conditions for constructive interference (i.e. phase matching) and the absorption of the medium. Constructive interference between the dipole fields from different atoms leads to the intensity of the generated light increasing as the square of the number of atoms in the high intensity region of the laser beam. In practice the N^2 factor is exploited by increasing the concentration to the highest value at which the generated output is still increasing as a function of concentration. The optimum concentration is usually determined by the onset of strong absorption. Several examples will be given which illustrate the order of magnitude of the number of photons generated per pulse at new frequencies.

9.2 Introduction to non-linear processes

In Chapters 4 and 5 it was noted than when intense, narrow band width light enters a gas cell, the interaction between individual atoms and the laser field is well represented by the Hamiltonian

$$\hat{\mathcal{H}} = \hat{\mathcal{H}}_0 - \hat{\boldsymbol{D}} \cdot \boldsymbol{E} \tag{9.1}$$

where $\hat{\mathcal{H}}_0$ is the electronic Hamiltonian of the unperturbed atom, $\hat{\boldsymbol{D}} = \Sigma_i e \boldsymbol{r}_i$ is the electronic dipole operator, and $\boldsymbol{E}$ is the laser field described as a classical electromagnetic wave. Situations where this treatment fails include problems such as resonance fluorescence where fluctuations related to spontaneous emission play a dominant role, and situations where high Rydberg states are involved. The high Rydberg states invalidate the multipole expansion involved in arriving at the $-\hat{\boldsymbol{D}} \cdot \boldsymbol{E}$ form of the interaction. Resonance fluorescence is not described properly because classical electromagnetic theory does not account for spontaneous emission. A review of Chapter 4, with special attention being given to equations (4.113) to (4.117), will be useful as preparation for the rest of this chapter.

If the laser is tuned to a wavelength which is well away from any one-, two-, or three-photon resonance and the laser power is less than or equal to $10^{11} \, \text{W cm}^{-2}$, the effects of the laser fields are usually described accurately by time-dependent perturbation theory. We expand the time-dependent state vector of an atom at $\boldsymbol{R}$ in terms of the complete set of eigenvectors of $\hat{\mathcal{H}}_0$:

$$|\Psi(\boldsymbol{R}, t)\rangle = \sum_{\varepsilon_n, \mu} a(\boldsymbol{R}, \varepsilon_n, \mu, t) e^{-i\omega_n t} |\varepsilon_n, \mu\rangle \tag{9.2}$$

where $\hat{\mathcal{H}}_0 |\varepsilon_n, \mu\rangle = \varepsilon_n |\varepsilon_n, \mu\rangle$, and $\varepsilon_n = \hbar\omega_n$. The set of quantum numbers μ may be regarded as angular momentum quantum numbers, and the sum over ε_n is to be interpreted as a sum over the discrete eigen-energies and an integral over the continuous part of the eigen-energy spectrum of $\hat{\mathscr{H}}_0$. The coefficient $a(R, \varepsilon_n, \mu, t)$ is properly interpreted as a probability amplitude for an atom at R being in state $|\varepsilon_n, \mu\rangle$ at time t. We now borrow some results from near the end of Chapter 4:

$$a(R, \varepsilon_n, \mu, t) = \langle \varepsilon_n, \mu | \hat{S} | \varepsilon_0, \mu_0 \rangle \tag{9.3}$$

where $|\varepsilon_0, \mu_0\rangle$ is the atomic ground state and

$$\hat{S} = \hat{1} + \sum_{k=1}^{\infty} \hat{S}_k \tag{9.4a}$$

with

$$\hat{S}_k = (1/i\hbar)^k \int_{-\infty}^{t} dt_1 \ldots \int_{-\infty}^{t_{k-1}} dt_k \hat{V}_I(t_1) \ldots \hat{V}_I(t_k) \tag{9.4b}$$

and

$$\hat{V}_I(t) = \exp(i\hat{\mathscr{H}}_0 t/\hbar)(-\hat{D}\cdot E)\exp(-i\hat{\mathscr{H}}_0 t/\hbar). \tag{9.5}$$

In equations (9.4) the entire solution for $\hat{S}$ is written as a series in $\hat{V}_I$. The result is equivalent to ordinary time-dependent perturbation theory.

In a neutral gas the laser beam induces dipoles oscillating at the laser frequencies and at the odd harmonics of these frequencies. In Chapter 4 it was seen that the polarisability P at the laser frequency leads to a modified phase velocity for the beam. With more than one laser beam overlapping, each having an angular frequency ω_{L1}, ω_{L2} etc, there are dipole oscillations at frequencies such as $2\omega_{L1} - \omega_{L2}$ and $2\omega_{L1} + \omega_{L2}$, as well as other combinations. The sources of the dipoles are the atoms in the medium as they respond to the intense laser fields. A concentration of oscillating dipoles is equivalent to a current density $J = \partial P/\partial t$. With only a current density present, Maxwell's equations can be manipulated to obtain the following wave equation for the E field.

$$\nabla^2 E - (1/c^2)(\partial^2 E/\partial t^2) = (4\pi/c^2)(\partial^2 P/\partial t^2). \tag{9.6}$$

In addition, there is a charge density associated with the polarisability $\rho = -\nabla\cdot P$. However, if the laser beams are parallel, either unfocused or focused with long focal length lenses, then $-\nabla\cdot P$ produces negligible effects since the propagation vector and the E field are orthogonal.

If we could evaluate P without ambiguity for rather general forms of the E field, then the problem of calculating the fields generated in the medium would involve the solution of equation (9.6) and the evaluation of some quantities related to the atomic response. The electric polarisability, i.e. the dipole moment per unit volume, is just the atomic concentration multiplied by the time-dependent expectation value of $\hat{D}$. Thus,

$$P(R, t) = N \langle \Psi(R, t) | \hat{D} | \Psi(R, t) \rangle \tag{9.7}$$

$$= N \sum_{\varepsilon_n, \mu} \sum_{\varepsilon_m, \mu_1} \langle \varepsilon_n, \mu | \hat{D} | \varepsilon_m, \mu_1 \rangle \, a^*(R, \varepsilon_n, \mu, t) a(R, \varepsilon_m, \mu_1, t) e^{-i(\omega_m - \omega_n)t}.$$

Consider first the contributions to P which are linear in $\hat{V}_I$. Within the framework of perturbation theory the population of the atomic ground state remains undepleted, so that $|a(R, \varepsilon_0, \mu_0, t)| \approx 1$, and for all excited states $|a(R, \varepsilon_n, \mu, t)| \ll 1$. As a consequence of equations (9.2)–(9.7) the contribution to $P(R, t)$ which is linear in $\hat{V}_I$ leads to a separate term for each laser beam, and for each coherent eam generated in the medium. For a particular beam at frequency ω

$$P^{(1)}_\omega(R, t) = \varkappa_1(\omega) E_L(R, t) \tag{9.8}$$

where the susceptibility $\varkappa_1(\omega)$ derived in equation (4.55) is

$$\varkappa_1(\omega) = (Ne^2/m) \sum_{\varepsilon_n, \mu} f_{n,\mu;0,\mu_0} / [(\omega_n - \omega_0)^2 - \omega^2] \tag{9.9}$$

where $f_{n,\mu;0, \mu_0}$ is the oscillator strength for the transition from the ground state to the state $|\varepsilon_n, \mu\rangle$. Equation (9.9) is not valid on resonance due to the omission of line width effects and memory effects in the region near resonance. The expression also omits small corrections due to the presence of gas dimers. Nevertheless, equation (9.9) is adequate in accounting for most off-resonance phenomena in atomic gases or vapours. In a gaseous media the next non-zero contribution to $P(R, t)$ is of third-order in $\hat{V}_I$ because of the rotational and inversion symmetries that control selection rules in atomic vapours.

If there are laser beams which coincide in space and time at frequencies ω_{L1} and ω_{L2}, then there will be third-order terms in $P(R, t)$ at frequencies $3\omega_{L1}$, $3\omega_{L2}$, $2\omega_{L1} \pm \omega_{L2}$, and $2\omega_{L2} \pm \omega_{L1}$, as well as terms which are linear in the laser field amplitudes at the same frequencies. The field amplitudes at the sum and difference frequencies have their origin in third-order contributions of $\hat{V}_I$ to $P(R, t)$, and serve as source terms at these frequencies in equation (9.6). Any term at a frequency ω, together with any non-linear source terms at the same frequency, can be considered to obey a separate equation like equation (9.6), which becomes

$$\nabla^2 E_\omega - (1/v^2)(\partial^2 E_\omega / \partial t^2) = (4\pi/c^2)(\partial^2 P^{NL}_\omega / \partial t^2) \tag{9.10}$$

$v^{-2} = c^{-2}[1 + (4\pi \varkappa_1(\omega)/c^2)] = n^2(\omega)/c^2$ where $n(\omega)$ is the index of refraction of the medium at frequency ω. In arriving at equation (9.10) the term at ω which is linear in the corresponding field has been brought to the left-hand side of the equation to give a modified phase velocity for the generated wave. In the case under consideration, the new frequencies generated in the medium are weak, and of third order in the laser field amplitudes or perhaps second order in one field and linear in the other. Consequently they do not appear in $P_\omega^{NL}(R, t)$. However, in fifth-order contributions to P^{NL}, the third-order fields generated coupled with two laser fields, can be just as important (or more so) than terms that are directly fifth order in the laser fields.

In principle the $P_\omega^{NL}(R, t)$ for a particular new frequency generated in the medium can be calculated. It is just a matter of evaluating equation (9.3) by using $\hat{S}_3$, as given by equation (9.4b), and inserting unit operators in the form $\hat{1} = \Sigma_{\varepsilon_n,\,\mu}|\varepsilon_n, \mu\rangle\langle\varepsilon_n, \mu|$ between pairs of $\hat{V}_I$. We also use the fact that $\exp(\pm i\hat{\mathcal{H}}_0 t/\hbar)$ operating on these bras and kets can be evaluated immediately since they are eigenstates of $\hat{\mathcal{H}}_0$. To see how the evaluation works note that

$$\langle\varepsilon_n, \mu|e^{i\hat{\mathcal{H}}_0 t/\hbar} = (e^{-i\hat{\mathcal{H}}_0 t/\hbar}|\varepsilon_n, \mu\rangle)^\dagger$$

and that

$$(e^{-i\hat{\mathcal{H}}_0 t/\hbar}|\varepsilon_n, \mu\rangle)^\dagger = (e^{-i\varepsilon_n t/\hbar}|\varepsilon_n, \mu\rangle)\dagger$$

$$= e^{i\varepsilon_n t/\hbar}\langle\varepsilon_n, \mu|.$$

As a consequence

$$\langle\varepsilon_{n1}, \mu_1|\hat{V}_I(t)|\varepsilon_{n2}, \mu_2\rangle = \langle\varepsilon_{n1}, \mu_1|e^{i\omega_{n1}t}\hat{V}(t)e^{-i\omega_{n2}t}|\varepsilon_{n2}, \mu_2\rangle$$

$$= e^{i(\omega_{n1} - \omega_{n2})t}\langle\varepsilon_{n1}, \mu_1|\hat{V}(t)|\varepsilon_{n2}, \mu_2\rangle. \quad (9.11)$$

From equations (9.3) and (9.4) we have, through looking at third-order terms in $\hat{V}_I(t)$

$$a(R, \varepsilon_n, \mu, t) = \langle\varepsilon_n, \mu|\hat{S}_1 + \hat{S}_2 + \hat{S}_3|\varepsilon_0, \mu_0\rangle. \quad (9.12)$$

We will write out explicitly the $\hat{S}_1$ and $\hat{S}_3$ terms:

$$\hat{S}_1 = (1/i\hbar)\int_{-\infty}^{t} dt_1 \hat{V}_I(t_1)$$

$$\hat{S}_3 = (1/i\hbar)^3 \int_{-\infty}^{t} dt_1 \int_{-\infty}^{t_1} dt_2 \int_{-\infty}^{t_2} dt_3 \hat{V}_I(t_1)\hat{V}_I(t_2)\hat{V}_I(t_3). \quad (9.13)$$

The part of $a(R, \varepsilon_n, \mu, t)$ due to $\hat{S}_1$ is easily evaluated using equation (9.11) and yields a term equivalent to that evaluated in Chapter 4, equation (4.43). The higher order term which arises from $\hat{S}_3$ is much smaller unless the laser wavelengths are such that there is a nearby two- or three-photon resonance. However, it is very important because it gives rise to a part of the polarisability oscillating at frequencies other than that of the laser. After the insertion of unit operators (expressed in terms of the eigen bras and kets of $\hat{\mathcal{H}}_0$ between $\hat{V}_I(t_1)$ and $\hat{V}_I(t_2)$ and $\hat{V}_I(t_2)$ and $\hat{V}_I(t_3)$) the contribution of $\hat{S}_3$ to $a(R, \varepsilon_n, \mu, t)$ becomes

$$\langle\varepsilon_n, \mu|\hat{S}_3|\varepsilon_0, \mu_0\rangle = (-i/\hbar^3)\int_{-\infty}^{t}\int_{-\infty}^{t_1}\int_{-\infty}^{t_2} dt_1 dt_2 dt_3 S(t_1, t_2, t_3) \quad (9.14)$$

$$S(t_1, t_2, t_3) = \sum_{\varepsilon_{n1}, \mu_1} \sum_{\varepsilon_{n2}, \mu_2} V(n, n1, t_1) V(n1, n2, t_2) V(n2, 0, t_3)$$

$$V(ni, nj, t_k) = \langle \varepsilon_{ni}, \mu_i | \hat{V}_I(t_k) | \varepsilon_{nj}, \mu_j \rangle$$

$$= e^{i(\omega_{ni} - \omega_{nj})t_k} \langle \varepsilon_{ni}, \mu_i | \hat{V}(t_k) | \varepsilon_{nj}, \mu_j \rangle.$$

Once the explicit sinusoidal time dependencies of the laser fields are introduced, the resulting time integrals are all of the type

$$\int_{-\infty}^{t_k} d\tau Q(\tau) e^{iv\tau} \approx -iQ(t_k) e^{ivt_k}/v.$$

In evaluating equation (9.12), the fact that $|v| \gg |d[\ln(Q(\tau)]/dt$ is used. In evaluating the time integrals the only rapidly oscillating time dependence which does not come from the laser fields is an $\exp[i(\omega_n - \omega_0)t]$ term, which itself is eliminated in the evaluation of the polarisability in equation (9.7). This is the reason for the earlier statement that the non-linear interaction leads to parts of the polarisability at frequencies which are multiples, or sums and differences, of the laser frequencies. In order to obtain all of the frequency components properly one must include all the coherent fields in the total electric field E in the $-\hat{D} \cdot \hat{E}$ term and pick out all products of the strong laser fields which lead to the frequency under consideration. Inserting the resulting terms into equation (9.7) then leads to a very untidy expression for $P_\omega^{NL}(R, t)$ in terms of a non-linear susceptibility for the atomic species multiplied by a product of three laser fields. The non-linear susceptibility depends only on the concentration of atoms and upon their properties, but involves the sum of several terms that are themselves sums over two sets of intermediate states. These sums involve *resonant denominators* which give enhancements to the susceptibility whenever there is a near coincidence with a one-, two-, or three-photon resonance with the combinations of laser amplitudes involved in generating the frequency in question.

9.3 An example of a non-linear process with an unfocused laser beam: third harmonic generation near three-photon resonances in xenon

Consider the special case of third harmonic generation near a three-photon resonance. This special case is particularly simple because the existence of the three-photon resonance makes two kinds of simplification possible. First, in calculating the third-order contribution to $|\Psi(R, t)\rangle$ there are significant contributions to the amplitude $a(R, \varepsilon_n, \mu, t)$ only from the near three-photon resonance between $|\varepsilon_0, \mu_0\rangle$ and $|\varepsilon_n, \mu\rangle$. Second, in the absence of any near resonance through one- or two-photon processes, contributions to $P_{3\omega_L}$ from the product of the first and second order terms are small compared with the resonant third-order correction multiplied by $a(R, \varepsilon_0, \mu_0, t) \simeq 1$. Following the prescription from the previous section one finds

$$\langle \varepsilon_n, \mu | \hat{S}_3 | \varepsilon_0, \mu_0 \rangle = e^{-i(\delta t - 3k_{\omega_L}x)} \Omega_3 / \delta \qquad (9.15)$$

where

$$\delta = 3\omega_L - (\omega_n - \omega_0) \qquad (9.16)$$

$$\Omega_3 = (E_0(t)/2\hbar)^3 \sum_{\varepsilon_{n1}, \mu_1} \sum_{\varepsilon_{n2}, \mu_2} \left[\frac{D(n, n1)D(n1, n2)D(n2, 0)}{(\omega_{n2} - \omega_0 - \omega_L)(\omega_{n1} - \omega_0 - 2\omega_L)} \right]$$

$$D(ni, nj) = \langle \varepsilon_{ni}, \mu_i | \hat{D}_z | \varepsilon_{nj}, \mu_j \rangle$$

and Ω_3 is one half of the three-photon Rabi frequency. This is exactly what is obtained if Ω_N from equation (4.126) is evaluated. The concept of Rabi frequency was introduced in spin resonance studies to describe the angular frequency with which the population oscillated between the two states. Such oscillations would only occur with three-photon excitation of an isolated atom at extremely high power densities (i.e. greater than or equal to 10^{11} W cm^{-2}) where there are typically AC Stark shifts in the transition which are much larger than the power broadening due to the three-photon pumping. In the case of the off-resonant coupling under consideration here, there will never be any Rabi flopping, but the parameter is still useful in estimating the non-linear response. In equations (9.15) and (9.16) we have assumed plane-polarised light with the direction of propagation being the x axis and the direction of polarisation being the z axis. Specifically, the laser field was taken to be

$$E = e_z E_0[t - (x/v_{\omega_L})] \cos(\omega_L t - k_{\omega_L} x). \qquad (9.17)$$

The quantity in equation (9.15) yields a contribution to equation (9.7) at a frequency $3\omega_L$, which then provides a source term in equation (9.10) at $\omega = 3\omega_L$. The part of $P(R, t)$ at the third harmonic of the laser frequency is

$$P_{3\omega_L}(R, t) = \varkappa_1(3\omega_L)E_{3\omega_L}(R, t) + Ne_z(e^{i(3k_{\omega_L}x - 3\omega_L t)}D(0, n)\Omega_3/\delta + \text{cc}). \qquad (9.18)$$

We have allowed for the fact that there is a source term at the third harmonic so that the total polarisability is due both to the three-photon term and to the third-harmonic field which is nearly one-photon resonant. The first term has already been moved to the left-hand side when equation (9.10) is applied with $\omega = 3\omega_L$. Also, the only source term is in the z direction so that we can reduce equation (9.10) to a one-dimensional scalar equation for the z component:

$$(\partial^2 E_{3\omega_L}/\partial x^2) - [1/v^2(3\omega_L)](\partial^2 E_{3\omega_L}/\partial t^2)$$
$$= (4\pi N/\delta c^2)(\partial^2/\partial t^2)(D(0, n)\Omega_3 e^{3i(k_{\omega_L}x - \omega_L t)} + \text{cc}). \qquad (9.19)$$

Equation (9.19) is of the form

$$(\partial^2 Y/\partial x^2) - (1/v^2)(\partial^2 Y/\partial t^2) = (\partial g/\partial t) \qquad (9.20)$$

which, for no incoming waves, has the formal solution

$$Y(x, t) = -(v/2)\int_0^L dx' g(x', t - |x - x'|/v). \qquad (9.21)$$

Note that

$$k_{3\omega_L} = 3\omega_L/v(3\omega_L).$$

From equation (9.21) we find, with $v_1 \equiv v(3\omega_L)$,

$$E_{3\omega_L} = \left(\frac{6\pi\omega_L v_1 N}{c^2\delta}\right)(e^{-3i\omega_L[t-(x/v_1)]}D(0, n)i\Omega_3\int_0^x dx' e^{3i[k_{\omega_L}-(\omega_L/v_1)]x'} + \mathrm{cc}). \qquad (9.22)$$

In equation (9.22) we have neglected the integral from x to L. Over this region the integrand oscillates with a spatial periodicity of about $1/6$ of the wavelength of the laser light and averages to a value near zero. On the other hand, if one could arrange for $|k_{\omega_L} - (3\omega_L/v_1)|$ to be small, the integral between 0 and x would evaluate to x. This condition is met when the velocity of the *polarisation wave* is equal to the phase velocity of the third harmonic field, corresponding to complete constructive interference between the dipole fields generated by each atomic dipole in the laser beam. More generally

$$E_{3\omega_L} = -\frac{6\pi\omega_L N v_1}{c^2\delta}\left[D(0, n)\Omega_3 e^{3i\omega_L[(x/v_1)-t]}\left(\frac{e^{3i[k_{\omega_L}-(\omega_L/v_1)]x}-1}{k_{3\omega_L}-3k_{\omega_L}}\right) + \mathrm{cc}\right]. \qquad (9.23)$$

Once $E_{3\omega_L}$ is determined, the flux of third harmonic photons is calculated from the Poynting vector and the photon concept to be

$$\mathscr{F}_{3\omega_L} = \frac{c\overline{E}^2_{3\omega_L}}{4\hbar\omega_L\pi} \qquad (9.24)$$

The overbar in equation (9.24) indicates a time average over several oscillations of the laser field is used.

To go further we must introduce new information regarding both the indices of refraction and the order of magnitude of the three-photon Rabi frequency. We begin with some phenomenology concerning the indices of refraction. The index of refraction of a mixture of gases A and B is given by

$$n(\omega) = 1 + N_A F_A(\omega) + N_B F_B(\omega) \qquad (9.25)$$

where $F_A(\omega)$ represents the following sum over states for gas A, and $F_B(\omega)$ is the corresponding sum for gas B:

$$F_A(\omega) = (2\pi e^2/m)\sum_{\varepsilon_n,\mu\in S_A} F_{n,\mu;0,\mu_0}(A)/[(\omega_n(A) - \omega_0(A))^2 - \omega^2]. \qquad (9.26)$$

The sum over S_A represents the eigenvalue spectrum of $\mathcal{H}_0$ for atom A, and the eigen energies of this Hamiltonian are $\hbar\omega_n(A)$. Typically, a few oscillator strengths are known for the stronger and lower lying states of an inert gas. For instance, in the case of Xe there are more than 20 accurately known oscillator strengths. In the case of Ar the number of well known absorption oscillator strengths between the ground state and various excited states is only seven. The sum of the known oscillator strengths between the ground state and excited states is nearly always less than 2.0. However, it is well known from the conventional sum rule that the oscillator strength summed over all transitions starting from the ground state is 54 for Xe, 36 for Kr, and 18 for Ar. The unknown part of the oscillator strength is due partly to transitions to Rydberg states and to the near-threshold photo-ionisation continuum, and to a much greater degree to inner shell excitation and multi-electron excitation resonances which lie at very high photon energies. The unknown part of the oscillator strength plays a very important part in determining $n(\omega) - 1$. As long as the wavelength of interest is longer than the shortest wavelength for which all lower lying states have known oscillator strengths, a major simplification is possible. The contribution to $n(\omega) - 1$ from the unknown parts of the oscillator strength is approximated by just two terms. The first term is represented by an effective oscillator strength and an effective ω_m chosen to lie just above the first ionisation limit, while the second has an effective oscillator strength and an effective ω_m lying near the lowest doubly excited resonances. The magnitudes of the effective oscillator strengths are chosen so as to give accurate indices of refraction at an IR frequency and at the shortest wavelength at which an accurate oscillator strength (not dominated by a resonance) is known. This very simple two-parameter approach provides adequate indices for Xe and Ar at wavelengths longer than 110 nm. A more detailed method has been described by Mahon *et al* (1979). We have tabulated index of refraction data for Xe for $\lambda > 110$ nm. Extensive use was made of the information on the indices of refraction for inert gases for $\lambda > 200$ nm given in a review by Leonard (1974). Inert gas oscillator strengths for Kr and Xe were taken from a paper by Geiger (1977).

Figures 9.1 and 9.2 show $(n(\omega) - 1)/N$ against wavelength for pure Xe. For the pure gas $(n(\omega) - 1)/N$ is equivalent to $F_{Xe}(\omega)$ as defined by equation (9.26). Figure 9.3 shows less-detailed information at longer wavelengths for pure Xe, Kr and Ar. Important features of figures 9.1 and 9.2 are the peaks at the resonant wavelengths. The contribution to equation (9.26) from the nearest resonance dominates in the region near a strong one-photon resonance. On the high-energy side of the resonance, the dominant resonant contribution to $(n(\omega) - 1)/N$ is negative. The term $(n(\omega) - 1)N$ remains negative as the wavelength is shortened

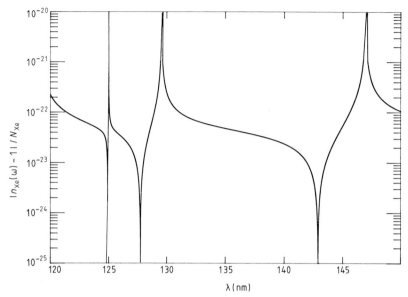

Figure 9.1 Plot of the concentration-independent quantity $|(n_{Xe}(\omega) - 1)|/N_{Xe}$ against the wavelength for the wavelength region between 120 and 150 nm. The deviation of the index of refraction from unity is large near strong dipole-allowed absorption resonances. On the short wavelength side of each resonance there is a region where the phase velocity of the light is greater than the vacuum speed of light, i.e. a region of negative dispersion.

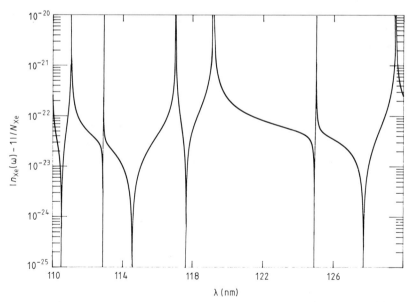

Figure 9.2 Plot of the concentration-independent quantity $|n_{Xe}(\omega) - 1|/N_{Xe}$ against wavelength for the wavelength region 110 to 130 nm.

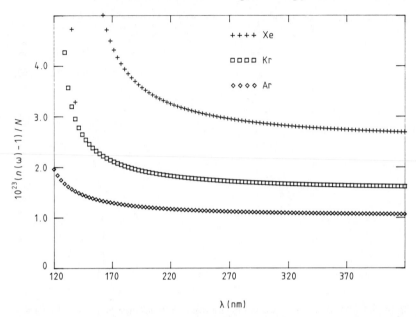

Figure 9.3 Gross features of the indices of refraction of Xe, Kr and Ar between 120 and 420 nm. The Ar data is smooth down to 120 nm, while Xe exhibits rapid variations for wavelengths less than 150 nm. The Kr data is slowly varying above $\lambda = 150$ nm, but it varies rapidly for less than 130 nm.

even further on the high-energy side of the resonance. When the resonance ceases to be dominant the sign changes. The very sharp dips and rises in figures 9.1 and 9.2 occur when the change of sign occurs and are only sharp due to the singular property of the logarithm for arguments near zero. In the region of wavelength between each resonance and the next sharp dip on the high-energy side of the resonance, the medium exhibits a phase velocity greater than the speed of light.

Suppose that the third harmonic frequency is to be generated at a laser wavelength corresponding to a near-three-photon resonance in Xe, and with a gas mixture of Xe and Ar. In equation (9.23) we saw that the generation of the third harmonic field depended on the magnitude of $k_{3\omega_L} - 3k_{\omega_L}$. We can write

$$k_{3\omega_L} = (3\omega_L/c)(1 + N_{Xe}F_{Xe}(3\omega_L) + N_{Ar}F_{Ar}(3\omega_L))$$
$$3k_{\omega_L} = (3\omega_L/c)(1 + N_{Xe}F_{Xe}(\omega_L) + N_{Ar}F_{Ar}(\omega_L)). \tag{9.27}$$

In the region near a strong resonance the difference between $k_{3\omega_L}$ and $3k_{\omega_L}$ is dominated by the resonance term from $F_{Xe}(3\omega_L)$. The contribution from Ar will be small unless we allow for the possibility that the Ar concentration is very much higher than the Xe concentration. We find

$$k_{3\omega_L} - 3k_{\omega_L} = -(\kappa/\delta) + (3\omega_L/c)N_{Ar}(F_{Ar}(3\omega_L) - F_{Ar}(\omega_L)) \tag{9.28}$$

where, by keeping just the resonance term from equation (9.26),

$$\kappa = \pi N_{Xe} f_{\varepsilon_n,\,\mu;\varepsilon_0,\,\mu_0} e^2/m_e c$$

$$= 8.73 \times 10^{14} f_{\varepsilon_n,\,\mu;\varepsilon_0,\,\mu_0} P_{Xe}. \tag{9.29}$$

In evaluating κ it was assumed that the gas was at room temperature and P_{Xe} is the Xe pressure in torr. Note that κ has units of $s^{-1} cm^{-1}$ and δ is defined in equation (9.16).

From figure 9.3 it can be seen that $F_{Ar}(3\omega_L)$ and $F_{Ar}(\omega_L)$ are both positive, and $F_{Ar}(3\omega_L)$ is largest. Further, the difference between these slowly varying quantities is nearly constant over a several nanometre region for third harmonic wavelengths longer than 120 nm. On the high-energy side of a resonance one can choose N_{Ar}/N_{Xe} so that $\Delta k \equiv k_{3\omega_L} - 3k_{\omega_L} = 0$. The required ratio depends on the detuning from the three-photon resonance. If δ corresponds to the region near the three-photon resonance the required ratio will generally be quite large. As an example, use figures 9.3 and 9.4 to determine $F_{Ar}(3\omega_L) - F_{Ar}(\omega_L)$ in the region near the $5p^5 6s(J = 1)$ resonance of Xe. The VUV resonance transition is at $\lambda = 146.96$ nm and it has an absorption oscillator strength of 0.276. The quantity κ is found from

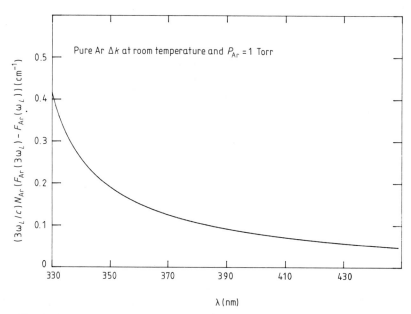

Figure 9.4 Plot of the quantity $(3\omega_L/c)N_{Ar}(F_{Ar}(3\omega_L) - F_{Ar}(\omega_L))$ against wavelength ($\omega_L/c \equiv 2\pi/\lambda$) for room temperature and an Ar pressure of 1 Torr. If the part of the phase mismatch in equation (9.28) which depends on the Ar concentration is written at room temperature as CP_{Ar}, with the Ar pressure in torr, then C can be read directly from this graph.

equation (9.29) to be $\kappa \simeq 2.41 \times 10^{14} P_{Xe}\ \text{s}^{-1}\,\text{cm}^{-1}$, while the part of the phase mismatch (i.e. Δk) due to Ar can be read directly from figure 9.4 to be $0.051 P_{Ar}$. Consequently, we see by using these values in equation (9.28) that if $\Delta \lambda$ is the detuning of the laser from exact three-photon resonance at which $k_{3\omega_L} - 3k_{\omega_L} = 0$, then $\Delta \lambda \simeq -160(P_{Xe}/P_{Ar})$. Here, as in the next example, $\Delta \lambda$ is in nanometres and the contribution to Δk due to the buffer gas is in cm^{-1}; P_{Ar} and P_{Xe} are in torr. As another example, consider the $5p^5 5d(J = 1)$ resonance at 119.2 nm. The oscillator strength of this transition is 0.395, so that $\kappa \simeq 3.45 \times 10^{14} P_{Xe}$. At this wavelength the part of Δk due to Ar is $0.159 P_{Ar}$. Determining the δ at which $\Delta k = 0$, we find the required detuning of the dye laser from exact three-photon resonance to be $\Delta \lambda \simeq -50(P_{Xe}/P_{Ar})$.

Before actually discussing the amount of vuv which can be generated under given circumstances we need to cover two other important effects which play dominant roles in third harmonic generation. As seen above in the region to the high-energy side of a resonance, the contribution to Δk due to the Xe is negative. However, by adding a much larger amount of Ar, Δk can be made to be zero. It follows that when unfocused laser beams are used, a gas mixture is required for purposes of achieving constructive interference. One of the components must be present in high concentrations. In the situation where constructive interference (or *phase matching*) is achieved the third harmonic field intensity will be proportional to the square of the concentration of the negatively dispersive gas for concentrations where the absorption of the medium is negligible. In the Xe–Ar example it is desirable to increase the Xe pressure as much as possible, while keeping the ratio of concentrations fixed so as to preserve phase matching at the desired third harmonic frequency. With narrow band width laser light the optimum third harmonic production occurs at a concentration determined by the trade-off between the N^2 increase in signal and the decrease due to absorption of the medium. Once the mean free path of the third harmonic photons becomes as short as twice the cell length, further increases in concentration will soon start to cause a decrease in the generated vuv light. The effect is fairly sudden due to the fact that absorption causes exponential effects on photon propagation distances. The absorption coefficient of the medium, α, depends on the concentration as follows

$$\alpha = \alpha_s + \alpha_P + \alpha_M. \tag{9.30}$$

The term α_s is due to near-resonant scattering and it is only important quite near the resonance. This elastic scattering part, which in the case of many Xe resonances is dominant, is

$$\alpha_s = \kappa \gamma_{n,0}/\delta^2$$

where $\gamma_{n,0}$ is the spontaneous decay rate between the excited state and the ground state. The term α_P is a part of the absorption coefficient due to resonance pressure broadening of the transition. In the region relatively near the resonance it can be written as (Ferrell *et al* 1987)

$$\alpha_P = (6/\pi)(\kappa^2\lambda_{3\omega_L}/\delta^2) \qquad (9.31)$$

where $\lambda_{3\omega_L}$ is the vacuum third harmonic wavelength, and κ is still defined by equation (9.29). Another contribution to α_p proportional to N_{Xe}^2 is due to absorption by bound Xe_2 dimers. Except for the concentration dependence, the latter correction has no simple, universal dependence on laser frequency. Equation (9.31) will typically yield the dominant absorption very near the resonance at high concentrations. Some distorted form of equation (9.31), which is appropriate to the very far wing of the pressure-broadened line, is responsible for the fact that vuv generation is nearly always more efficient further from the three-photon resonance, i.e. beyond the first several hundred wavenumbers of a three-photon resonance. The third contribution, α_M, represents absorption due to Xe–Ar mixed dimers and is proportional to $N_{Xe}N_{Ar}$ (Castex 1977). The electronic excited states resulting from the excitation of the mixed dimers are unbound and this component of the absorption results in the following process

$$XeAr + \hbar(3\omega_L) \rightarrow Ar + Xe^*$$

where Xe^* represents a xenon atom in the nearby resonant excited state. Consequently, one of the more efficient laser ionisation processes occurs when third harmonic photons are absorbed by dimers, and the resulting excited states are ionised later by laser photons. Such a process ordinarily totally dominates direct multiphoton ionisation on the high-energy side of three-photon resonances. The easiest way to demonstrate this ionisation effect is to study a three-photon resonance which requires five photons for photo-ionisation. In this case the addition of a weak dye laser beam tuned to resonance between the nearby resonance and a higher excited state which can be ionised by one photon is found to greatly increase the ionisation signal. The absorption of mixed dimers in various mixtures of inert gases has been studied by Castex (1977) and others (see, for instance, Ferrell *et al* (1987), and Payne *et al* (1983)). The importance of absorption effects in third harmonic generation makes it imperative that the index of refraction be considered a complex quantity. Thus, we write

$$\Delta k = k_{3\omega_L} - 3k_{\omega_L} + (i\alpha/2) \qquad (9.32)$$

where we have included only the real part of the index of refraction in $k_{3\omega_L}$, with the imaginary part giving rise to the absorption coefficient.

The other important factor in third harmonic generation is the non-linear coupling. One sees from equation (9.23) that it is measured by the ratio $|\Omega_3/\delta|$. The coupling parameter is largest near the resonance, where absorption is extremely high. The power dependence of the third harmonic field enters through Ω_3 which is

$$|\Omega_3| = cI^{3/2} \tag{9.33}$$

where I is the laser power density in $W\,cm^{-2}$ and $|\Omega_3|$ is in units of s^{-1}. For several three-photon transitions, c lies between 10^{-8} and 10^{-6} for the units described above. When $I \simeq 10^8\,W\,cm^{-2}$, $|\Omega_3| \simeq 10^5\,s^{-1}$.

Most of the physical effects have now been discussed and we can evaluate the flux of third harmonic photons:

$$\mathcal{F}_{3\omega_L} = (\kappa N_{Xe}/4)|\Omega_3/\delta|^2\{(1 + e^{-\alpha x} - 2e^{-\alpha x/2}\cos\Delta kx)/[\Delta k^2 + (\alpha/2)^2]\}. \tag{9.34}$$

A numerical example should help readers to understand. Consider the three-photon resonance in Xe at 146.96 nm. Suppose that the laser has a power density of $10^8\,W\,cm^{-2}$ and that the dye laser is tuned about 1.2 nm to the blue of the resonance. In this case $\delta \simeq 5 \times 10^{13}\,s^{-1}$ and $\Omega_3 \simeq 10^5\,s^{-1}$, thus $|\Omega_3/\delta|^2 \simeq 10^{-18}$. Ferrell *et al* (1987) have found the absorption coefficient at this third harmonic frequency to be $\alpha \simeq 2.6 \times 10^{-4}P_{Xe}P_{Ar}$. For 5 Torr of Xe we need about 650 Torr of Ar to phase match at this wavelength. With a cell of length 10 cm the exponential factors will be small and $\Delta k = 0$. Notice that for Xe and Ar pressures a factor of two higher, α increases by a factor of two and the vuv generated decreases by a factor of four. The decrease is due to the photon mean free path decreasing faster than $1/N_{Xe}$ so that the number of atoms that can constructively interfere starts to decrease with increasing concentration once the mean free path becomes shorter than the cell length. With $P_{Xe} = 5$ Torr and $P_{Ar} = 650$ Torr we find $\mathcal{F}_{3\omega_L} \simeq 5 \times 10^{14}\,s^{-1}$. With a 1 mm beam and a pulse length of 10 ns, about 50 000 photons are generated. This estimate is only accurate to an order of magnitude, but it tells us that the vuv generated is not nearly enough to be interesting for use in RIS. The vuv generation can be increased greatly by either focusing the laser beam to increase the power density by three orders of magnitude, or by using two colours—with one colour being tuned near a two-photon resonance. In the latter instance light is generated at $2\omega_{L1} \pm \omega_{L2}$. With this method the non-linear coupling at a particular power density can be increased by more than three orders of magnitude relative to the coupling in the absence of the two-photon resonance. We will see in later sections that either of these methods can yield vuv light intensities which are useful for RIS.

Before leaving the present topic we will discuss an interesting effect on the ionisation as the three-photon resonance is approached. We assume that the pressure is high enough so that before δ is decreased to within a Doppler width of the resonance, Δk becomes very large and $\exp(-\alpha L)$ (L is the cell length) becomes very small. Under this circumstance $E_{3\omega_L}$ starts to propagate at a phase velocity equal to that of the laser. In particular

$$k_{3\omega_L} - 3k_{\omega_L} \rightarrow -\kappa/\delta$$

$$E_{3\omega_L} \rightarrow [2\pi(3\omega_L)N/c\kappa][D(0, n)\Omega_3 e^{3i(-\omega_L t + k_{\omega_L} x)} + \text{CC}]. \quad (9.35)$$

The three-photon resonance is being pumped resonantly by the three-photon process as well as by the third harmonic field. The amplitude for the near-resonant excited state can be written as

$$a(\boldsymbol{R}, \varepsilon_n, \mu, t) = \langle \varepsilon_n, \mu | \hat{S}_1 + \hat{S}_3 | \varepsilon_0, \mu_0 \rangle \quad (9.36)$$

where the $\hat{S}_1$ is the first-order perturbation theory term for the interaction of the third harmonic field with the atom and $\hat{S}_3$ is the third-order interaction with the laser field. We find

$$a(\boldsymbol{R}, \varepsilon_n, \mu, t) = (e^{-i(\delta t - 3k_{\omega_L} x)})[\Omega_3 - (D(n, 0)eE^0_{3\omega_L}/\hbar)]\delta^{-1}$$

$$= 0$$

where $E^0_{3\omega_L}$ is the amplitude of the $e^{-3i\omega_L t}$ part of the third harmonic field in the limit of equation (9.35), and we have made use of the fact that the spatial dependence of each of the coherent coupling terms is $\exp(3ik_{\omega_L} x)$. We have also made use of the rotating wave approximation and an alternative expression for κ in which $\kappa = [2\pi(3\omega_L)|D(0, n)|^2 N_{\text{Xe}}]/(\hbar c)$. On approaching the resonance the two pumping terms become equal in magnitude, but they are 180° out of phase at all points in space. Consequently, due to destructive interference, the two coherent coupling terms yield a value of zero for the total amplitude of the state. The implication is that as one approaches resonance the enhancement to multiphoton ionisation due to the resonance cancels. This is also what is found experimentally (Miller *et al* (1980); see also Payne *et al* (1980), Payne and Garrett (1982), Payne *et al* (1983), Ferrell *et al* (1987)). We will not go further here, but it turns out that in the inert gases all odd non-linear resonances exhibit this cancellation, but when the laser beams are reflected back on themselves, so that there are photons propagating in both directions, a sizeable proportion of the resonant enhancement returns. The above effect on laser ionisation is but one of the striking effects that can affect laser ionisation once concentrations become as high as 10^{12} cm^{-3}.

We have seen above that as the resonance is approached the phase mismatch becomes huge and the medium becomes strongly absorbing, so that the resulting third harmonic field exhibits no enhancement due to constructive interference. The third harmonic field can be as much as several thousand times smaller near the resonance than it is near a detuning where phase matching occurs. It is the interaction of the atoms with this greatly reduced third harmonic field that produces a coupling which is exactly large enough to cancel the three-photon pumping of the resonance. It follows that in a region of phase matching the multiphoton ionisation due to the absorption of a third harmonic photon plus other

ionisation than multiphoton ionisation due to laser photons. This enhancement is easily seen experimentally (Payne *et al* 1983, Ferrell *et al* 1987). The dominance of the role of the third harmonic field persists with focused beams, but the enhancement is not nearly so large due to the reduced number of atoms which contructively interfere.

Jackson *et al* (1983) first observed that three-photon resonances were easily observed when the laser beam is reflected back on itself, so that there are photons propagating in both directions in the medium. The reappearance of the three-photon resonance in the presence of counter-propagating beams was explained independently by Jackson *et al* (1983) and by Payne and Garrett (1983). In the counter-propagating beam situation coherent cancellation still occurs between the third harmonic beams (propagating in both directions now) and the corresponding three-photon pumping involving the simultaneous absorption of three photons propagating in the same direction. However, in the presence of counter-propagating beams there can also be absorption processes in which the two photons propagating in one direction and one propagating in the other direction are absorbed. The latter pumping process has no corresponding third harmonic field to interfere with it, and an excited state population is produced.

9.4 Third harmonic generation with focused laser beams

Third harmonic generation (THG) in gases is an old subject (see, for example, New and Ward (1967), Ward and New (1969), Hsu *et al* (1976), Cotter (1979) and Bjorklund (1975). Almost all of the earlier work on THG was carried out with focused laser beams. The Bjorklund (1975) reference will be particularly useful if the reader wants to study some of the results which we will derive here from another point of view.

When an initially unfocused laser beam is focused with a lens having a focal length F, the focal spot has a diameter approximately equal to $F\Delta\theta$. The quantity $\Delta\theta$ is the full angle beam divergence. The lower limit on the magnitude of $\Delta\theta$ is set by diffraction effects due to the finite diameter of the unfocused beam, d_0. For a Gaussian radial intensity profile beam with its beam divergence determined by diffraction, the beam divergence is $\Delta\theta = \lambda/\pi d_0$. Actually, the value of d_0 used above is related to the diameter of a Gaussian beam at which the intensity drops to $1/2$ the peak value by $d_{1/2} = (2\ln 2)^{1/2}d_0 \simeq 1.2d_0$. To see that this beam divergence is of the right order of magnitude we apply the relation $\Delta P_z \Delta z \geqslant \hbar$ to the problem. The uncertainty in the radial position is of the order of the beam diameter, and the uncertainty in z momentum for the nearly parallel beam is $P_x\Delta\theta = \hbar\omega_L\Delta\theta/c$. Solving for $\Delta\theta$ we find that $\Delta\theta \geqslant \lambda/2\pi d_0$.

Most commercial dye lasers have beam divergences which are considerably larger than the diffraction limit as a consequence of imperfections in the optics and of off-diagonal modes. Even though the peak power density with such imperfect beams cannot be estimated while assuming a diffraction-limited beam, there are still aspects of the effects of phase matching with focused beams which are easiest to interpret by supposing the beam to be made up of several independent diffraction-limited modes, each propagating in a slightly different direction. The different directions of propagation account for the beam divergence. The effective diameter of the beam is estimated to be the diameter of sharpest structure in the high power density region of the beam. Having a very good laser is the best way to obtain predictable results, but in the absence of an ideal beam the use of the effective beam diameter frequently leads to approximate predictability. We will now discuss third harmonic generation with focused, diffraction-limited beam divergence, Gaussian laser beams.

Most of the features of a focused laser beam can be understood from Huygens' principle (which itself follows from the scalar wave equation). According to the elementary form of Huygens' principle, if the wave is known at all points on a surface of constant phase, then the wave at other points in space can be calculated as being due to a superposition of spherical waves emanating from each surface element on the wavefront and having amplitudes proportional to the wave amplitude at the surface element. We will use Huygens' principle to construct a function that is a solution to the wave equation and which has the characteristics of a focused E field with a Gaussian radial intensity profile.

We begin by investigating the field due to a wave which has a planar wavefront corresponding to $x = 0$, with the wave amplitude decreasing as $\exp[-(z^2 + y^2)/d^2]$ off the axis. Let $\rho = (z^2 + y^2)^{1/2}$, then according to Huygens' principle the field at a field point corresponding to $x_p > 0$ is the sum over the wavefront at $x = 0$ of the field due to spherical wave sources located at each point on the wavefront, with the spherical wave having amplitudes proportional to the field amplitude at the point on the wavefront. Thus,

$$E(x_p, y_p, z_p, t)$$
$$= \mathrm{Re} \int_0^{2\pi} \int_0^\infty d\theta d\rho K \exp{(-\rho^2/d^2)} \{\exp{[i(k|r_p - r| - \omega t)]}\}/|r_p - r|.$$

(9.37)

In equation (9.37) (x_p, y_p, z_p) is a field point, where x_p is measured from the source plane at $x = 0$. The vector $r = e_y y + e_z z$ extends from the origin at $x = 0$, $y = 0$, $z = 0$ to a source point. The distance between source and field points is

$$|r_p - r| = [x_p^2 + \rho^2 + \rho_p^2 - 2\rho\rho_p \cos{(\theta_p - \theta)}]^{1/2}.$$

(9.38)

Note the use of cylindrical coordinates with z and x interchanged because of the convention used here for the direction of propagation and of the plane of polarisation. The coordinate set $(\rho, \theta, 0)$ is a point in the source plane at $x = 0$, while (ρ_p, θ_p, x_p) are the cylindrical coordinates of a field point with $y_p = \rho_p \cos{\theta_p}$ and $z_p = \rho_p \sin{\theta_p}$. We will eventually identify x_p as the distance from the focal point of a focused laser beam which originally had a diffraction-limited beam divergence. To evaluate equation (9.37) we use the fact that $[\exp{(ik|r_p - r|)}]/|r_p - r|$ satisfies $\nabla^2\phi + k^2\phi = 0$ and solve the latter equation subject to the existence of a pole at $r_p = r$ by the technique of separation of variables in cylindrical coordinates. This expansion of the Greens function yields a Fourier series expansion in the azimuthal angle which permits the θ integral to be carried out immediately. The ρ integral then involves the integral of the Gaussian and the zero-order Bessel function. Many of the details concerning the evaluation of integrals of this type can be found in a paper by Payne and Garrett (1983). Using the approximation that $kd \gg 1$ and for $x_p > 0$,

$$E(x_p, y_p, z_p, t) = \mathrm{Re}(\{k \exp{i(kx_p - \omega t)}/[1 + (2ix_p/kd^2)]\}$$
$$\times \exp{\{-(\rho_p^2/d^2)/[1 + (2ix_p/kd^2)]\}}.$$

(9.38)

The proper interpretation of k is as the amplitude of the field on the axis and in the plane $x = 0$. Note that we also have a solution to the wave equation for $x_p < 0$ if we extrapolate equation (9.38) analytically into that region of space.

An interesting aspect of this field is the fact that the beam increases in radius as $x_p > 0$ increases. In fact, the radial intensity of the predicted E field is a wave propagating to the right, with the radial intensity profile that is Gaussian. The e-fold diameter of the beam increases with x_p having a value ρ_0 given by

$$\rho_0(x_p) = d[1 + (2x_p/b)^2]^{1/2}$$

(9.39)

$$b = kd^2.$$

The quantity b is called the confocal parameter. It is a measure of how much x_p must be increased to cause an appreciable increase in the beam diameter. As the beam diameter increases with x_p, the intensity on the axis decreases as

$$I(\rho = 0, x_p) = I(\rho = 0, 0)/[1 + (2x_p/b)^2]. \qquad (9.40)$$

This corresponds with a decrease in intensity with increasing $|x_p|$ on the axis as required to be consistent with the increase with the beam diameter. What we have is a solution to the wave equation which corresponds to a beam moving in the x direction with wavefront curvature causing the beam radius to decrease starting at $x_p \ll 0$ and moving towards the right. At $x_p = 0$ the beam radius is a minimum and the wavefront is a plane. For $x_p > 0$ the curvature of the wavefront develops again, but with the centre of curvature in the opposite direction. Equation (9.38) is a solution to the wave equation which represents a wave propagating along the positive x axis with the amplitude being small for large negative x_p and increasing to a maximum at $x_p = 0$ before starting to decrease again. At the same time that the amplitude increases, the radial extent of the wave is decreasing before becoming a minimum at $x_p = 0$. We have used Huygens' solution to construct a solution to the wave equation which has all of the characteristics of a focused Gaussian beam with focal point at $x_p = 0$. One of the most important features associated with the diffraction-controlled focusing of a laser beam is the phase slip of π as the beam passes through the focal point. The origin of this phase change is the complex factor

$$1/[1 + (2ix_p/b)] \equiv \{1/[1 + (2x_p/b)^2]^{1/2}\} \exp[-i \arctan(2x_p/b)].$$

When x_p is much greater than b we obtain $\rho_0 \simeq 2dx_p/b$. If x_p corresponds to the focal length F of a lens, then ρ_0 corresponds to the e-fold distance for the unfocused beam d_0. The relation between the focused size of the beam, the focal length and the unfocused size is given by solving $d_0 = 2dF/b$ for d. Using $b = kd^2$ we find

$$d = 2F/kd_0 = F\lambda/\pi d_0 \qquad (9.41)$$

which agrees with the beam divergence, $\Delta\theta = \lambda/\pi d_0$. As the beam diameter decreases in approaching the focal point, the power density increases accordingly.

Above, Huygens' principle was used to construct a paraxial approximation solution to the wave equation which corresponds to a beam being focused by a lens. In the same paraxial approximation we can neglect the charge density $\rho = -\nabla \cdot P_{3\omega_L}$ and find the third harmonic field for a focused beam by solving equation (9.10) with $\omega = 3\omega_L$ and a non-linear polarisability given by the non-linear part of equation (9.18). Of course, Ω_3 must be expressed in terms of a focused laser beam instead of an unfocused one. The resulting equation can be solved directly by Fourier transform techniques, with approximations being made in the position part of the transform which allow for the paraxial approximation. The equation can also be solved by noting that equation (9.10) is exactly like the equation for the vector potential, but with a current density replaced by the second partial of the non-linear polarisability divided by c. Almost any electricity and magnetism book (see Jackson (1962)) shows how Fourier transform techniques enable one to write the vector potential as a space integral of the current density evaluated at a retarded time. By analogy

$$E_{3\omega_L} = \int_V (d^3r'/|\mathbf{r} - \mathbf{r}'|)(-1/v_1^2)(\partial^2/\partial t^2)P_{3\omega_L}^{NL}[\mathbf{r}', t - (|\mathbf{r} - \mathbf{r}'|/v_1)] \quad (9.42)$$

where we need only combine the functional form of the focused field with the polarisability in equation (9.18) and carry out the volume integral. This approach has some appeal because the same machinery can be utilised which was used in evaluating the integral in equation (9.37). This same functional form for the integrand arises because of the retarded time factors. Readers who are interested in working through the details of evaluating the integral in equation (9.42) are referred to a paper by Payne and Garrett (1983). The details in the latter paper will also make evident the evaluation of the integral in equation (9.37). If the distance to the windows of the cell is many times larger than the confocal parameter, we find for the number of third harmonic photons generated

$$N_{3\omega_L} = (N_{Xe}d^2b^2\pi^3\kappa/6\delta^2)|\Delta kb|^2 e^{\Delta kb}\int_{-\infty}^{\infty} dt|\Omega_3^{(0)}(t)|^2 \qquad \text{for } \Delta k < 0$$

$$= 0 \qquad \text{for } \Delta k > 0 \qquad\qquad (9.43)$$

where we have neglected absorption and $\Delta k = k_{3\omega_L} - 3k_{\omega_L}$. The quantity $\Omega_3^{(0)}(t)$ is the three-photon coupling parameter at the focal point of the focused Gaussian beam. Typically, with focused beams a focal length is chosen which makes the power density at the focal point close to the level at which laser-induced breakdown occurs. Notice that the optimum value of Δkb is -2, but that any value of Δkb between -4.0 and -0.5 gives appreciable THG. This is in sharp contrast to the unfocused beam case where THG only occurs within a very narrow wavelength region about $\Delta k = 0$. With focused beams third harmonic light can only be generated on the blue side of a three-photon resonance where Δk can be negative. In such a region of wavelength THG can occur at a chosen wavelength even without using a gas mixture. However, the use of a buffer gas can frequently improve the output by making possible the achievement of $\Delta kb = -2$ for a given wavelength, while using a high concentration of the gas that contributes most of the non-linear polarisability (the active gas). As with unfocused beams, there is an optimum total pressure determined by the onset of absorption. The effect of absorption is even more serious with focused beams due to the fact that the third harmonic light is mostly generated in the focal region. The focal region cannot be too close to an exit window because of the possibility of window damage. With most of the generation occurring in the high-intensity region, the attenuation of the intensity is exponential with distance from the focal point to the output window.

Very little work has been done on THG with diffraction-limited beam divergence lasers. In practice, much of the work has been done with commercial dye lasers having a beam divergence from three to five times larger than the diffraction limit. Even with these lasers it is possible to push the power densities into the range of 10^{11} W cm^{-2}, so that at pressures of several torr the threshold for laser breakdown is of concern. With lasers of this non-ideal variety several workers have reported the generation of 10^{10} to 10^{11} photons per pulse. The observed third harmonic output is within an order of magnitude of the output estimated from equation (9.43) when corrections are made for the reduced power density that results due to having a beam divergence much larger than the diffraction limit. This quantity of VUV photons has been shown in Chapter 5 to be of interest to RIS. If two laser beams of the same radius and direction of propagation are merged and focused with the same confocal parameter, equation (9.43) still applies for the case where the absorption of two photons from one laser and one photon from the second laser is near three-photon resonance. In this situation Ω_3 is proportional to the power density at the focal point of the first laser and to the square root of the corresponding power density for the second laser. The definitions for δ and Δk must also be modified to

$$\delta = 2\omega_{L1} + \omega_{L2} - \omega_n + \omega_0$$

$$\Delta k = k(2\omega_{L1} + \omega_{L2}) - 2k(\omega_{L1}) - k(\omega_{L2}).$$

This process is sometimes referred to as four-wave sum mixing. A very convenient form of this process which uses a single dye laser will be described later.

In this section we have seen how the VUV output can be substantial by making the power density just below the threshold for laser breakdown. We will see in the next section that the output can also be increased greatly by using two dye lasers so that the process can make use of a large resonant enhancement due to having a near three-photon resonance and a two-photon resonance. With both a two- and three-photon near-resonance, Ω_3 can be increased as much as four orders of magnitude at a given power density relative to its value without a two-photon resonance. In the next section we will describe a sum-mixing process with unfocused beams which can sometimes permit the generation of 10^{11} to 10^{12} photons per pulse.

9.5 Sum-mixing with unfocused laser beams

To have a better physical picture of four-wave sum mixing near two- and three-photon resonances consider two unfocused, concentric, plane-polarised (with the same plane of polarisation) laser beams of beam diameter d_0 entering a gas cell of length l. If $(l\lambda)/(\pi d_0^2) \ll 1$, where λ is the wavelength of either beam, then diffraction effects are unimportant during passage through the cell. One can consider the effects of the laser beams on the atoms to be that of plane waves propagating in the x direction. Suppose also that the laser at angular frequency ω_{L1} is tuned on, or very near, a dipole-allowed, two-photon resonance between the ground state $|0\rangle$ and an excited state $|1\rangle$, and that $2\omega_{L1} + \omega_{L2}$ is close to three-photon resonance with state $|2\rangle$. An example of the situation described is shown in figure 9.5 for the special case where the desired vuv light is at 116.48 nm and the active gas for the four-wave sum mixing is Xe.

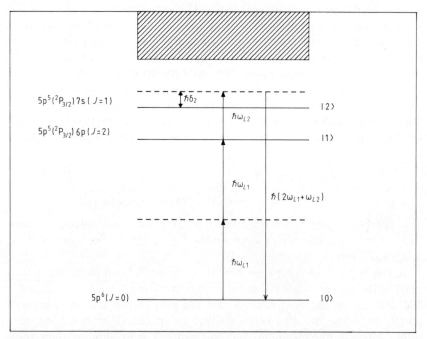

Figure 9.5 Energy level diagram for Xe showing the two-photon and near three-photon resonances used to enhance the non-linear polarisability at $2\omega_{L1} + \omega_{L2}$. These levels were used in Xe in order to generate light at 116.48 nm for use in carrying out the RIS of Kr (Hurst *et al* 1985).

Assuming that the laser at ω_{L1} is too weak to produce saturation effects in the two-photon resonance, one can show that the amplitude for being in $|2\rangle$ because of three-photon absorption is

$$a(R, 2, t) = [\Omega_2(0 \to 1)/\Gamma_1][\Omega_1(1 \to 2)/\delta_2] \exp i[\delta_2 t - (2k_{\omega_{L1}} + k_{\omega_{L2}})x] \quad (9.44)$$

where $\Omega_2(0 \to 1)$ is the Rabi frequency for the $|0\rangle \rightleftharpoons |1\rangle$ transition, $\Omega_1(1 \to 2)$ is the Rabi frequency for the $|1\rangle \rightleftharpoons |2\rangle$ transition, $\delta_2 = 2\omega_{L1} + \omega_{L2} - \omega_2 + \omega_0$, and Γ_1 is an effective level width for the two-photon transition. The laser at ω_{L1} is assumed to be detuned from resonance by just enough so that the VUV signal has started to drop due to a decrease in non-linear susceptibility. The drop coincides with the detuning becoming larger than the effective level width. For a broad band laser the parameter Γ_1 would correspond to about half of the laser line width, while for a narrow band width laser and high pressures it corresponds to either the pressure-broadened width or a width induced by an AC Stark shift for the two-photon transition. Comparing equation (9.44) with equation (9.15), we see that the two expressions are nearly equivalent expressions for the part of the excited state amplitude due to three-photon pumping. The major difference is that in equation (9.44) two colours have been used in order to enhance Ω_3 due to a near two-photon resonance, which reduces this quantity to a product of a two-photon Rabi frequency times a one-photon Rabi frequency divided by a detuning from two-photon resonance. There is also a part of the amplitude due to the field at $2\omega_{L1} + \omega_{L2}$ which contributes the dominant resonant term to the index of refraction. When there is a small detuning from the two-photon resonance and the lasers are tuned to very small δ_2 the total amplitude approaches zero so that ionisation due to the three-photon resonance is cancelled in the absence of a counter-propagating laser beam at one of the two laser frequencies. We will not supply the details of the latter effect since it is analogous to the treatment of third harmonic generation near a three-photon resonance given in §9.3. In the region near, or on, the two-photon resonance one will inadvertently generate amplified spontaneous emission and stimulated Raman beams in the near IR region of the spectrum, Whether the latter beams can limit the conversion efficiency will be discussed in a later section.

As pointed out earlier, the simplicity of equation (9.44) is due to the detuning from two- and three-photon resonances being so small that a dominant resonance reduces two of the three sums over intermediate states to single terms. We can use equation (9.44) to obtain the non-linear polarisability

$$P_{2\omega_{L1} + \omega_{L2}}(x, t) = e_1 N |D_{20}| [\Omega_2(0 \to 1)/\Gamma_1][\Omega_1(1 \to 2)/\delta_2] e^{i\phi(x, t)} + \text{cc} \quad (9.45)$$

where $\phi(x, t) = (2\omega_{L1} + \omega_{L2})t - (2k(\omega_{L1}) + k(\omega_{L2}))x + \phi_0(t)$. Above, e_1 is a unit vector parallel to the electric vector of the laser beams. Notice that if the two laser beams were circularly polarised in the same sense they could only drive $\Delta M_J = 3$ transitions with three-photon processes, and that for such transitions D_{02} is zero. With the latter state of polarisation there can be no non-linear generation.

Using the plane wave feature of the laser beams, equation (9.10) becomes independent of the y and z coordinates and can be solved:

$$E_{\text{vuv}}(x, t) = - (2\pi v/c^2)\int_0^x \mathrm{d}x_1 \partial P_{2\omega_{L1} + \omega_{L2}}[x_1, t - (|x - x_1|/v)]\partial t$$

(9.46)

where $v = (2\omega_{L1} + \omega_{L2})/k(2\omega_{L1} + \omega_{L2})$.

If we use equation (9.45) in equation (9.46), the resulting integral is elementary and we find for the flux of vuv photons,

$$\mathcal{F}_{\omega_s} = \kappa N \left|\frac{\Omega_2(0 \to 1)\Omega_1(1 \to 2)}{\Gamma_1\delta_2}\right|^2 \left(\frac{1 - 2e^{-\alpha x/2}\cos(\Delta kx) + e^{-\alpha x}}{\Delta k^2 + (\alpha/2)^2}\right)$$

(9.47)

where $\omega_s = 2\omega_{L1} + \omega_{L2}$, $\kappa = (2\pi\omega_s N|D_{02}|^2/\hbar c$, $\Delta k = k(\omega_s) - 2k(\omega_{L1}) - k(\omega_{L2})$, and the absorption of the medium has been introduced through α. The extreme similarity between equation (9.47) and equation (9.34) should be noted. In these two cases we have solved what is nearly the same problem, except for the much larger three-photon Rabi frequency which occurs here. If the laser fields are Gaussian and drop to $1/e$ at a distance d_0 from beam centre, we find for the total number of photons generated with $\Delta k = 0$ that

$$N_{\omega_s} = (\pi d_0^2 \kappa N \tau/3)|\Omega_2\Omega_1/\delta_2\Gamma_1|^2(1 - e^{-\alpha x/2})^2/(\alpha/2)^2.$$

It is very clear from the expression for the vuv photon flux that a peak occurs when $\Delta k = 0$. With unfocused laser beams the condition $\Delta k = 0$ makes the phase velocity of the generated wave just equal to the effective phase velocity of the non-linear polarisability. This is the condition for constructive interference; and indeed we see that with $\Delta k = 0$ the photon flux depends on the atomic concentration as the function N^2. In order to achieve $\Delta k = 0$ at a chosen wavelength a gas mixture is ordinarily used, with the 'active' gas being chosen so that it is negatively dispersive (i.e. $\delta_2 > 0$) and a 'buffer' gas is added which is positively dispersive. In the latter circumstance, if the ratio of concentrations is chosen properly the condition $\Delta k = 0$ is achieved. By keeping the ratio of concentrations fixed while increasing the concentration of the 'active' gas the value of N^2 can be made very large while still preserving phase matching. This cannot be continued indefinitely due to the fact that β generally increases either as the square of the concentration of one of the gases, or as a product of concentrations of the two components. This fact ultimately leads to a decreasing vuv output as N is increased.

As an example of an application of vuv generation to RIS consider the laser ionisation of Kr. Hurst *et al* (1985) have used four-wave sum mixing in Xe and Ar mixtures (which were purified to remove Kr) in order to generate light at 116.64 nm. This light was used to resonantly pump the ground state to the Kr $4p^55s'(J = 1)$ transition. This transition was the first step in the laser ionisation scheme shown in figure 9.6. In order to generate sizeable quantities of 116.48 nm light, two laser wavelengths were used at $\lambda_1 = 252.5$ nm and at 1507 nm. The 252.5 nm radiation is two-photon resonant with the $5p^5(^2P_{3/2})6p(J = 2)$ transition, and the 1507 nm radiation is close to resonance for the $5p^5(^2P_{3/2})6p(J = 2)$ to $5p^5(^2P_{3/2})7s(J = 1)$ transition. Consequently, we have both a nearby two-photon and a nearby three-photon resonance, as shown in figure 9.5.

With the wavelengths used here, phase matching is predicted to occur with $N_{Ar}/N_{Xe} = 8.9$. This prediction, based on the phenomenology described in §9.3, is very close to the experimentally determined ratio. In the study the laser beams had diameters of 0.14 cm, pulse lengths of 5–7 ns, and energies per pulse of around 1 mJ. We find for the peak

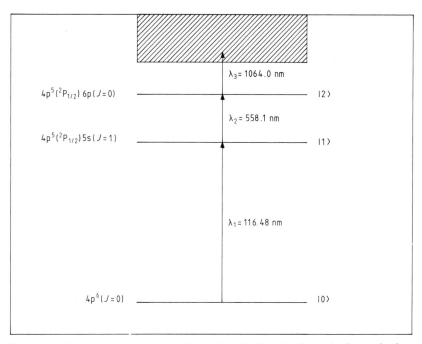

Figure 9.6 Resonance ionisation scheme for Kr. The hard step is the excitation of the first resonance level, requiring vuv photons.

power densities $I_1 = I_2 \simeq 1.2 \times 10^7 \, \text{W cm}^{-2}$. The two-photon Rabi rate for this transition has been measured (Chen *et al* 1980) and calculated (Payne *et al* 1981) and in radians per second it is given by $4I_1$, with I_1 in W cm^{-2}. The one-photon Rabi frequency is not known, but reasonable order of magnitude estimate is $10^8 I_2^{1/2}$, with I_2 in W cm^{-2}. With 30 Torr of Xe and about 270 Torr of Ar the output is still increasing, so that we may assume that absorption is not serious. Since the ground state to 7s oscillator strength is about 0.09 we find

$$|\Omega_1| \simeq 5 \times 10^{11} \, \text{s}^{-1}$$

$$|\Omega_2| \simeq 7.5 \times 10^7 \, \text{s}^{-1}$$

$$\kappa = 2.4 \times 10^{15} \, \text{cm}^{-1} \text{s}^{-1}$$

$$\Gamma_1 \simeq 2.7 \times 10^{11} \, \text{s}^{-1}$$

$$\delta_2 \simeq 440 \, \text{cm}^{-1} = 7.8 \times 10^{13} \, \text{s}^{-1}.$$

We find for the 5 cm cell with no absorption that $N_{2\omega_{L1} + \omega_{L2}} = 3 \times 10^{11}$ photons, which corresponds to about 0.5 μJ. This is very close to the VUV output measured experimentally. In view of the poorly known one-photon Rabi frequency, only an order of magnitude agreement was expected.

The most impressive demonstrations of VUV generation have been based on the sum generation method described above (see Tomkins and Mahon (1981) and Hurst *et al* (1985)). The main drawback to this scheme is that it frequently requires doubling or doubling plus sum mixing to get the beam at ω_{L1}. In addition, ω_{L2} is frequently in the IR and may require a stimulated Raman process for its generation. The ionisation of Xe can be based on the work of Tomkins and Mahon. These workers use four-wave sum mixing in Hg in order to demonstrate a method which can give approximately 15 μJ at a wavelength of 125.02 nm. Even with a band width of 0.2 cm^{-1} such a large VUV output enables one to overcome the small oscillator strength of the $5p^6 \rightarrow 5p^5(^2P^0_{3/2})5d(J = 1)$ transition and to saturate the transition while using a 3 mm laser beam. This compares well with the 1 mm beam that can be used in ionising Kr with the 300 nJ generated by Hurst *et al* (1985) at a band width of 0.2 cm^{-1}. The band width used in the Kr study was actually greater than 1 cm^{-1}, but generating the same output with a narrower band width should be straightforward. In generating the 116.48 nm light for the ionisation of Kr great care must be exercised in ensuring that the Xe–Ar mixture is free of Kr. Even concentrations of PPM of Kr cause a severe absorption problem.

In the above discussion phase matching was achieved by making use of a positively dispersive buffer gas. The two laser beams which supply the two colours were concentric and propagated in the same direction. Since absorption due to mixed dimers is frequently dominant, it may in some situations be useful to utilise a pure gas or vapour as the non-linear medium, with phase matching achieved by introducing a small angle between the direction of propagation of the two laser beams. Consider what happens to equation (9.45) when the plane-polarisation vector of both beams is the z direction, but the propagation vectors of the two beams are $k_{\omega_{L1}}$ and $k_{\omega_{L2}}$. The expression is found to remain unchanged if the x axis is taken to lie along k_p, where

$$k_p = 2k_{\omega_{L1}} + k_{\omega_{L2}}$$

and where $\phi(x, t)$ is modified to

$$\phi(x, t) = (2\omega_{L1} + \omega_{L2})t - |k_p|x + \phi_0(t).$$

When the two beams are relatively large and the medium is short enough so that the small angle between the two beams does not destroy the beam overlap in the length of the cell, we obtain equation (9.47) for the photon flux if we interpret Δk as

$$\Delta k \equiv |k_{2\omega_{L1} + \omega_{L2}} - (2k_{\omega_{L1}} + k_{\omega_{L2}})|. \tag{9.48}$$

The phase matching corresponds to the polarisation wave in the direction of $2k_{\omega_{L1}} + k_{\omega_{L2}}$, with the four-wave mixing signal having to propagate in the same direction with the same speed in order for constructive interference to occur. It is evident that phase matching (i.e. $\Delta k = 0$) does not occur for just any angle between the laser beams. The desired situation which would yield $\Delta k = 0$ is shown in figure 9.7.

If the angle between $k_{\omega_{L1}}$ and $k_{\omega_{L2}}$ is θ, and the angle between $k_{\omega_{L1}}$ and the propagation vector for the four-wave mixing signal is β in figure 9.7, then

$$k_{2\omega_{L1} + \omega_{L2}} \cos \beta = 2k_{\omega_{L1}} + k_{\omega_{L2}} \cos \theta$$

$$k_{2\omega_{L1} + \omega_{L2}} \sin \beta = k_{\omega_{L2}} \sin \theta. \tag{9.49}$$

Let

$$\Delta k_0 = k_{2\omega_{L1} + \omega_{L2}} - (2k_{\omega_{L1}} + k_{\omega_{L2}})$$

then for perfect phase matching we must choose θ so that

$$\theta = \{[(2\omega_{L1} + \omega_{L2})/\omega_{L1}](-\Delta k_0/k_{\omega_{L2}})\}^{1/2}. \tag{9.50}$$

The angle between the first laser beam and the four-wave mixing signal will be

$$\beta = \theta \omega_{L1}/(2\omega_{L1} + \omega_{L2}). \tag{9.51}$$

In solving for θ and β we have assumed that Δk_0 is much smaller than the length of the propagation vector for either laser, so that the k vectors have lengths which are close to their vacuum lengths in terms of percentage and the angles are small.

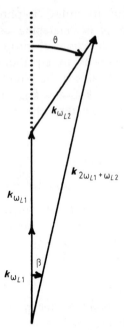

Figure 9.7 Phase matching for four-wave sum mixing can be achieved in a negatively dispersive pure gas by introducing an angle between the laser beams to achieve $k_{2\omega_{L1} + \omega_{L2}} = 2k_{\omega_{L1}} + k_{\omega_{L2}}$.

A very similar analysis applies to a case where the lasers are tuned near a three-photon resonance which is pumped by the absorption of two photons at frequency ω_{L1}, but with a stimulated emission occurring at ω_{L2}. Energetically, this corresponds to $\hbar(2\omega_{L1} - \omega_{L2}) \simeq \hbar(\omega_2 - \omega_0)$, where $\hbar(\omega_2 - \omega_0)$ is the excitation energy of the three-photon resonance. In the latter case a polarisability is produced at $2\omega_{L1} - \omega_{L2}$ and with proper phase matching a coherent beam is generated at this frequency. This process, referred to as four-wave difference mixing, can be phase matched by introducing an angle between the two laser beams in order to achieve

$$k_{2\omega_{L1} - \omega_{L2}} = 2k_{\omega_{L1}} - k_{\omega_{L2}}.$$

The four-wave sum mixing case gives a phase matched, four-wave mixing signal propagating in a direction lying between the directions of the two laser beams. In order for phase matching to be achieved by angle tuning in the case of sum mixing, it is necessary for the parallel beam phase mismatch (i.e. Δk_0) to be negative. Conversely, for four-wave difference mixing phase matching can again be achieved by angle tuning providing the parallel beam Δk_0 is positive (i.e. $\Delta k_0 \equiv k_{\omega_{L1} - \omega_{L2}} - 2k_{\omega_{L1}} + k_{\omega_{L2}} > 0$). Also, the direction of propagation of the generated wave lies in the plane of the laser beams, but not between them. One finds for difference mixing that θ must be chosen so that

$$\theta = \{(\Delta k_0/k_{\omega_{L2}})[2 - (\omega_{L2}/\omega_{L1})]\}^{1/2} \qquad (9.52)$$

and

$$\beta = -\omega_{L2}\theta/(2\omega_{L1} - \omega_{L2}).$$

In the region near three-photon resonance with a pure atomic gas or vapour one can frequently use a very simple expression for the parallel beam phase mismatch in which the nearby resonance dominates the deviation of the index of refraction from one. We have for both sum and difference mixing

$$\Delta k_0 \simeq -\kappa/\delta_2 \qquad (9.53)$$

where δ_2 is the detuning from three-photon resonance and κ is defined in equation (9.29). This makes the estimation of the angles for angle-tuned phase matching quite simple.

A wealth of references to the literature on vuv generation can be found in a review paper by Jamroz and Stoicheff (1983). This review contains references to four-wave mixing in both inert gases and metal vapours in high-temperature heat pipes.

9.6 Four-wave sum and difference mixing in Xe and Kr

The work which we will now describe (Hilbig and Wallenstein 1982) was carried out with just two 'active' gases: Xe and Kr. In the regions where Xe was negatively dispersive either Ar or Kr was used as the buffer gas; while in the negatively dispersive regions of Kr the Ar served as a buffer gas. The region of the spectrum between 110 and 130 nm was investigated by using a dye laser tuned in the region between 550 and 650 nm. Part of the dye laser output was frequency doubled to give ω_{L1} in the wavelength region $275 < \lambda < 325$ nm, while ω_{L2} was the remainder of the dye laser beam. The process $2\omega_{L1} + \omega_{L2}$ then yielded vuv light at 1/5 the wavelength of the dye laser. By restricting the wavelength of the light used in this way one gives up the large non-linear susceptibility which results from having a two-photon resonance, and tries to gain back the efficiency by making use of the excellent dye laser output available when pumping is done by the second harmonic of a Nd:YAG laser. By focusing the laser beams tightly, and by using a buffer gas in order to phase match at the desired wavelength with high concentrations of the active gas, excellent results were obtained. Figure 9.8 shows the output generated in this way.

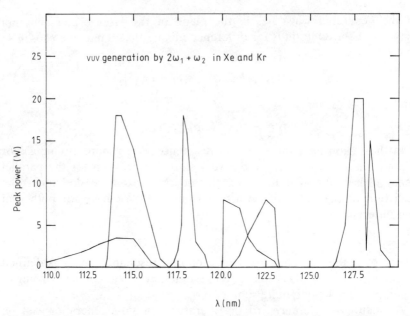

Figure 9.8 Four-wave sum generation in Xe and Kr (from Hilbig and Wallenstein 1982).

In order to generate light at a sum frequency the active gas must be negatively dispersive. However, in the case of difference four-wave mixing (i.e. generating $2\omega_{L1} - \omega_{L2}$) the requirement with focused beams is that Δk (where $\Delta k = k(2\omega_{L1} - \omega_{L2}) - 2k(\omega_{L1}) + k(\omega_{L2})$) multiplied by the length of the high intensity region (i.e. the confocal parameter) should not be large compared with unity. The latter quantity can be either positive or negative, with optimum phase matching occurring for $\Delta k = 0$. With a non-zero Δk a derivation similar to the one used in deriving equation (9.43) shows that the amount of $2\omega_{L1} - \omega_{L2}$ light generated decreases as $\exp(-|\Delta kb|)$, where b is the confocal parameter. To generate light between 160 and 210 nm Hilbig and Wallenstein used Xe as the active gas. A dye laser in the wavelength region 550 to 650 nm was frequency doubled and the doubled output was used as ω_{L1}, with either the fundamental of the dye laser or the fundamental of the Nd:YAG being used as ω_{L2}. All of the generation was carried out in a positively dispersive region far from the lowest Xe resonance, so that relatively high Xe pressures could be used without producing a large Δk. The output achieved by this process is shown in figure 9.9.

It is clear that even though the methods described in this section often yield less power than a method which uses a two-photon resonant enhancement, the output can still be useful for spectroscopy and sensitive detection methods.

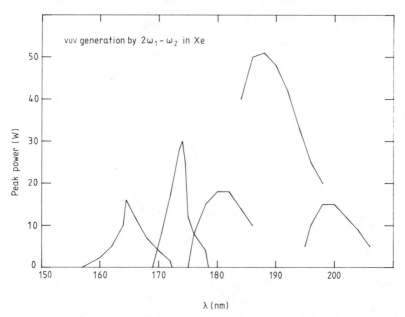

Figure 9.9 Four-wave difference mixing in Xe (from Hilbig and Wallenstein 1982).

9.7 Two-photon excitation and the stimulated Raman process

This section will serve two diverse purposes. First, it provides a more detailed discussion of two-photon excitation which, along with one-photon excitation, is used for selective excitation schemes in RIS. Secondly, two-photon excitation is intimately related to the simplest stimulated Raman process which provides another method for extending the range of tunability outside the range 217 to 1000 nm which is routinely generated with commercial dye laser systems. We will present here a simplified rate equation theory of both two-photon excitation and the stimulated Raman process. This discussion will serve to introduce both two-photon excitation and the generation of new wavelengths by the stimulated Raman process. Further details can be found in the literature.

The equations of motion for two-photon excitation and three-photon ionisation are very similar to those for one-photon excitation. The major difference involves the replacement of the one-photon Rabi frequency by the two-photon Rabi frequency. This is most easily seen in equations (4.125) to (4.127), which are the equations of motion and the expressions for the N-photon Rabi frequency and AC Stark shifts in a two-state model of N-photon excitation. This treatment assumes that the laser is a broad band width device having a continuous frequency spectrum with a width much larger than either the AC Stark shift in the transition or the two-photon Rabi frequency. From our discussion of excitation with a broad band width source in §5.4 we expect that a rate analysis will apply with the rate of excitation given by

$$R \simeq \langle \langle |\Omega_2(t)|^2 \rangle \rangle / \Gamma_L. \tag{9.54}$$

This equation is written in analogy to the corresponding relation for one-photon excitation, while allowing for the fact that the equations of motion are nearly identical except for the replacement of the one-photon Rabi frequency by the two-photon Rabi frequency and the omission of the AC Stark shift. The quantity Γ_L is the half width at half maximum of the laser frequency spectrum and Ω_2 is half of the two-photon Rabi frequency. From equation (4.126) we find

$$\Omega_2 = (i/\hbar^2) e^{-i\delta t} \langle 0 | \hat{V}_H(t) \int_{-\infty}^{t} dt_1 \hat{V}_H(t_1) | 1 \rangle \tag{9.55}$$

where $|0\rangle$ and $|1\rangle$ are the upper and lower states and M_J has been suppressed for simplicity. Only the slowly varying part obtained in evaluating equation (9.55) should be retained in order to be consistent with the rotating wave approximation. When a single laser beam is present and is tuned very near a two-photon resonance we can use techniques similar to those used in §9.2 in order to obtain

$$\Omega_2(t) = \sum_k (\hat{D}_{0,k} \cdot E_0/2\hbar)(\hat{D}_{k,1} \cdot E_0/2\hbar)/(\omega_L - \omega_1 + \omega_k). \tag{9.56}$$

Above, the sum over intermediate states involves a sum over the discrete part of the eigenspectra and integrals over continua. The k index involves a sum over all appropriate quantum numbers (including energy). In equation (9.56) the E_0 is the amplitude of the laser field.

The individual terms in equation (9.56) are of the form of a product of one-photon Rabi frequencies divided by a detuning from the intermediate state. If some intermediate state is close to one-photon resonance at the laser frequency ω_L, a single term (or a few closely spaced levels) can dominate and

$$\Omega_2 \simeq \Omega_1(0 \to k)\Omega_1(k \to 1)/\delta_1 \tag{9.57}$$

where $\delta_1 = \omega_L - \omega_k + \omega_0$, $|\delta| \equiv |2\omega_L - \omega_1 + \omega_0| \ll |\delta_1|$. Above, $\Omega_1(0 \to k)$ and $\Omega_1(k \to 1)$ are half of the Rabi frequencies for the $|0\rangle$ to $|k\rangle$ and $|k\rangle$ to $|1\rangle$ transitions, respectively. An example of a situation where there is a dominant one-photon resonance in two-photon excitation is the 3s → 4d resonance in sodium. When the laser is tuned to two-photon resonance with the 4d state the 3p levels are within approximately 300 cm^{-1} of one-photon resonance. All other intermediate resonances have resonance denominators which are more than an order of magnitude larger, and these other levels also have much smaller dipole matrix elements. Averaging over fine structure levels one finds that the two-photon Rabi frequency is $\Omega_2 \simeq 440I(\mathrm{W\,cm^{-2}})$. At a power density of $10^8\,\mathrm{W\,cm^{-2}}$ the two-photon Rabi frequency would be $4.4 \times 10^{10}\,\mathrm{s^{-1}}$. The rate for pumping population from the ground state to the excited state for a laser having a band width of $0.1\,\mathrm{cm^{-1}}$ is $8 \times 10^{-6}I^2(\mathrm{W\,cm^{-2}})$. At a power density of $10^7\,\mathrm{W\,cm^{-2}}$ the pumping rate is approximately $10^9\,\mathrm{s^{-1}}$. With a pulse length of a few ns the transition is strongly saturated, with the equilibrium between the ground and excited states occurring in about 1 ns.

A near one-photon resonance enhances the two-photon Rabi frequency by several orders of magnitude. This is similar to the enhancement to the three-photon Rabi frequency due to a two-photon resonance which was used to increase the generation of vuv by four-wave mixing in §9.5. In some situations the desirable property of two-photon excitation is the mechanism that it provides for reaching high-lying excited states, without the use of vuv light. In this case there is no intermediate state closer to resonance than several eV. In fact, in the inert gases the lowest excitation energy is typically more than 70% of the ionisation potential and the nearest intermediate one-photon transition is 5 eV away from resonance when a laser is tuned to a two-photon resonance. The one-photon electric dipole matrix elements between the ground state and excited states are only large for a range of levels lying between the lowest $J = 1$ level and a point a little above the ionisation potential. Consequently, as a crude estimate one can replace the resonant denominator by a constant and use closure to estimate the two-photon Rabi frequency (Payne *et al* 1981):

$$\Omega_2 \simeq [\langle 0|(\hat{\boldsymbol{D}}\cdot\boldsymbol{E}_0/2\hbar)^2|1\rangle]/\delta. \tag{9.58}$$

One situation has been studied both theoretically and experimentally. This is the two-photon excitation and ionisation of the Xe 6p $(J = 0)$ and 6p $(J = 2)$ levels (Chen *et al* 1980, Payne *et al* 1981). Chen's measurements used two-photon excitation and three-photon ionisation of Xe in a low-pressure cell. When ions were produced they were accelerated and implanted in the ion detector. Consequently, as time increased the number of Xe atoms remaining in the cell decreased exponentially. The effective volume of ionisation was found to be $2 \times 10^{-4}\,\mathrm{cm^3}$, which was in good agreement with theory (Payne *et al* 1981). In the theory the two-photon Rabi frequency was calculated both in the closure approximation of equation (9.58) and by explicit summation. Different approximations led to a variation of about a factor of two on the two-photon Rabi frequency. The ionisation volume was found both from the decrease of the Xe signal with time and from the power-density dependence of the ionisation signal. The two values agreed to better than 40%. In the latter situation of the two-photon Rabi frequency was $\Omega_2 \simeq 10I(\mathrm{W\,cm^{-2}})$. This is a rather large two-photon Rabi frequency for a transition in the inert gases. The laser used in this study generated about 0.7 mJ at 249.6 nm in a 7 ns pulse. The laser band width was close to 1 cm^{-1}. The lifetime of the excited state is much longer than the laser pulse length so that saturation of the discrete transition requires $R\tau \gg 1$, where R is the pumping rate and τ is the pulse length. Using $\Omega_2 \simeq 10I$, with I in W cm^{-2}, saturation starts for power densities greater than 5×10^8 W cm^2. With the broad band width laser used here and a photo-ionisation cross section of nearly 10^{-17} cm^2, the ionisation of the excited state becomes very efficient before the two-photon transition is saturated. With a narrow band width source and counter-propagating beams the excitation is Doppler free and saturation starts to occur as soon as $\Omega_2 \tau > 1$. The saturation condition is satisfied at power densities of greater than 3×10^7 W cm^{-2}. With the very best available lasers strong two-photon transitions can be saturated with unfocused beams having diameters close to 1 mm. This is particularly true of those elements with relatively low ionisation potentials where one could use a resonant enhancement and carry out very efficient photo-ionisation free from Doppler effects.

As an introduction to the stimulated Raman process, consider a two-photon excitation process in which two colours are used for resonant excitation. The first laser frequency is ω_L and a second beam has an angular frequency ω_R, as shown in figure 9.10. This two-photon excitation process is assumed to be resonant when $\omega_L - \omega_R = \omega_2 - \omega_0$. If the beam at ω_L is very close to resonance the evaluation of equation (9.55) will have a dominant intermediate state and will reduce to one term given by

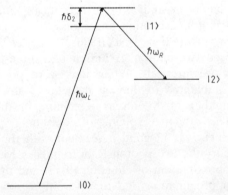

Figure 9.10 Two-photon resonance excitation of a state with excitation energy $\omega_L - \omega_R = \omega_2 - \omega_0$. This excitation process involves absorption of photons at ω_L and stimulated emission into the beam at angular frequency ω_R. The two-photon excitation process is greatly enhanced by a near one-photon resonance at ω_L between states $|0\rangle$ and $|1\rangle$.

$$\Omega_2(t) \simeq \Omega_1(0 \to 1)\Omega_1(1 \to 2)/[\omega_L - (\omega_1 - \omega_0)]. \qquad (9.59)$$

In equation (9.59) the quantity $\Omega_1(0 \to 1)$ is proportional to the amplitude of the laser beam with angular frequency ω_L and $\Omega_1(1 \to 2)$ is proportional to the amplitude of the beam at frequency ω_R. We can use equation (9.54) to write an expression for the rate of change of the excited state occupation probability in terms of Ω_2. Letting $\delta_2 = \omega_L - (\omega_1 - \omega_0)$,

$$R = [\langle\langle\Omega_1^2(0 \to 1)\rangle\rangle\langle\langle\Omega_1^2(1 \to 2)\rangle\rangle]/\Gamma_L\delta_2^2 \qquad (9.59)$$

$$= \sigma_{eff}\mathscr{F}_R$$

where $\mathscr{F}_R$ is the flux of photons at the angular frequency ω_R and σ_{eff} is an effective cross section (proportional to the intensity of the beam with frequency ω_L) for stimulating an atom to emit a photon at frequency ω_R. To estimate the order of magnitude of this effective cross section as a function of δ_2 and the laser power density I_L let

$$\langle\langle\Omega_1^2(0 \to 1)\rangle\rangle \simeq 10^{15}I_L \ \text{W cm}^{-2}$$

$$\langle\langle\Omega_1^2(1 \to 2)\rangle\rangle \simeq 10^{16}I_R \ \text{W cm}^{-2}$$

$$\Gamma_L \simeq 1.9 \times 10^{10} \ \text{s}^{-1} \simeq 0.1 \ \text{cm}^{-1}$$

$$\delta_2(\text{s}^{-1}) \simeq 1.9 \times 10^{11}\delta_2 \ \text{cm}^{-1}. \qquad (9.60)$$

Assuming a photon energy of 0.5 eV so that I_R can be related to a photon flux, we estimate for the cross section

$$\sigma_{eff}(\text{cm}^2) \simeq 1.2 \times 10^{-21}I_L(\text{W cm}^{-2})/\delta_2^2(\text{cm}^{-1}). \qquad (9.61)$$

We have assumed an average Rabi frequency for the first step and a strong one for the second. One-photon Rabi frequencies of the assumed magnitude are not rare in alkali metals. As an example let $I_L = 10^7 \ \text{W cm}^{-2}$ and $\delta_2 = 30 \ \text{cm}^{-1}$ so that $\sigma_{eff} \simeq 10^{-17} \ \text{cm}^2$. Even with this large detuning from resonance and a modest power density, a concentration of $3 \times 10^{17} \ \text{cm}^{-3}$ for the atomic species gives 0.3 cm for the average distance between stimulated emissions at ω_R. In a 10 cm path a single photon at ω_R is amplified to give a mean number of photons $\exp(\sigma_{eff}NL) = \exp(33)$ photons. This exponential gain, which can start from a single spontaneous Raman scattered photon emitted along the laser beam, is finally limited by attenuation of the laser beam.

The process which we have described above is the stimulated Raman process. In alkali vapours the conversion efficiency can be very high with a large fraction of the laser photons being absorbed due to their conversion to a new wavelength by the stimulated Raman process. It is not uncommon for the number of generated Raman photons to be 30% of the number of laser photons. Each one-photon resonance (except for the lowest p state) in an alkali metal has a region below and above it such that the Raman gain will be high at elevated pressures. High efficiency conversion to tunable IR can be achieved in many wavelength regions. Such an efficient frequency conversion method can be very useful for generating tunable laser beams in the IR. Pulsed sources of tunable IR can be very useful in the RIS of small molecules. A great deal of isotopic selectivity can be obtained by starting the RIS process with a vibrational excitation.

References

Bjorklund G 1975 *IEEE J. Quant. Electron.* **QE-11** 287
Bloembergen N 1965 *Nonlinear Optics* (Reading, MA: Benjamin)
Castex M C 1977 *J. Chem. Phys.* **66** 3854
Chen C H, Hurst G S and Payne M G 1980 *Chem. Phys. Lett.* **75** 473
Cotter D 1979 *Opt. Lett.* **4** 134
Ferrell W R, Payne M G and Garrett W R 1987 *Phys. Rev.* A **35** 5020
Garrett W R, Ferrell W R and Payne M G 1986 *Phys. Rev.* A **34** 1165
Geiger J 1977 *Z. Phys.* A **282** 129
Hilbig R and Wallenstein R 1982 *Appl. Opt.* **21** 913
Hurst G S, Payne M G, Kramer S D, Chen C H, Phillips R C, Allman
    S L, Alton G D, Dabbs J W T, Willis R D and Lehman B E 1985
    Rep. Prog. Phys. **48** 1333
Hsu K S, Kung A H, Zych L J, Young J F and Harris S E 1976 *IEEE
    J. Quant. Electron.* **QE-12** 60
Jackson D J, Wynne J J and Kes P H 1983 *Phys. Rev.* A **28** 781
Jackson J D 1962 *Classical Electromagnetic Theory* (Reading, MA:
    Addison-Wesley)
Jamroz W and Stoicheff B P 1983 Generation of Tunable Coherent
    Vacuum-Ultraviolet Radiation in *Progress in Optics XX* ed E Wolf
    (Amsterdam: North Holland)
Leonard P J 1974 Refractive Indices, Verdet Constants and Polarizabili-
    ties of the Inert Gases in *At. Data and Nucl. Data Tables* **14** 22
Levenson M D 1982 *Introduction to Nonlinear Laser Spectroscopy* (New
    York: Academic)
Mahon R, McIlrath T J, Myerscough V P and Koopman D W 1979
    IEEE J. Quant. Electron. **QE-15** 444
Miller J C, Compton R N, Payne M G and Garrett W R 1980 *Phys.
    Rev. Lett.* **45** 114
New C H and Ward J F 1967 *Phys. Rev. Lett.* **19** 556
Payne M G, Chen C H, Hurst G S, Kramer S D, Garrett W R and
    Pindzola M 1981 *Chem. Phys. Lett.* **79** 142
Payne M G, Ferrell W R and Garrett W R 1983 *Phys. Rev.* A **27** 3053

Payne M G and Garrett W R 1982 *Phys. Rev.* A **26** 356
Payne M G, Garrett W R and Baker H C 1980 *Chem. Phys. Lett.* **75** 468
Tomkins F S and Mahon R 1981 *Opt. Lett.* **6** 179
Ward J F and New C H 1969 *Phys. Rev.* **185** 57

10

Maxwell's demon and other noble concepts

10.1 Concept of the Maxwell demon

A unique type of atom counter was made possible when methods of resonance ionisation of the noble gases were developed, as discussed in Chapter 9. Noble gas atoms have high ionisation potentials and large energy gaps between the ground states and the first excited states. Consequently, special effort was needed to provide vuv radiation for the first excitation step in the RIS process. The same electronic properties which make RIS difficult account for the chemical inertness of the noble gases, and therefore confer uniqueness on these few types of atoms. Because a few atoms of a noble gas can be separated from thousands of tons of a material, it is possible to use large targets for the detection of rare events. Application of the noble gas detector for environmental research and for solar neutrino studies motivated the development of the RIS schemes for the noble gases and the detector to be discussed in this chapter.

The applications which provided the driving force for the development required that atoms of one isotope of atomic mass A be counted even when atoms of the neighbouring isotope $(A \pm 1)$ were far more abundant (in some cases by ten orders of magnitude). Furthermore, it is required to count as few as 100 atoms of the desired isotope, independent of its half-life for radioactive decay. Therefore, the concept was developed (Hurst *et al* 1980, 1981, 1983, 1984a, 1985a, Chen 1984, Chen *et al* 1980, 1984a, b, Kramer *et al* 1984) in which each atom in the sample is Z-selected using RIS, A-selected with a quadrupole mass filter, and counted as it is stored in a detector.

As the concept developed, a parallel with Maxwell's sorting demon (named by Lord Kelvin 1889) became quite clear, as illustrated in figure

10.1. The demon, as visualised by Maxwell (1872), could sort atoms either by their velocity or by the type of atom—in apparent violation of the second law of thermodynamics. This serious conceptual problem was not resolved until Brillouin (1951) proved that the demon must have a light source to see the atom. The entropy increase in the flashlight more than offsets the entropy decrease due to information on individual atoms. The modern demon must be more intelligent than the Maxwell version since we require isotopic selection. Brillouin's flashlight has become a laser—a much more powerful entropy generator!

The basic idea involved in the modern realisation of Maxwell's demon

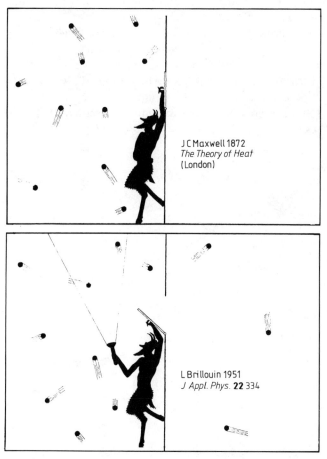

Figure 10.1 Conceptualisation of Maxwell's sorting demon which requires a light source to see the atoms. Such a demon can function legally without violating the second law. (Artwork courtesy of Jimmy Green, while a student at Western Kentucky University.)

is shown in figure 10.2. Lasers are used for the selective ionisation of noble gas atoms in the RIS process. Atoms of a particular Z which are within the small volume ΔV are ionised, and a fraction of these pass through a mass filter. For instance, a quadrupole mass spectrometer would select the atom according to A. The transmitted ions are then accelerated to 10 keV and implanted into a target that emits a burst of electrons which can be detected to record each implanted atom. Any ion not transmitted will be neutralised by wall collisions and returned to the gaseous sample in the static system. After a large number of laser shots, all of the Z- and A-selected species are implanted, and the count rate approaches zero. The total number of counts is (neglecting interference from $A \pm 1$) just equal to the number of atoms having atomic number Z and mass A (i.e. $N(Z, A)$).

What was described above had two deficiencies which were eliminated by adding other features to the Maxwell demon. A good quadrupole mass filter will have an abundance sensitivity of about 10^{-4}, i.e. the transmitted fraction at $A \pm 1$ is about 10^{-4} times the value of that at A. This limitation can be overcome by pumping the system (after all species of mass A have been implanted) to remove essentially all of the other

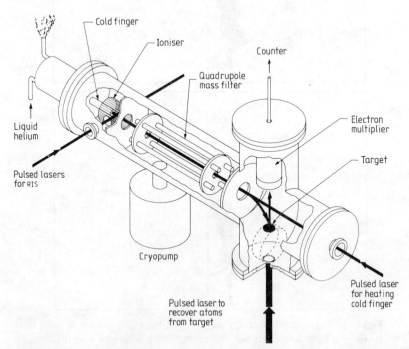

Figure 10.2 Schematic diagram of a modern Maxwell demon suitable for sorting and counting noble gas atoms with isotopic selectivity.

isotopes, then releasing the atoms from the implanted target back into the enclosure for another cycle through the mass filter. After n such cycles, the undesired isotopes can be attenuated by the factor 10^{4n}. Secondly, our demon is inherently very slow because the volume where RIS occurs is small (see Chapter 9 for the magnitudes of ΔV) and the mass spectrometer volume is a few litres. This problem was overcome by the development of an atom buncher, which greatly increases the chance that an atom will be in ΔV at the time of interest.

To describe more fully how the atom counter (figure 10.2) should work, assume we need to count 100 or so ^{81}Kr atoms in a sample of 10^8 atoms of ^{82}Kr. (This simulates a requirement in solar astrophysics, as described in Chapter 13.) The Kr atoms condense onto the cold finger, an essential part of the atom buncher, at liquid helium temperature. When the light of a pulsed visible laser (i.e. the 'buncher' laser) strikes the cold finger, Kr atoms are quickly released and travel a few mm in a few μs. A system of lasers can be pulsed (after a short time delay) just above the cold finger to ionise a significant fraction of the Kr atoms in the Z-selective RIS process. The Kr$^+$ ions enter a quadrupole mass filter tuned to mass 81. After leaving the mass filter, Kr$^+$ ions (now both Z- and A-selected) are implanted at approximately 10 kV into a silicon target. With an abundance sensitivity of 10^{-4}, about 10^4 atoms of ^{82}Kr are also implanted by the time that nearly all of the 100 atoms of ^{81}Kr are implanted in the target, amounting to an unacceptable background. After most of the signal atoms are safely implanted, the remaining gas is pumped out. The silicon target is then annealed using a laser pulse, releasing the implanted atoms. This step completes a cycle that returns the 100 atoms of ^{81}Kr and 10^4 atoms of ^{82}Kr to the static vacuum system. A final count is made by repeating the process in which 100 atoms of ^{81}Kr and only one atom of ^{82}Kr are counted with an activated copper–beryllium target. This final count is not only free of background atoms of mass $A \pm 1$ but is also nearly absolute, since three or more electrons are emitted when a 10 keV ion strikes activated copper–beryllium.

10.2 The atom buncher

The need for an atom buncher (Hurst *et al* 1984b) arose from the fact that some of the applications of Maxwell's demon require counting 10 to 100 atoms of a particular isotope, which are free to move in a 4 l vacuum enclosure. However, our laser scheme which ionises the atoms in the RIS process sweeps out a volume of less than 10^{-3} cm^3 per laser pulse. A large number (greater than 10^7) of laser shots would be required to ionise and count all the atoms. In view of laser repetition rates of about 10 Hz, this is unacceptable. Thus, the concept of an atom buncher was conceived which would put a large fraction of the target atoms into the laser beam at the time of the laser pulse. The basic idea of the atom buncher is very simple (see figure 10.3). A cold surface is used to condense the atoms of interest and a suitable pulse of laser light momentarily heats a thin layer of the cold surface. (For a discussion of surface heating with laser pulses see Ready (1965).) Inert gas atoms are evaporated, as a consequence of the laser heating, and pass through a region of space just above the cold surface after a short flight time. Thus, there is a high probability that the atoms will be in the laser ionisation volume at the desired time. Long before atoms can return by random walk, the surface is again cold enough to condense them.

A brief discussion of the laser evaporation process can be helpful. Physical adsorption of noble gases on cooled surfaces can be characterised by the concept of mean stay times (Wilmoth and Fisher 1978), i.e. $\tau = \tau_0 e^{\varepsilon/kT}$. Values for τ_0 for Xe and Kr on copper and nickel surfaces

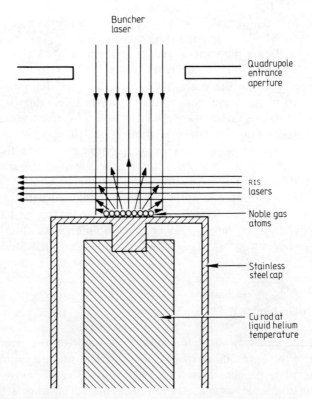

Figure 10.3 Schematic diagram illustrating the atom-buncher concept.

range from 10^{-15} to 10^{-20} s, while ε values range from 0.22 to 0.28 eV, depending on the surface treatment of the samples that were studied. We define a critical temperature T_c as the temperature where the mean stay time τ is 1 μs. If a laser pulse can heat a surface and keep $T > T_c$ for several μs, the entire noble gas sample, which is initially trapped on the cold surface, will leave the surface. From the data published, one estimates that $T_c = 110$ K for Kr and $T_c = 130$ K for Xe for the case of a Ni surface.

Recurrence times to stick onto a small area A_R in an open system of volume V are approximately $t_R = 4V/A_R \bar{v} \xi$, where $\bar{v}$ is the mean speed of the free atoms and ξ is the sticking probability. This recurrence time describes the number of atoms N in the free state at time t according to $N = N_0 e^{-t/t_R}$, where N_0 is the number of free atoms at $t = 0$. (The single exponential behaviour assumes that all apertures in the vacuum system have an area which is large compared with that of the atom buncher.) Even where V is one litre and A_R is a few mm^2, t_R can be as small as a few seconds. Thus, noble gas atoms can be recycled frequently.

The volume V of an apparatus required so that a mass spectrometer can be used to provide isotopic resolution is about 4 l. On the other hand, the laser system (Kramer *et al* 1984) for generating vuv radiation at 116.5 nm for one-photon excitation (the first step of resonance ionisation) of Kr will saturate a volume, ΔV, of only about 4×10^{-4} cm^3 (see Chapter 9). The probability of counting in this uncorrelated case is $P_i = \Delta V/V$. To detect 95% of the atoms would require nearly 3×10^7 laser pulses or 833 hours with a system that pulsed at 10 Hz. In the correlated case the probability is $P_c(t) = P_b P_I(\Delta t)$, where P_b is the probability that an atom is on the buncher, and $P_I(\Delta t)$ is the probability that an atom leaving the cold tip is in the laser volume ΔV after the laser delay Δt. Typically, the laser volume ΔV is defined by a laser beam that is approximately 0.05 cm in diameter and projects 0.2 cm of length onto a collection aperture (i.e. $\Delta V = 4 \times 10^{-4}$ cm^3). If the small ionisation volume is centred about 1 mm from the cold tip, it takes about 10 μs for Kr atoms (at 120 K) to fill it, if the atoms have a mean velocity distribution characteristic of release at $T = 120$ K. In a typical case $P_I(\Delta t = 10 \mu$s) can be as large as 10%. Thus, under steady state conditions, $P_c(t) = 0.1 t_L/t_R$, where t_L is the laser repetition time, which is small compared to the recurrence time t_R. If $t_R = 10$ s and $t_L = 0.1$ s, we have $P_c = 10^{-3}$ compared to $P_i = 10^{-7}$, i.e. use of the buncher increased the probability of detection by a factor of 10^4.

For a lower laser repetition of the buncher laser, the enhancement of P_c/P_i is even more dramatic; P_c approaches 10% when t_L is long compared to t_R. With a small number of atoms (e.g. 10^3 or less), digital counting using a 10 Hz repetition rate is ideal. For large numbers of atoms (e.g. 10^4), analogue counting where more than ten atoms are counted during each pulse is advisable and may be completed in a reasonable period of time by using the buncher.

A theoretical treatment was made (Hurst *et al* 1984b), using the relevant heat transport considerations, to determine both the temperature of the buncher tip in the steady state and the transient temperature during a laser pulse. The calculated temperatures (in K) at various distances from the centre of a stainless steel disc with a Ni core are shown in figure 10.4. Some representative stay times at various radii are also shown for Kr on stainless steel, based on the data of Wilmoth and Fisher (1978).

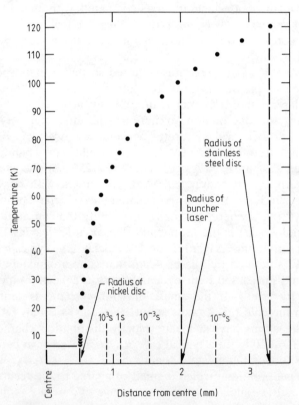

Figure 10.4 Calculations of the temperature profile of the buncher tip for the steady state and some representative stay times for Kr atoms at various distances from the centre of a disc made of stainless steel with a Ni core as indicated.

Calculations of the surface-heating transient were also made (Hurst *et al* 1984b) for the Ni portion and the stainless steel portion of the cold tip. In the laser that was actually used to heat the cold tip of the buncher about 100 mJ of energy at 600 nm was produced in a pulse of about 0.8 μs. Of the energy incident on Ni or stainless steel, about 60% is reflected while the remaining 40% is absorbed within 20 nm of the surface. The maximum surface temperature for the Ni portion is given approximately by $T_m = 1.15 \, (Q_0^2/\kappa_0 \tau A_T)^{1/5}$, where Q_0 is the absorbed laser energy per cm^2, κ_0 is the constant thermal conductivity (equal to 2×10^7 erg cm^{-1}s^{-1}K^{-1} for Ni from about 20 to 150 K), τ is the laser pulse width in seconds, and A_T appears in $\rho C_v(T) = A_T T^3$ as a parameter characterising the temperature dependence of specific heat C_v (about 40 for Ni). For instance, if $Q_0 = 0.284$ J cm^{-2}, the maximum temperature is 120 K. If $Q_0 = 0.142$ J cm^{-2}, T_m is 91 K. The transient behaviour of the surface temperature does not depend in a critical way on the initial T.

The temperature transient on the surface of a stainless steel surface was also studied. In this case, the maximum surface temperature is given by $T_m = 1.17(Q_0^2/A_T c\tau)^{1/6}$, where the new quantity c is derived from a new dependence of thermal conductivity on temperature; thus, $K(T) = cT = 10^4 T$ on stainless steel if $7 < T < 120$ K. As expected, stainless steel is easier to heat than Ni. For example, for $Q_0 = 0.142$ J cm^{-2}, the maximum temperature rises to 159 K. Therefore, if $Q_0 = 0.284$ J cm^{-2}, Kr atoms will have a short stay time when the temperature peaks either on the Ni or on the stainless steel portions of the cold tip. This stay time following the laser pulse (see figure 10.4) is short compared to the time for the tip to cool again, and is short compared to the time for an atom to travel from the cold tip to the RIS laser beam.

Calculations were then made of the atoms in flight following release from the cold tip of the atom buncher. Assume that all of the atoms leave at the same time and consider distances that are small compared to the radius of the cold tip. The fraction $F dx$ of the released atoms between x and $x + dx$ at time t following their release is, for x less than the radius of the cold spot,

$$F = (xm/t^2 kT_c) \exp[- mx^2(2kT_c t^2)^{-1}]$$

where m is the mass of released atoms, k is the Boltzmann constant and $T_c = 110$ K. Figure 10.5 shows the plot in two forms. The variation of F with distance at various fixed times, $F(x, t)_t$, is convenient for evaluating the probability $P_I(\Delta t)$ that the atoms will be ionised in the laser beam of a finite diameter at a time delay Δt. The form $F(x, t)_x$ is convenient since the delay time to maximise the signal can be quickly

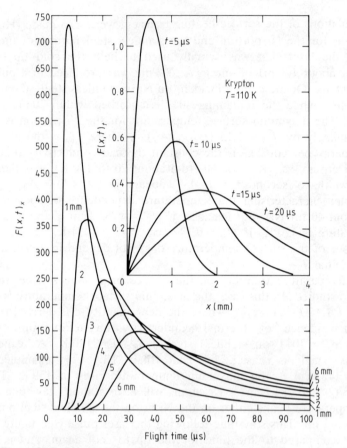

Figure 10.5 Calculations of the atoms in flight from the cold finger following a heating laser pulse. The plot shows $F(x, t)_x$, the relative probability that atoms are near the indicated distance as a function of time, and $F(x, t)_t$, the spatial distribution for various delay times.

determined experimentally. Hence the distance of the laser beam to the buncher surface can be confirmed. The atom buncher was designed and constructed for use with liquid helium as a coolant, with dimensions suitable for use inside the ionisation region of a quadrupole mass spectrometer. The three traces on the upper portion of figure 10.6 show that the atoms come off the surface during each individual laser pulse and return to the surface with a recurrence time of the order of 10 s in a 1 l test volume using ^{85}Kr. When the laser irradiates the surface at a 1 Hz repetition rate, the count rate (centre graph) reaches a steady state consistent with the recurrence time measured with single laser pulses. If the entire cold surface where atoms are condensed were not being

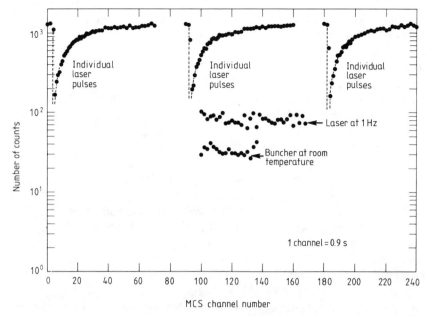

Figure 10.6 Experimental tests of the atom buncher. A small Geiger–Müller counter was used to view the ^{85}Kr atoms remaining on the cold tip as a function of time (0.9 s per channel). Each laser pulse caused nearly all of the atoms to leave the cold surface, as shown in the top portion of the figure. See text for additional interpretation of this figure.

heated to over 100 K, the count rate would steadily increase because all of the atoms would eventually collect on the unheated area.

10.3 Mass spectrometer

A mass spectrometer for separating atoms of different mass is essential, since the laser provides only Z and not A selection. Narrow band lasers can discriminate on the basis of A, but interference between the hyperfine levels limits the usefulness of this technique for ^{81}Kr. Magnetic deflection mass spectrometers, time-of-flight mass spectrometers, ion cyclotron traps and quadrupole mass spectrometers are the most frequently used. When selecting the appropriate mass analyser for the Maxwell demon, the properties of each were examined.

Mass spectrometers employing deflection in a magnetic field are widely used because of their reproducibility, stability and high throughput. Ions formed in the ion source are typically accelerated to a few keV energy and enter the magnetic field with nearly common kinetic energies and directions. Ions of different masses are deflected along circular paths of different radii, and the separate ion beams can be collected and measured. Resolutions up to 100 or so can be obtained with a single focusing instrument, using an ion accelerating voltage of 8 kV and a radius of curvature of 12 cm in the magnetic field. In order to obtain a large spread of ion energies or a resolution higher than 10 000, double-focusing magnetic mass spectrometers have been commonly used. Static systems using magnetic deflection for gas analysis have been pioneered by Nier (1940) and Reynolds (1956).

A time-of-flight mass spectrometer is a device in which ions of differing masses are given the same energy (a few keV) and are allowed to traverse a field-free space. Because of their differing velocities, ions with various masses arrive at the collector at various times. For time-of-flight mass spectrometers, the ion beams must be pulsed to achieve mass separation. The main advantage of the time-of-flight mass spectrometer is the speed at which a complete mass spectrum can be displayed. Also, time-of-flight methods have large input apertures. For example, in the absence of space charge, nearly 100% of the positive ions produced in a planar disc of several mm diameter can be transmitted. The disadvantage of the traditional time-of-flight mass spectrometer is limited resolution, unless the drift region is very long.

Ion cyclotron traps can store ions for long times and can also measure, using Fourier transform techniques, the complete spectrum at one time. However, resonance charge transfer makes them unsuitable for this use.

The heart of the quadrupole mass spectrometer is a quadrupole section, usually made of four stainless steel rods. A DC voltage and superimposed radiofrequency (RF) voltage are applied to the rods such that ions of a selected mass have stable trajectories through the quadrupole filter section. The advantages of the quadrupole mass spectrometer are high scanning speeds, small size, light weight, low cost and relatively low ion energies through the mass filter region. The disadvantage of the quadrupole mass spectrometer in many applications is its small transmission and moderate resolution (approximately 200). An excellent review and a theoretical treatment of quadrupole mass spectrometers are given by Dawson (1980).

A quadrupole mass filter was chosen for mass selection in the Maxwell demon since ion energies are low; thus, the probability of implantation of ions into any metal surfaces during the mass selection process is small. It was felt that memory effects due to implanted stray ions would be a problem in mass spectrometers using high energies. A commercial (Extranuclear Laboratory) quadrupole mass spectrometer was chosen for this application. Modifications of the ionisation region were necessary to allow the atom buncher to be installed, and some grid wires were removed to allow the RIS beam to be positioned just above the surface of the atom buncher. A typical value for the abundance sensitivity α is 10^{-4} when using laser ionisation; thus, each cycle of the atoms through the Maxwell demon should give about a factor of 10^4 enrichment of a selected isotope at mass number A compared to $A \pm 1$. With laser ionisation, it was found that values for α can be much smaller than with electron ionisation at equivalent throughput.

10.4 Atom bank

10.4.1 Requirements

The basic idea of a sorting demon requires a method for storing the selected atoms. We will discuss the idea of an 'atom bank' in which an atom can be stored by ion implantation, counted by electron emission and recalled by laser annealing for further enrichment if required. Basically, the target material should have the following special characteristics: (a) an implantation efficiency near unity; (b) an electron emission coefficient $\gamma_e > 1$; and (c) an atom recovery fraction near unity, following application of a convenient energy source such as a laser pulse. Because of the importance of the atom bank concept, we will give a brief discussion of the physics associated with ion implantation, followed by data on ranges of implanted ions, sticking coefficients and γ_e coefficients of energetic ion bombardment of materials, and the recovery of noble gas atoms from materials.

10.4.2 Ion implantation

Whenever a surface is irradiated by energetic heavy particles, several processes may occur, including; erosion (sputtering); radiation damage to the target; secondary emission of electrons, ions, and photons; and backscattering or trapping (implantation) of incident particles. These processes are a consequence of collisions between the incident ion and the atoms and electrons of the solid target material. Almost all of the projectile energy loss occurs through elastic scattering by the shielded nuclei or by excitation and ionisation of the target at projectile energies in the keV range. The projectile energy is thus partitioned by kinetic energy transfer to recoiling target atoms and electrons and by excitation of electronic states in the solid. The recoiling target atoms and electrons form a secondary cascade and, in turn, partition their energies amongst these same processes. The scattering and slowing down processes thus lead to lattice damage and erosion of the target surface whenever energy transfer to surface atoms exceeds the threshold energy for sputtering (for example, see Behrisch (1981)).

Ions may be interstitially or substitutionally trapped in the solid matrix at various energy levels, requiring a specific activation energy for release, repositioning, or reordering of the lattice, depending on the depth of the trap (Kornelsen and Van Gorkum 1979). Trapping may produce undesirable memory effects in mass spectrometer ion sources due to pumping and retention of feed materials which are subsequently released through sputtering or thermal processes at some later point in time (for example, see Willis *et al* (1984)). On the other hand, solids may be used effectively to retain ion-implanted gaseous material requiring rather high temperatures for desorption from the solid material (Kornelsen 1964, Lal *et al* 1969, Kornelsen and Van Gorkum 1979).

Losses due to reflection and backscattering of light ions from the surfaces of heavy targets may be significant due to the kinematics of the scattering system, particularly at low energies. Thus, a high sticking probability can usually be achieved by using a target having lower atomic weight than that of the projectile. Under continuous bombardment, the concentration of trapped particles initially increases, slows down due to sputtering losses at the surface, and finally reaches a state of dynamic equilibrium whenever saturation is reached. At this point, a previously trapped particle is ejected from the target through sputtering for every injected particle. The saturation value for a projectile in a particular solid material is inversely proportional to the sputtering yield (Van Wyk and Smith 1976). In our application, saturation of a target will seldom be a concern.

10.4.3 Range of implanted ions

Information concerning the range and distribution of energetic particles in solids is of fundamental importance towards better understanding of implantation doping of semiconducting materials, ion-beam alloy formation, dislocation damage and sputtering. Therefore, considerable efforts have been devoted towards experimental (e.g. Hofker *et al* (1975)) and theoretical (e.g. Brice (1975), Winterbon (1975) and Biersack and Haggmark (1980)) studies of these processes. Computer simulation programs have been developed for studying ion implantation, radiation damage and sputtering processes which predict ranges and distributions in reasonable agreement with experiment (e.g. Biersack (1973)). Figure 10.7 displays the distributions of 10 keV Kr ions in Be, Al, Si and Cu, calculated with the code described by Biersack (1973). These materials have been considered or used by the authors in the storage and detection of low-abundance Kr isotopes, using RIS for ion generation. Useful tabulations on ranges of various ions in a variety of materials can be found in Wilson and Brewer (1979).

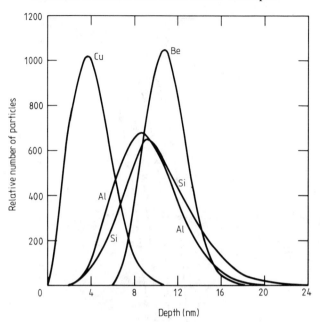

Figure 10.7 Calculated depth distributions of $10 \, keV \, Kr^+$ in poly-crystalline Al, Be, Cu and Si.

10.4.4 Sticking coefficients for ions

When energetic ions impact with a surface, some may be reflected from or backscattered from the surface as a consequence of single or multiple interactions with the atoms in the solid and thereby become lost, while others will be implanted or trapped within the surface. Thus, there is a sticking fraction or probability, η, for the process. The definition of η is simplified when the release of atoms due to diffusion can be neglected. The sticking coefficient, then, is a function of the type of ion and its energy, as well as the type of solid material and the number of particles previously implanted.

Early studies of η were motivated primarily by the need for information for ion pumps and ingassing (followed by outgassing) of vacuum systems (Redhead *et al* 1968). For Ne, Ar, Kr and Xe in W, η approaches unity for ion energies above 5 keV (see figure 10.8). Similarly, other authors (Lal *et al* 1969, Khaibullin *et al* 1980) conclude that for many metals η approaches unity for ion energies greater than 5 keV. Another use of ion implantation in thin metal and mylar films was considered for capturing ions in the solar wind (Lal *et al* 1969). Of the materials studied, aluminium was found to have the best properties for capturing the solar wind. For instance, η for $10 \, keV \, {}^{85}Kr^+$ was

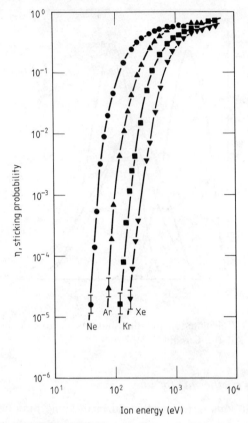

Figure 10.8 Sticking probability for ions of the noble gases in *W* (from Redhead *et al* 1968).

about 95% in aluminium foil. Many observers assume that the sticking probability in aluminium is unity, and it is often used as a reference foil. In table 10.1 some results for various materials selected as atom bank candidates are summarised (Hurst *et al* 1985a).

10.4.5 *Recovery of atoms; laser annealing of silicon*

A simple experimental facility was developed (Hurst *et al* 1985a) to study implantation of ions and recovery of noble gas atoms from targets that were candidates for the atom bank. This facility consisted of an electron source, a target at high potential and a Geiger–Müller tube mounted in a vacuum enclosure with suitable traps and getter pumps. Electron ionisation of ^{85}Kr was followed by ion implantation into various targets at 10 keV. As ions were implanted, the count rate of the Geiger–Müller tube decreased since it was positioned to detect atoms

Table 10.1 Sticking probabilities for atom bank candidates.

Target	Sticking probability, η (10 keV ^{85}Kr$^+$)	Notes
Al	1.0	Thin foil (reference material)
Al	1.0 ± 0.2	Al on kapton
Si	0.9 ± 0.2	Polished wafer
Cu–Be	0.9 ± 0.2	Electropolished
Cu–Be	0.9 ± 0.2	Activated for electron yield
Cu–Be	0.7 ± 0.2	Not activated
Cu	0.7 ± 0.2	Thin foil

from the gas phase and not from the target. The data in table 10.1 were obtained for several materials at a Kr$^+$ ion energy of 10 keV. As we will see below, silicon is of special interest because of the possible use of laser annealing for recovery of noble gas atoms, and Cu–Be because of its high electron emission coefficient, γ_e.

It is desirable to recall nearly all of the implanted noble gas atoms for further isotopic enrichment or for repeated counting. Several concepts for the recall of atoms from solids were investigated in this work. Early attention was focused on heating an aluminium target with an electric furnace after the method of Lal *et al* (1969). Microwave heating of thin aluminium discs was also studied. These methods give essentially 100% recovery of implanted krypton atoms, but they are not convenient. Laser ablation of a thin aluminium film on kapton plastic was evaluated, following a suggestion by Thonnard (1984, private communication), and this was found far more convenient than melting aluminium foils. However, laser ablation of 1 cm^2 of aluminium/kapton releases a large number of noble gas atoms and about 3×10^{15} molecules. The use of electronics-grade silicon wafers is now favoured because the sticking coefficient for silicon is close to unity, and tests show that more than 90% of the implanted krypton atoms can be removed by laser annealing. Since these silicon wafers are pure and do not release an appreciable number of atoms when annealed, they are suitable for including in the ultraclean vacuum system.

Research on laser annealing of silicon has grown enormously in the past few years (for example, see Wood (1981) and Stritzker *et al* (1981)) and has been the subject of many reviews (for example, see White *et al* (1982) and Poate and Mayer (1982)). Its use as a convenient atom bank was suggested to us by Appleton (1983, private communication). Laser annealing of silicon is now understood in some detail. When about

$1\,\mathrm{J\,cm^{-2}}$ is absorbed in the green proportion of the electromagnetic spectrum (e.g. frequency-doubled Nd:YAG laser), silicon melts to a shallow depth d_0 of about $1\,\mu\mathrm{m}$ determined by the absorption coefficient of light in the material, and the surface temperatures rise to about 3000 K with $2\,\mathrm{J\,cm^{-2}}$. As soon as the rapid absorption is over (approximately $10^{-8}\,\mathrm{s}$ laser pulse), the crystal begins to reform as the solid–liquid interface propagates back to the irradiated surface with a velocity of about $3\,\mathrm{m\,s^{-1}}$ (see figure 10.9). As this front propagates, atoms which are more soluble in the liquid silicon compared with the polycrystalline substrate will be continuously expelled into the liquid phase. As examples, copper atoms are segregated to the surface, whereas with boron atoms the implantation profiles are merely broadened by laser annealing (see figure 10.10). In the case of noble gases, one expects surface segregation since the silicon–krypton bond would be very weak and, in the absence of attractive forces which would adhere noble gas atoms to the surface, these atoms will be expelled to the gas phase. Furthermore, for $d_0 = 10^{-8}\,\mathrm{m}$, which is a typical implantation depth, and $v = 3\,\mathrm{m\,s^{-1}}$, the whole process should require only 3 ns.

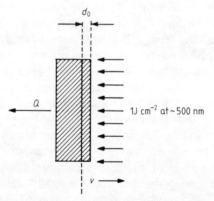

Figure 10.9 Schematic diagram of the laser annealing process.

Experiments were performed to verify the removal of krypton atoms from silicon by laser annealing. Frequency-doubled Nd:YAG radiation (of approximately 500 nm) was pulsed onto a silicon wafer at a level of about $1\,\mathrm{J\,cm^{-2}}$, but could not be uniformly applied because of poor beam quality. Several shots were used to release implanted [85]Kr atoms. It was found that the recalled fraction was more than 90% and we believe that it could approach 100% for uniform irradiation.

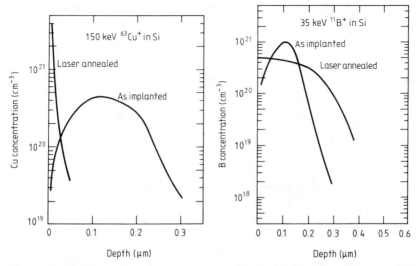

Figure 10.10 Illustration of the two types of redistribution phenomena associated with laser annealing of Si. The class of phenomena involving segregation of implanted species to the surface is of special interest here.

10.4.6 Secondary electron emission

There is considerable literature on secondary electron emission from solids due to the impact of noble gas ions. A review by Krebs (1968) summarises the field up to 1968. The γ_e coefficient (electrons emitted per ion incident) is a function of the mass and energy of the ion and a strong function of the material under bombardment. For the convenient region of ion energy below 10 keV, only a few materials have $\gamma_e \geqslant 1$ for ions of the noble gases. Alloys (Higatsberger *et al* 1954), or possibly thin film oxides (Dietz and Scheffield 1975), seem to be more satisfactory materials for the detection of low-energy (less than 10 keV) charged particles. For instance, silver–magnesium and nichrome are possibilities; however, copper–beryllium is definitely the leader, if not the standard. Allen (1942) used copper–beryllium to build an electron multiplier for the detection of low-energy ions. The definitive study of γ_e for copper–beryllium (98% Cu, 2% Be) is that of Baumhakel (1967), showing results for γ_e for He$^+$, Ne$^+$, Ar$^+$ and Xe$^+$ as a function of ion energy for both activated (see figure 10.11) and non-activated samples. For activated targets, γ_e ranges from 2 for Xe$^+$ to 6 for He$^+$ at 3 keV, and is 2.5 for Kr$^+$. The measured γ_e coefficient for Kr$^+$ ions on silicon at 10 keV is only about 1.5. However, even $\gamma_e = 1$ is an adequate monitor of the number of atoms being implanted.

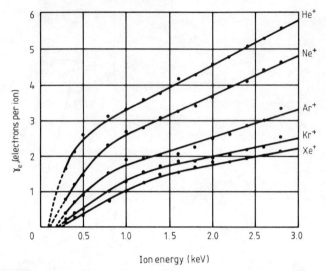

Figure 10.11 Gamma coefficient for noble gas ions in activated Cu–Be (from Baumhakel (1967), by permission).

10.4.7 Summary

Silicon has the following desirable features as an atom bank: (a) for Kr^+ ions of 10 keV, the sticking coefficient is nearly 100%; (b) following laser annealing, essentially 100% of the krypton atoms are recalled; and (c) the γ_e coefficient following laser annealing may be large enough to ensure nearly absolute atom counting. At the present time, silicon is the leading candidate for an atom bank. However, additional investigations could lead to a number of suitable materials. New studies with germanium (Jellison *et al* 1986a,b) suggest it as another very suitable material.

10.5 Atom counter

To actually count each atom, it is essential to count each ion transmitted by the mass spectrometer. An ion of a few kV impinging on a target can cause the release of more than one electron from the surface. Electron multiplier tubes of a variety of types can be used to detect even a single electron with nearly 100% efficiency. If γ_e is much greater than one, then the number of times that zero electrons are emitted will be a small fraction. Specifically, if we assume that even one electron will be counted by the multiplier if it is emitted from the target, the fraction of times that an ion will not be counted is $e^{-\gamma}$ if electron emission is random. We need $\gamma_e \geqslant 3$ for losses under 5% and $\gamma_e \geqslant 6$ for losses under 0.025%.

In figure 10.12, we show the arrangement of an ion target and a Johnston multiplier in basically the Daly (1960) configuration. A computer simulation of the ion optics was used to calculate ion trajectories from the quadrupole exit to the target, and electron trajectories from the target to the electron multiplier (Henry McKown of the ORNL Analytical Chemistry Division provided this very convenient ion simulation program (in 1982) which originated at Latrobe University, Department of Physical Chemistry, Bundoora, Victoria, Australia.) A two-dimensional geometry with all relevant potentials can be fed into a program which solves Laplace's equation to obtain fields and equipotentials. Ions can be started at arbitrary positions with specified initial directions and energies. Trajectories are determined and presented as ray traces on a cathode-ray tube (CRT) display. Furthermore, the program was used to obtain trajectories for electrons produced at arbitrary locations on the target, until they were collected on the electron multiplier surface. A small indentation of the electron-emitting surface into the target plate provides modest initial focusing so that all the electrons strike the central portion of the electron multiplier in a

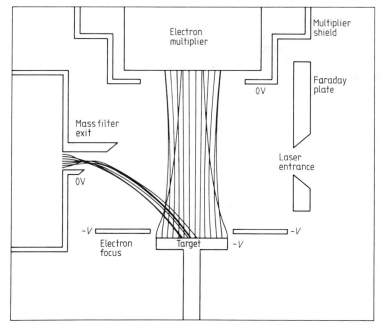

Figure 10.12 Configuration of the ion detector and associated ion and electron trajectories.

beam diameter of 2 or 3 mm. The ion trajectories and electron trajectories shown in figure 10.12 apply to target potentials from 2 to 10 kV.

The concept for data acquisition is simple. Buncher laser energy per
pulse, the vuv component of the ris lasers and the amplitude of the
pulse from the electron multiplier are all stored in a computer. Real-
time displays are used to monitor the buncher laser output and the vuv
laser output. The number of atoms counted per group of laser shots is
monitored as a function of time, and the pulse height spectrum of the
electron multiplier is displayed as data are acquired.

For absolute counting, one must also be concerned about the number
of electrons in the first stage of the electron multiplier. High-gain
electron multipliers are made commercially by several companies. Standard copper–beryllium dynodes (Laurenson and Koch 1965) have a
yield, δ, of about 1.5 to 2.0 secondary electrons per primary electron (at
about 300 eV). Special activation procedures used by Johnston Laboratories Inc. (Tice 1981, private communication) increase these to about
three when the primary electron has its optimum energy of about
500 eV. However, in our case it is convenient to let the primary electron
have the energy of the target potential (i.e. about 10 keV); hence, δ will
be about 1.0 at the first multiplier surface. The ion-counting efficiency is
governed by the statistics of electron multiplication in the early stages of
the multiplier. In particular, the average number of electrons, n, created
in the first stages of the multiplier (which equals $\gamma_e \delta$) determines the
probability that a single ion will be recorded (i.e. $\xi = 1 - e^{-n}$, where ξ
is the counting efficiency). Figure 10.13 shows integral pulse height
spectra for 7 keV Ar^+ ions striking three different targets with γ_e
coefficients of 1.2, 2.1, and 3.6, respectively. Both the slopes and the
intercepts depend on γ_e. Since δ is estimated to be about one, the
intercept for $v \to 0$, or the total number of particles counted, should be
0.7, 0.9 and 0.97 for the three targets. The actual convergence as γ_e
increases is assurance that nearly all of the ions are counted.

10.6 A demonstration using ^{81}Kr atoms

The concept for counting small populations of atoms required the
development of several basic components of the complete apparatus
before crucial demonstrations could be made. With the progress made
on (a) the atom buncher, (b) the vuv generation for the ris of krypton,
(c) the adaptation of the mass spectrometer, and (d) the atom bank, it
was possible to prove the concept of atom counting. Various tests,
conducted after an integration of all of the major components, were
viewed as proof that the Maxwell demon can work (Hurst *et al* 1985a).

Since the krypton atoms must be counted in a static enclosure isolated

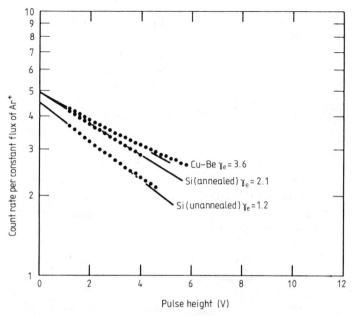

Figure 10.13 Integral pulse height spectra for $7\,\text{keV}$ Kr^+ ions on indicated targets with various γ_e coefficients.

from the vacuum system, outgassing rates were critical. During the counting period the chamber pressure must be kept below 10^{-5} Torr. The outgassing rate of krypton was measured to be 50 atoms per s, or about 10 atoms per s of ^{82}Kr, and the total pressure rise when the apparatus was in the counting mode was about 6×10^{-10} Torr h^{-1}, with only the getter pump open to the enclosure.

A four-wave mixing scheme (see Chapter 9) was used to generate 116.5 nm laser beams with energies up to approximately 500 nJ per pulse. Thus, krypton atoms could be efficiently excited by resonance radiation and subsequently ionised. With a xenon pressure of 40 Torr and argon pressure of 364 Torr in the VUV generation cell to achieve phase matching, the energy per pulse generated in the sum process $2\omega_1 + \omega_2$ near 116.5 nm was found to be approximately 500 nJ at a band width of $1.5\,\text{cm}^{-1}$. By using a known amount of krypton in the chamber, an effective detection volume (RIS ionisation volume multiplied by the mass spectrometer implantation factor) was found to be $2 \times 10^{-4}\,\text{cm}^{-3}$. This corresponds to a time of more than 700 hours to count 63% $[1 - (1/e)]$ of the atoms in the 5 l volume when running all lasers at 10 Hz, assuming that the sticking fraction at the target is unity.

The atom buncher was then employed to reduce the time to count the atoms. Some initial studies were made by time delaying the RIS lasers with respect to the buncher laser. By comparing the data obtained with the calculated curves (figure 10.5), it was estimated that the RIS laser beams were 0.2 cm from the buncher tip. At this distance and with the optimum laser delay time, about 10% of the atoms on the buncher tip should be ionised in a single laser pulse. However, at equilibrium the probability of counting one of the sample atoms in the system is much reduced if the lasers repeat at 10 Hz because of the long recurrence time. This buncher recurrence time was measured in the Maxwell demon apparatus by changing the repetition rate of the lasers and was found to be about 50 s. Therefore, at 10 Hz the probability of counting one of the sample atoms should be $0.1 \times (0.1/50) = 2 \times 10^{-4}$ or 5000 pulses for counting down to $1/e$ of the sample atoms.

With a large number (60 000) of atoms of ^{81}Kr, it was found that 2.2 hours at 10 Hz, or nearly 80 000 shots, were required. This implies that the total efficiency for ion extraction, transmission of the mass filter and ion implantation (mass spectrometer implantation factor) was about 6%. Space charge effects decrease the transmission if the number of implanted ions exceeds 3000 per pulse. Even with the 6% transmission factor, the RIS scheme combined with the atom buncher is rather effective. The demonstrated reduction of a factor of approximately 1000 in counting time by the atom buncher is crucial with present VUV schemes. Note that the buncher can also be used for analogue measurements to detect about 10% of the atoms on the cold tip; in this application, the buncher enhancement factor would be about 2×10^6 in a 5 l system.

After krypton atoms were ionised and isotopically selected, the ions were accelerated to 10 kV onto a copper–beryllium target where they were implanted. An electron multiplier with gain higher than 10^6 was used to count each implanted ion by detecting the secondary electrons emitted by the target. The ions take about 50 μs to travel through the mass spectrometer which means that time gating of the electron multiplier signal can be used to reduce background. Since the implanted krypton atoms stayed in the copper–beryllium target indefinitely, nearly all of the isotopically selected krypton atoms were eventually ionised and counted.

After mixing a sample of enriched ^{81}Kr (obtained from the National Bureau of Standards) with helium, 1000 atoms of ^{81}Kr with 2×10^5 other krypton atoms and 1×10^{10} atoms of helium were introduced into the chamber. Experimental data (Chen *et al* 1984b) for counting 1000 atoms of ^{81}Kr are shown in figure 10.14. The buncher laser was started before the RIS lasers to make sure that only a small fraction of krypton atoms were sitting on the cold spot at any given time. Thus, the probability of ionising and counting one atom of ^{81}Kr by a single laser pulse was less than 5%, even at the beginning of the run. This procedure ensured digital counting in which the atoms are counted one at a time. The results in figure 10.14 imply that 2100 atoms of ^{81}Kr were counted. However, for this measurement the particular unactivated copper–beryllium target used had a sticking coefficient of 0.6; thus, about 1300 atoms were actually counted. This good agreement between our RIS counting and decay counting at the NBS (a [81]Kr sample was decay counted at NBS by F J Schima in 1984 and provided to us for this work) proves the concept of Maxwell's demon.

Since most applications require enrichment of the 'signal atoms' compared to background or 'noise atoms', it is essential to demonstrate that isotopic enrichment can be done in the Maxwell demon before final counting. Figure 10.15 shows that an isotope of krypton could be stored

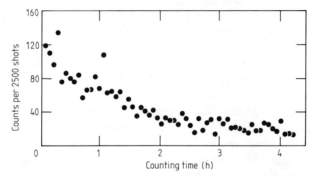

Figure 10.14 Atom-counting demonstration using 1000 atoms of [81]Kr. Exponential decay of the counting rate, as well as good agreement with decay counting, is offered as proof that the Maxwell demon can work.

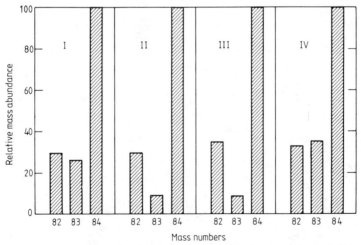

Figure 10.15 Bar graph showing the selective implantation of [83]Kr into Si and its subsequent recovery by laser annealing. Mass scan I was made before implantation of mass 83—scans II (30 minutes of implantation) and III (60 minutes of implantation). Scan IV, made after laser annealing to recover the implanted [83]Kr atoms, compares well with the original mass scan I.

in the atom bank and then recalled by laser annealing. In difficult cases, even pre-enrichment is required, as described in the next section.

It is interesting to compare this RIS counting of ^{81}Kr with decay counting. In all applications of ^{81}Kr to date, information has been obtained by counting the number of decays of the 2×10^5 year ^{81}Kr atoms. We note that the signal in figure 10.14 decreases with a half-life of about one hour, illustrating the rate at which the demon can sort, store and count atoms. While it may appear that ^{81}Kr atoms are made to decay in 1 hour instead of 2×10^5 years, nothing is decaying. Atoms are stored in the bank but can be recalled for further use or for repeated counting. In Chapters 11 and 12 we discuss in detail some applications of this new way of counting atoms.

10.7 A Maxwell demon using time-of-flight principles

A new version of Maxwell's demon was introduced (Thonnard *et al* 1984) which uses time-of-flight (TOF) principles for mass selection. Again, an atom buncher and RIS laser scheme were used for selective and efficient ionisation of a particular noble gas. However, mass selection is based on time of flight and is incorporated into the demon concept in a novel way. As shown in figure 10.16, an 'ion switch' is used which can be operated such that a selected isotope is either reflected or

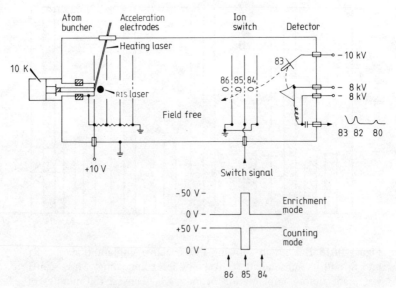

Figure 10.16 Schematic diagram of the Maxwell demon using a time-of-flight principle. (Courtesy N Thonnard, Atom Sciences Inc.)

transmitted, depending on the phase relationships of the switch signal. As with the Maxwell demon (MAXD), using a quadrupole mass filter (MAXDQP for abbreviation), the MAXDTOF can first be operated in an enrichment mode (if needed) followed by a counting mode.

Consider first the operation of the MAXDTOF in the enrichment mode. For example, suppose the sample contains 10^8 atoms of krypton and only 10^3 atoms of ^{85}Kr. Suppose that in a particular way of operating (Thonnard *et al* 1984) the krypton ions reach the ion switch at the end of the field-free drift tube in about 330 μs, and contiguous mass peaks are separated by about 2 μs in time or about 8 mm spatially. Soon after the ions of lowest mass clear the final grid of the ion switch they are accelerated (by 10 kV) to the target and implanted. But if the centre grid is pulsed 50 V positive when, for example, mass 85 is between the first two grids, ions of this selected mass will be reflected. These reflected ions strike a wall at low energy, are neutralised and return to the closed system of the sample. Now, if the centre grid returns to 0 V before ions of mass 86 enter the first section of the switch, these ions (and those at all higher masses) will be transmitted and implanted just as were all of the ions of mass below the selected level. Thus, in the enrichment mode all masses except the desired mass are continuously implanted! During the counting mode the phase of the switch signals takes on the complementary values shown in the inset; thus, only the selected mass is transmitted and implanted while all others are reflected.

A new time-of-flight concept was developed to take advantage of the sudden release of atoms from the buncher and the fact that atoms can be ionised in a narrow time-window in the RIS beam to improve mass resolution. By proper choice of the time delay, T_D, between the buncher laser and the RIS laser and the accelerating electric field, it was possible to nearly eliminate effects of velocity spread and position in the RIS beam (Thonnard *et al* 1984).

10.8 RISTRON

A recently proposed (Hurst and Allman 1983, Hurst 1984, Hurst *et al* 1985b) atom counter utilises the idea that ions can be implanted in silicon wafers, removed as neutral atoms by laser annealing, ionised with nearly 100% efficiency using RIS, filtered through a mass analyser and implanted into another silicon wafer. A complete cycle can be operated as shown in the RISTRON concept in figure 10.17. With only moderate abundance sensitivity in the mass analyser (e.g. 10^3), a sample containing, for example, ten atoms of ^{85}Kr and 10^9 atoms of ^{84}Kr would converge like 10^6, 10^3, 10, 10, . . . with each laser pulse. Of course, the RIS process will not be 100% efficient; however, in view of this rapid convergence, 80% to 90% efficiency would be adequate. The laser requirement for the RISTRON could be met by building a slab laser (Byer 1983, private communication) to produce about 10 J per pulse. These can then be used to produce about 5 μJ of VUV radiation. This approach to counting the atoms has several advantages over either type of the Maxwell demon. One of these is the very rapid rate of isotopic enrichment and final counting, since each step could occur at whatever rate the lasers (both annealing and RIS) can be pulsed (e.g. ten times per second). Another important advantage is derived from the fact that the system can be continuously pumped. Hence, outgassing and memory effects should be eliminated.

Several other options for mass selection are available in the RISTRON concept. If adequate isotopic enrichment can be built into the RIS process itself, the rest of the device is extremely simple, as shown in figure 10.18. In this example, annealing lasers and RIS lasers service both targets simultaneously, and a controller reverses the direction of the

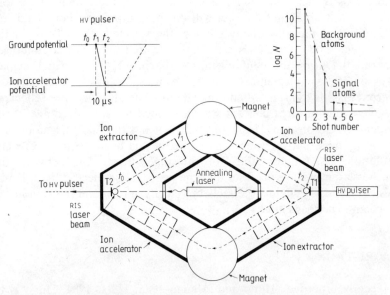

Figure 10.17 Schematic diagram of the RISTRON. Not shown is a RIS laser routed parallel to the front face of both targets, available at each target on each pulse. The annealing laser must be on for about 1 μs before the RIS lasers to allow atoms to travel into the RIS beam. Also not shown are electron multipliers to count the number of secondary electrons from ions striking each Si target. Pulsing the target potentials ensures that positive ions could leave T1 and T2 simultaneously and by following the arrows arrive at opposing targets after a few microseconds delay, allowing samples to be used in both targets.

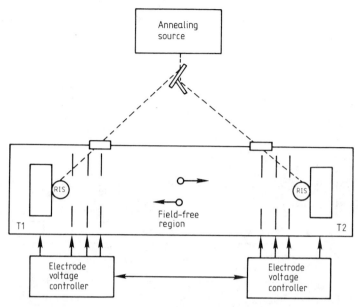

Figure 10.18 Illustration of the RISTRON concept in which isotopic selection is built into the RIS process. Unidirectional or bidirectional operating modes are possible.

electrical field to shuttle the atoms between targets. A field-free region could be provided so that atoms can be transmitted in both directions simultaneously; thus, two samples can be counted at the same time—for example, an unknown and a reference sample could be compared to cancel laser fluctuations. This feature was also provided in the magnetic sector design of figure 10.17 by pulsing the target potentials. In figure 10.19 a Wien filter is illustrated for mass selection. This type of mass filter uses both a magnetic and an electrical field ($E \times B$) and detailed treatments of its design have been given (Seliger 1972, Wilson and Brewer 1979). Particles of the desired mass are transmitted without deflection; thus, the linear design of figure 10.19 is possible. We suggest that it can be designed such that the direction of transmission of a positive ion can be reversed merely by changing the direction of E (normal to the ion vector). If it is desirable to process both targets simultaneously, the Wien filter could be situated closer to one ion source than to the other so that after ions from one source are analysed, there is time to reverse E to accommodate ions from the more distant source. Clearly, combinations of mass selections are possible—for example, time of flight could easily be added to the design of figure 10.18 so that mass selection is improved.

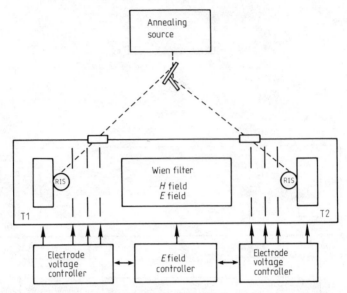

Figure 10.19 Illustration of the RISTRON concept incorporating laser isotopic enrichment with the Wien filter.

10.9 Other methods of atom counting

All of the methods described above use straightforward RIS schemes for the noble gas atoms which involve excitation from ground states. See Chapter 9 for detailed discussions of these schemes. While these schemes are direct, they are nevertheless difficult because of the problem of generating the necessary radiation in the VUV region. Thus, others have conceived of ingenious methods for resonance ionisation from metastable states of the noble gases. Efficient preparation of these populations would then eliminate the need for the VUV radiations.

Snyder *et al* (1985) suggested a combination of magnetic mass selection (in the form of an ion storage ring), resonant charge exchange and resonance ionisation from metastable states for the analysis of ^{90}Sr. This concept was extended to the noble gases and described especially for ^{81}Kr at a recent conference (Bonanno *et al* 1987). The method depends on charge exchange between Kr$^+$ and rubidium vapour in a heat pipe. If this process always leads to a particular metastable state, then it is possible to develop a simple RIS scheme. Further, from metastable levels it is possible to incorporate isotopic selectivity in the RIS process by taking advantage of optical isotope shifts (Lucatorto *et al* 1984, Miller *et al* 1985, Cannon and Whitaker 1985).

10.10 Isotopic enrichment

In each of the three types of atom counters described above, isotopic enrichment is an intrinsic feature of the sorting and counting process. Yet, each case differs from the others in rather fundamental ways. We need to examine these principles used for enrichment in the counters themselves, since they have a direct impact on the amount of external enrichment required to eliminate isotopic interferences.

The three types of sorting principles are compared in figure 10.20. In MAXDQP the demon attempts to find just the few desired atoms amid a huge sea of atoms of other isotopes, whose population is essentially constant until all of the desired atoms have been sorted and counted. On the other hand, in the MAXDTOF the demon attempts to first sort all undesired atoms into an inactive compartment and then counts the remaining desired atoms by sorting into a third compartment. A three-compartment demon certainly has some advantages over a two-compartment one. Finally, the RISTRON concept is a three-compartment device but again is fundamentally different from both demons in that all of the atoms are tossed from one compartment and simultaneously accumulated into two new compartments (for desired and undesired atoms), as in a winnowing process. In the demons, only a small fraction of the atoms is sorted in each trial, whereas in the RISTRON all of the atoms are involved in each step of the winnowing.

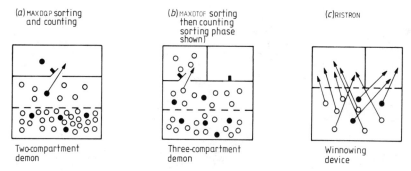

(a) MAXDQP sorting and counting — Two-compartment demon

(b) MAXDTOF sorting then counting (sorting phase shown) — Three-compartment demon

(c) RISTRON — Winnowing device

Figure 10.20 Summary of the atom-sorting and counting principles described in the text. In part (*a*) the small number of desired isotopes is sorted (and immediately counted) from the larger number of undesired isotopes. In part (*b*) the large number of undesired isotopes is first removed and then the desired isotopes are sorted (and counted) from the relatively small number of undesired isotopes. In part (*c*) both the undesired and desired isotopes are sorted as in a winnowing process. The winnowing process can be repeated until excellent isotope enrichment is obtained. Furthermore, each step of the winnowing process is monitored by counting the desired isotopes.

Let us first compare the two demons in a more quantitative way. Let α be the abundance sensitivity of the mass filter and β the rate of implantation of the Z-selected ions into the target. We define an enrichment factor, $E(t)$, by

$$E(t) \equiv (N_s(t)/N_{s0}) \, (N_x(t)/N_{x0})^{-1}$$

where $N_s(t)$ and N_x are the numbers of signal atoms and the number of undesired atoms (background) kept in the sample to be analysed. Thus, corresponding to figure 10.20(a),

$$E_a(t) = (1 - e^{-\beta t}) \, (1 - e^{-\alpha\beta t})^{-1}$$

and corresponding to figure 10.20(b),

$$E_b(t) = e^{-\alpha\beta t}/e^{-\beta t} = e^{\beta t(1 - \alpha)}.$$

These differ fundamentally and are plotted in figure 10.21 for good

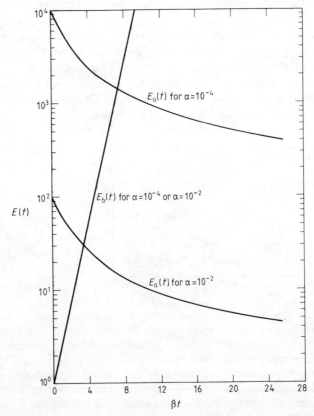

Figure 10.21 Enrichment factors as a function of time. The term $E_a(t)$ refers to the method of figure 10.20(a) and is shown for abundance sensitivity $\alpha = 10^{-4}$ and 10^{-2}. In the method of figure 10.20(b), $E_b(t)$ increases with time and is insensitive to α.

resolution ($\alpha = 10^{-4}$) and for poor resolution ($\alpha = 10^{-2}$). For the three-compartment demon, $E_b(t)$ grows exponentially and is quite insensitive to α, but some time is required for the enrichment factor to exceed the declining enrichment factor of the two-compartment demon.

The fraction of the mass-selected atoms retained (not lost in the background atoms) for the two cases must also be considered for the two demons. These are simply

$$S_a(t) = (1 - e^{-\beta t})$$

and

$$S_b(t) = e^{-\alpha \beta t}.$$

Some values are included in table 10.2 where one sees that the two-compartment demon must continue to $\beta t = 5$ to find 99% of the signal atoms, whereas the three-compartment demon experiences losses if isotopic enrichment continues too long. But this is where the advantage of a good mass filter reappears.

Table 10.2 Some values of $S_a(t)$ and $S_b(t)$ for moderate and poor abundance sensitivity.

| | $S_a(t)$ | | $S_b(t)$ | |
βt	$\alpha = 10^{-4}$	$\alpha = 10^{-2}$	$\alpha = 10^{-4}$	$\alpha = 10^{-2}$
1	0.633	0.633	1.0	0.99
2	0.865	0.865	1.0	0.98
5	0.993	0.993	1.0	0.95
10	1.0	1.0	0.999	0.91
20	1.0	1.0	0.998	0.82
40	1.0	1.0	0.996	0.67

In figure 10.20(c) for the RISTRON we see that

$$E(n) = (\alpha^{-1})^n$$

where n is the number of times all of the atoms are tossed. The fraction of the signal retained is

$$S(n) = S_1^n$$

where the fraction retained in a single toss S_1 will be determined almost entirely by the ionisation efficiency of the RIS lasers.

In practice, there are limits on the total number of atoms that can be processed in a sample admitted to either type of atom counter. The most severe of these is space charge (Chapter 2) which, if excessive, can alter ion optics in the extraction region. For the MAXDQP this limit is about 10^5 ions per laser pulse and perhaps as low as 10^4 ions per laser pulse in the MAXDTOF. If it is desired to do an isotopic enrichment in 1 hour (with the MAXDQP) or about 4×10^4 laser pulses, the maximum sample size is about 4×10^9 atoms. Whenever a sample contains 1000 signal atoms and about 10^6 times more atoms of other isotopes, there can be space charge effects. This limitation has been dealt with by developing external isotopic enrichment.

One system for external isotopic enrichment (Chen *et al* 1984a, c) is virtually identical to the demon itself (figure 10.2) except that it employs conventional electron-impact ionisation instead of the laser and the atom buncher. Ions are extracted from the source by a series of extraction and focusing lenses and are passed through the quadrupole mass filter. The mass-selected ions are then accelerated and implanted at 10 kV into a suitable collector. Under typical operating conditions, the throughput of the device for krypton is 3×10^{-3} A Torr^{-1} at an operating pressure of 10^{-5} Torr with an abundance sensitivity of 10^{-3}. This throughput corresponds to a time of approximately 100 minutes to process 63% (one *e*-fold) of the gas enclosed in the 3.6 l volume. Both aluminised kapton foils and silicon wafers have been employed as collectors, with good results. After a sufficient fraction of the desired isotope has been stored in the collector, the remainder of the sample is pumped away and the collector can then be processed (laser annealed for silicon or laser ablated for aluminised kapton) to recover the enriched sample for additional pre-enrichment, or transferred to the demon for final enrichment and counting. With this device, it is important to operate the electron gun at low voltage (about 30 V) to avoid pumping and unwanted effects due to atom entrapment in the ionisation source region (Willis *et al* 1984). A second type of enrichment facility has been developed (Willis and Thonnard 1984) and is based on the Wien filter. This device was based on a commercial instrument known as the colutron (Wahlin 1964) and has now been used successfully in a closed loop operation to achieve a high degree of isotopic enrichment (Lehmann 1985, private communication). Some comparisons of the characteristics of the colutron and the quadrupole isotopic enrichment devices are made in table 10.3. Fortunately, they play complementary roles if a sample is large (greater than 2×10^{-3} cm^3 STP) since it is necessary to first process it with the colutron before enriching a second stage with the quadrupole. In tandem, the two stages give a combined isotopic enrichment factor of 10^8.

10.11 Concluding remarks

We have discussed in this chapter the emergence of entirely new concepts for counting noble gas atoms with isotopic selectivity, indepen-

Table 10.3 Characteristics of two enrichment systems.

	Colutron (open loop)	Quadrupole
Ion source	Plasma	Electron impact
Abundance sensitivity	5×10^{-5}	2×10^{-4}
Throughput for 5×10^{-7} Torr Kr	0.3 A per Torr Kr 9.4×10^{11} Kr per s	0.005 A per Torr Kr 1.6×10^{10} Kr per s
Sample requirements	Greater than 2×10^{-3} cm^3 STP; gas recirculation source required for small samples	Less than 2×10^{-5} cm^3 STP; no minimum sample size
Additional comments	Ideal for large samples or initial enrichment step	Not suited for large samples; good for subsequent enrichment steps

dent of the radioactivity of these atoms. This was made possible by taking advantage of the Z-selectivity and high ionisation efficiency inherent in the RIS process. Important applications are numerous and some of these are under exploration by Thonnard *et al* (1987), Lehmann *et al* (1987) and Turner (1987), where many novel variations have been introduced to further improve these new methods.

References

Allen J S 1942 *Phys. Rev.* **61** 1692
Baumhakel R 1967 *Z. Phys.* **199** 41–55
Behrisch R ed 1981 *Sputtering by Particle Bombardment* (New York: Springer) vol. 47
Biersack J P 1973 *Radiat. Eff.* **19** 249
Biersack J P and Haggmark L G 1980 *Nucl. Instrum. Meth.* **174** 257
Bonanno R E, Snyder J J, Lucatorto T B, Debenham P H and Clark C W 1987 in *Resonance Ionization Spectroscopy 1986* ed G S Hurst and C Grey Morgan (Inst. Phys. Conf. Ser. 84) pp 85–90
Brice E 1975 *Ion Implantation, Range, and Energy Deposition Distribution, Vol 1: High Energy* (New York: Plenum)
Brillouin L 1951 *J. Appl. Phys.* **22** 334
Cannon B D and Whitaker T J 1985 *Appl. Phys.* B **38** 57

Chen C H 1984 in *Resonance Ionization Spectroscopy 1984* ed G S Hurst and M G Payne (Inst. Phys. Ser. 71) pp 189–94

Chen C H, Hurst G S and Payne M G 1980 *Chem. Phys. Lett.* **75** 473

—— 1984a in*Progress in Atomic Spectroscopy* ed F Beyer and H Kleinpoppen Part C, Ch. 4 (New York: Plenum) pp 115–50

Chen C H, Kramer S D, Allman S L and Hurst G S 1984b *Appl. Phys. Lett.* **44** 640

Chen C H, Willis R D and Hurst G S 1984c *Vacuum* **34** 581

Daly N R 1960 *Rev. Sci. Instrum.* **31** 720

Dawson P H 1980 *Advances in Electronics and Electron Physics Suppl. 13B Applied Charged Particle Optics* ed A Septier (New York: Academic) pp 173–256

Dietz L A and Scheffield J C 1975 *J. Appl. Phys.* **46** 4361

Higatsberger M J, Demorest H L and Nier A O 1954 *J. Appl. Phys.* **25** 883

Hofker W K, Oosthoek D P, Koeman N J and DeGrefte H A 1975 *Radiat. Eff.* **24** 223

Hurst G S 1984 in *Resonance Ionization Spectroscopy 1984* ed G S Hurst and M G Payne (Inst. Phys. Conf. Ser. 71) pp 309–18

Hurst G S and Allman S L 1983 Noble Gas Atom Counter Utilizing Laser Annealing and Resonance Ionization Spectroscopy *Patent disclosure* CNID-4403

Hurst G S, Allman S L and Thonnard N 1985b *US Patent disclosure* 4 658 135 (assigned to Atom Sciences Inc.)

Hurst G S, Chen C H, Kramer S D, Cleveland B T, David R Jr, Rowley R K, Gabbard F and Schima F J 1984a *Phys. Rev. Lett.* **53** 1116

Hurst G S, Chen C H, Kramer S D, Payne M G and Willis R D 1983 in *Science Underground* ed M M Nieto, W C Haxton, C M Hoffman, E W Kolb, V D Sandberg and J W Toevs (American Inst. Phys. Conf. Ser. 96) pp 96–104

Hurst G S, Payne M G, Chen C H, Willis R D, Lehmann B E and Kramer S D 1981 in *Laser Spectroscopy* V ed A R W McKellar, T Oka and B P Stoicheff (New York: Springer) pp 59–66

Hurst G S, Payne M G, Kramer S D and Chen C H 1980 *Phys. Today* **33**(9) 24

Hurst G S, Payne M G, Kramer S D, Chen C H, Phillips R C, Allman S L, Alton G D, Dabbs J W T, Willis R D and Lehmann B E 1985a *Rep. Prog. Phys.* **48** 1333

Hurst G S, Payne M G, Phillips R C, Dabbs J W T and Lehmann B E 1984b *J. Appl. Phys.* **55** 1278

Jellison G E Jr, Lowndes D H, Mashburn D N and Wood R F 1986a *Phys. Rev. B* **90** 2407–15

Jellison G E Jr, Lowndes D H and Wood R F 1986b in *Excimer Lasers and Optics* SPIE vol. 710 (Washington, DC: The Society of Photo-

Optical Instrumentation Engineers) pp 24–34

Khaibullin I B, Shtyrkov E I and Zaripov M M 1980 *J. Phys. Soc. Japan Suppl.* A **49** 1281

Kornelsen E V 1964 *Can. J. Phys.* **41** 364

Kornelsen E V and Van Gorkum A A 1979 *Radiat. Eff.* **42** 113

Kramer S D, Chen C H, Allman S L, Hurst G S and Lehmann B E 1984 in *Laser Techniques in the Extreme Ultraviolet Spectroscopy* ed S E Harris and T B Lucatorto (New York: American Institute of Physics) pp 246–52

Krebs H K 1968 *Fortschr. Phys.* **16** 419

Lal D, Libby W F, Wetherill G, Leventhal J and Alton G D 1969 *J. Appl. Phys.* **40** 3257

Laurenson L and Koch J W 1965 *Br. J. Appl. Phys.* **16** 889

Lehmann B E, Rauber D F, Thonnard N and Willis R D 1987 in *Resonance Ionization Spectroscopy 1986* ed G S Hurst and C Grey Morgan (Inst. Phys. Conf. Ser. 84) pp 81–4

Lucatorto T B, Clark C W and Moore L J 1984 *Opt. Commun.* **48** 406

Maxwell J C 1872 *Theory of Heat* (New York: Appleton) pp 308–9

Miller C M, Engleman R and Keller R A 1985 *J. Opt. Soc. Am.* **2** 1503

Nier A O 1940 *Rev. Sci. Instrum.* **11** 212

Poate J M and Mayer J W 1982 ed *Laser Annealing of Semiconductors* (New York: Academic)

Ready J F 1965 *J. Appl. Phys.* **36** 462

Redhead P A, Hobson J P and Kornelsen E V 1968 *The Physical Basis of Ultrahigh Vacuum* (London: Chapman and Hall)

Reynolds J H 1956 *Rev. Sci. Instrum.* **27** 928

Seliger R L 1972 *J. Appl. Phys.* **43** 2352

Snyder J J, Lucatorto T B, Debenham P H and Geltman S 1985 *J. Opt. Soc. Am.* B **2** 1497

Stritzker B, Pospieszczyk A and Tagle J A 1981 *Phys. Rev. Lett.* **47** 356

Thonnard N, Payne M G, Wright M C and Schmitt H W 1984 in *Resonance Ionization Spectroscopy 1984* ed G S Hurst and M G Payne (Inst. Phys. Conf. Ser. 71) pp 227–34

Thonnard N, Willis R D, Wright M C and Davis W A 1987 in *Resonance Ionization Spectroscopy 86* ed G S Hurst and C Grey Morgan (Inst. Phys. Conf. Ser. 84) pp 75–80

Turner G 1987 in *Resonance Ionization Spectroscopy 86* ed G S Hurst and C Grey Morgan (Inst. Phys. Conf. Ser. 84) pp 51–8

Van Wyk G N and Smith H J 1976 *Radiat. Eff.* **30** 91

Wahlin L 1964 *Nucl. Instrum. Meth.* **27** 55–60

White C W, Naramoto H, Williams J M, Narayan J, Appleton B R and Wilson S R 1982 *Laser and Electron-Beam Interactions with Solids* ed B R Appleton and G K Celler (New York: American Elsevier) pp 241–48

Willis R D, Allman S L, Chen C H, Alton G D and Hurst G S 1984 *J.*

Vac. Sci. Technol. A **2**(1) 57

Willis R D and Thonnard N 1984 in *Resonance Ionization Spectroscopy 1984* ed G S Hurst and M G Payne (Inst. Phys. Conf. Ser. 71) pp 213–18

Wilmoth R G and Fisher S S 1978 *Surf. Sci.* **72** 693

Wilson R G and Brewer G R 1979 *Ion Beams with Applications to Ion Implantation* (Huntington, New York: Krieger)

Winterbon K 1975 *Ion Implantation, Range, and Energy Deposition Distribution Vol 2: Low Energy* (New York: Plenum)

Wood R F 1981 *Appl. Phys. Lett.* **38** 357

11

Cosmology and particle physics

11.1 Introduction

As discussed in previous chapters, RIS provides some basic analytical measurement systems (atom-counting systems) with unique selectivity and sensitivity. In the remaining chapters some of the applications of the atom-counting systems will be illustrated. These are of three basic types. In the first type, a rare particle or event must be detected as it happens, i.e. atom counting must be done in 'real time'. In the second type, a stable rare gas atom is accumulated and counted at arbitrary time. In the third type any kind of atom in a solid can be counted at arbitrary time. Furthermore, the atoms to be counted can be in the ground state, or they could be in an excited state. They may be perfectly common atoms that happen to be rarely found in a particular environment, or they may be exotic atoms. Elementary particles which prepare unique populations of atomic species can also be detected with RIS.

Since detectors based on RIS have been considered for searches of particles which were relics of the early universe, it is convenient to organise the remaining chapters of this book along the lines of modern cosmology. In spite of the highly speculative nature of cosmology, it is useful to follow the time evolution of the universe as we discuss the detection of relic particles, solar processes and planetary-earth sciences as a compact way of organising our discussions.

In this chapter we consider the detection of the massive magnetic monopole which is predicted by grand unification theories (GUTs). These particles have a mass of about 10^{16} GeV and would have required the temperature of the 'big bang' itself for their production. Since these particles could not be produced in an accelerator, but could exist today as relics of the universe, we will be proposing a cosmic-ray search in real time for their detection. In Chapter 12 we will consider two other possible relic particles—quarked or fractionally charged atoms and superheavy atoms which must be searched for in solid materials. Solar neutrino experiments, in which the modern flux of neutrinos on the Earth would be measured by counting stable atoms induced in a large target, will be the subject of Chapter 13. Cosmic-ray production of long-lived atoms provides a natural tracer for the study of the Earth and planetary phenomena described in Chapter 14.

11.2 Connection of cosmology with particle physics

According to modern cosmology (see, for example, Weinberg (1972) and Zeldovich and Novikov (1975), or a convenient summary by Linde (1984)), the universe has been expanding from a state of infinite temperature and density for about ten billion years. Currently there is a remarkably strong coupling of cosmological with particle physics theories. The unified weak and electromagnetic interactions were developed by Glashow (1961), Weinberg (1967) and Salam (1968), while grand unification, which unifies the strong, weak, and electromagnetic interactions, was originated by Georgi and Glashow (1974) (see figure 11.1). The super gravity theories of Freedman *et al* (1976) and of Deser and Zumino (1976) attempt to unify all known forces. While cosmology and particle physics started independently, it is now difficult to make progress in one without the other. Some of the elementary particles are so massive that no accelerator on earth will ever be able to produce them and they can only be observed as relics of the 'big bang'. Particle physics theories or, in particular, theories that attempt to unify all of the

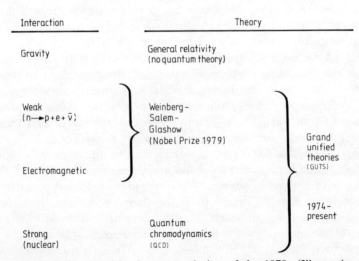

The Particle Theory Revolution Of The 1970s

Figure 11.1 The particle theory revolution of the 1970s (Illustration courtesy of Alan Guth.)

forces in nature require, therefore, a cosmological test. Conversely, new directions in modern cosmology may well rest on the outcome of searches for elementary particles as relics of the early universe. (See figure 11.2.)

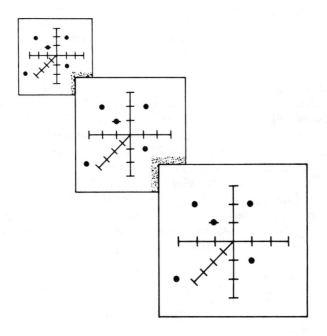

Physical distance =
$R(t) \times$ coordinate distance

Figure 11.2 The expanding homogeneous universe. (Illustration courtesy of Alan Guth.)

Preskill (1982) made a clear summary of the impacts of particle physics on cosmology. *First*, the interactions mediated by particles with masses of order M_{GUT} typically fail to conserve baryon number, leading to the prediction of proton decay. During the first 10^{-35} s, processes that did not require baryon number conservation could have been so numerous that any pre-existing memory was erased; thus, it is possible to calculate today's baryon density from cosmological models. The results of some of these models are in agreement with the observed relative abundance of photons to baryons, i.e. about 10^{10}. *Second*, grand unification leads to the prediction that the universe went through a phase transition at T_e of order M_{GUT}. As we will see in §11.5, this transition is the key idea of inflationary cosmology introduced by Alan Guth. *Third*, the GUTs predict that magnetic monopoles with masses of the order of M_{GUT} are produced copiously, and these stable particles should be observable today.

11.3 Time evolution of the universe

According to modern cosmology, the universe originated with a vacuum fluctuation about ten billion years ago, creating matter, geometry and time itself (see figure 11.2). We are totally lacking a means of discussing the situation prior to the 'big bang', and the event itself remains covered in mystery. Prior to the Planck time, 10^{-43} s, a quantum gravity theory is needed for the following reason. In 10^{-43} s, light will travel about 3×10^{-33} cm, and at this spacing elementary particles have gravitational attraction energies comparable to the energy of photons required to resolve such short distances. At about the Planck time, the first symmetry breaking occurs in grand unification and the gravitational force is split off from the three other fundamental forces (see figure 11.3). At 10^{-35} s, a second symmetry breaking isolates the strong from the electroweak force, and at about 10^{-11} s the final symmetry breaking separates the weak and the electromagnetic forces. As the universe expands, it cools down. In about 1 ms, baryons and mesons are created from quarks. The time period from milliseconds to three minutes is shown in figure 11.4. At the end of this period light elements are appearing on the scene. Neutral atoms did not appear until the universe

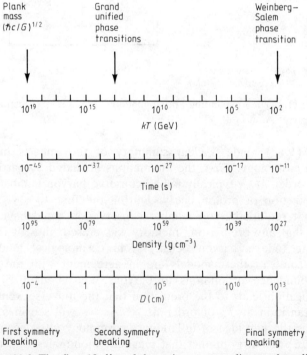

Figure 11.3 The first 10^{-11} s of the universe according to the adiabatic model. (Illustration courtesy of Alan Guth.)

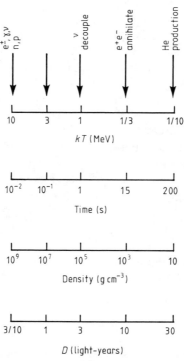

Figure 11.4 The first three minutes of the universe. (Illustration courtesy of Alan Guth.)

was about 500 000 years old. Galaxies, including our own Milky Way, the stars and our own solar system were formed much later.

One of the most startling predictions of grand unification theories is that baryons decay in about 10^{38} s (3×10^{30} years). Proton decay searches are one of the most active areas in particle physics, and verification would be the crucial test of the GUT. However, observation of grand unification monopoles (GUM) would be of comparable significance to particle physics and, in addition, would be a direct observation of a relic particle signalling the birth of the cosmos. Ironically, it is the beginning and the end of our familiar universe where grand unification theories are now being tested. We need to look in more detail at the brief interval of time following the big bang to examine the question of monopole production which depends critically on theories of the inflation of the universe.

11.4 Standard cosmology and its problems

The cepheid variable stars, first observed by John Goodrick in 1784, have been extremely useful in measuring astronomical distances. These stars show a regular variation of radius and luminosity with time. In 1912, Henrietta Leavitt found that the luminosity period, P, ranging from 1 to 100 days, increases with the relative luminosity, L, of the star. Astronomers have devised trigonometric methods of measuring the distance of the near stars and independent methods to measure the flux, F, of photons. Thus, for the near stars, F can be used to obtain absolute values of L, i.e. $L = 4\pi F d^2$, where d is the known distance, which quantifies the Leavitt relationship. In 1923, Edwin Hubble discovered cepheids in the Andromeda Nebula and, from the measured P, estimated L. Measurements of F revealed that the Andromeda galaxy was almost a million light years from us, compared to a distance of about 100 000 light years across our Milky Way galaxy.

Hubble soon made the even more profound observation that the light from the galaxies was red shifted by an amount that increases with distance. From the well known Doppler shift, it was concluded that the velocity at which matter is receding from itself increases with distance. The Hubble law (1929) states

$$v = lH$$

where v is the recession velocity, l is the distance to the galaxy and H is Hubble's constant. This law is the underlying reason for belief in the expansion of the universe. By simply reversing time, we are led to the conjecture that all matter originated from a point of infinite density. From these considerations, Hubble originally estimated the age of the universe to be 1 billion years, which was younger than the geological age (7 billion years) of the Earth. Recalibration of the cepheid variables, however, now gives 10 to 15 billion years as the 'Hubble age' of the universe, i.e. $H \approx 10^{-10}$ years^{-1}.

A stronger argument for the big bang came with the discovery (1965) of the 3 K microwave radiation by Penzias and Wilson. The discovery of this radiation coming from every direction in space and having a wavelength corresponding to 3 K is in agreement with independent theory which predicted that the big bang should have cooled down to 3 K in about 15 billion years. Even though the conclusions derived from the observations of Hubble and of the microwave radiation by Penzias and Wilson are in such remarkable agreement, the quotation from Mark Twain used by William Fowler (1984) in his Nobel lecture is just as appropriate here:

> There is something fascinating about science. One gets such wholesale returns of conjecture out of such a trifling investment of fact. (*Life on the Mississippi*, 1874)

Indeed, the standard scenario has serious problems which have been discussed in much detail in the popular press (see, for example, Weinberg (1977) and Trefil (1983)). Here we follow the outline of Linde (1984) who makes a clear separation of the problems coming from cosmology itself from those which are a consequence of new theories of elementary particles.

(i) *The singularity problem*. If our universe did not exist at $t < 0$, how could it originate from nothing?

(ii) *The flatness problem*. Presently we know that $0.03 \leq \rho/\rho_c \leq 2$ which is remarkably close to the critical density, ρ_c, to just close the universe. Since at the Planck time, $|\rho - \rho_c|/\rho_c \leq 10^{-59}$, it is most remarkable that our universe was created flat to such an amazing accuracy.

(ii) *The homogeneity problem*. The standard scenario assumes that the initial universe was perfectly homogeneous and isotropic; however, we know that the present universe is lumpy on a small distance scale.

(iv) *The horizon problem*. The isotropy of the 2.7 K background radiation (to a remarkable precision) is difficult to understand. It implies that at $t = 500\,000$ years (when the universe became transparent), matter was homogeneously distributed on a scale much larger than ct.

(v) *The galaxy formation problem*. The formation of galaxies is difficult to understand without some initial clumps of matter, and the standard scenario does not provide these in the very early universe.

(vi) *The antimatter (baryon asymmetry) problem*. In the observable part of the universe, the density of the baryons is many orders of magnitude greater than the density of antibaryons.

These problems were so severe in the 1940s that the big bang cosmology had strong competition from the steady state model. In this, as the name implies, the universe is eternal. The creation of less than one hydrogen atom per cubic metre per billion years maintains a constant density.

11.5 Inflationary cosmology and magnetic monopoles

The concept of the inflationary universe was introduced by Guth (1981) and pursued by Linde (1982) and Albrect and Steinhardt (1982). An excellent recent review is the article by Linde (1984). Spontaneous symmetry breaking in unified gauge theories allows massless vector fields to transform to massive vector bosons with strong (short-range) interactions. In these phase transitions the effective potential for the system may have more than one minimum over certain temperature ranges. At some critical temperature where two minima have equal potentials, a first-order phase transition occurs that can be compared with the formation and expansion of bubbles in water, except here reference is made to bubbles filled with matter in an energetically favourable phase.

When grand unification is combined with standard big bang cosmology, enormous numbers of massive (about 10^{16} GeV) particles having the property of isolated magnetic poles are predicted. In standard cosmology the very early history of the universe starts with a vacuum fluctuation, and at the Planck time (10^{-43} s) the gravitation force freezes out. This stage is described as a false vacuum in which the universe is in a special type of metastable state from which expansion occurs, due to quantum-mechanical tunnelling. Most of the energy is now in the Higgs field which is converted to ordinary matter as a consequence of expansion by tunnelling. Furthermore, expansion can occur from many centres, and as these grow and collide, kinks in space (described as domain walls, string and point defects) are produced. The point defects which are produced, as the Higgs field rapidly decays to create matter, are the grand unification monopoles.

Standard cosmology with grand unification has a number of special problems, one of the most difficult of which is the primordial monopole problem. Nearly all grand unification theories predict a large number of 't Hooft–Polyakov monopoles ('t Hooft 1974, Polyakov 1974) with masses 10^{16} times that of the proton. Monopole abundances predicted from these theories, combined with the standard scenario, predicts the universe to be 10^{15} times heavier and thus it would have collapsed long ago.

Mass was not an issue in the original monopole, since Dirac visualised it as an isolated end of a semi-infinitely long, but infinitesimally thin, solenoid. The magnetic charge of the monopole is given by $g = n/2e$, where n is an integer and e is the charge of the electron; $g_D = 1/2e$ is usually called the Dirac magnetic charge. This quantisation can also be turned around to show that the existence of a magnetic monopole would imply quantisation of electrical charge. Most particle physicists believe that fractional charge on quarks can exist inside a nucleon. The properties of a monopole of the 't Hooft–Polyakov type are very different from the Dirac monopole and can be summarised (Preskill 1982) as follows: charge $= g = g_D = 1/2e$; radius $= r \sim 10^{-28}$ cm and mass approximately 10^{16} GeV. The monopole is stable because it has the lowest magnetic charge.

The inflationary model of the universe introduced by Guth (1981) had the explicit purpose of suppressing monopoles since they had not been observed. In this picture the well depth of the false vacuum is less than in the older cosmology; therefore, tunnelling can occur much more rapidly, and the modified theory predicts that our universe was created more smoothly from one major centre. As a consequence, less kinking occurred and fewer point defects survived as relics of the big bang. The 'new' inflationary universe cosmology, first suggested by Linde (1982) further suppresses the estimates of the number of primordial monopoles. Clearly, these are highly speculative concepts, and one is not surprised that predictions of the number of monopoles vary widely. However, the conclusion of Preskill (1982) seems prudent, 'In the new inflationary universe scenario it is possible for the monopole abundance to be both small enough to be acceptable and large enough to be observable. Clearly we should look for them'. The new inflationary cosmology can no longer be taken lightly since it resolves a number of the problems of the standard cosmology.

11.6 Searches for magnetic monopoles

Searches for monopoles started more than 50 years ago with the theoretical predictions of Dirac; for a review see Giacomelli (1984). These included cosmic-ray searches and investigations made at accelerators, in the event that monopoles were not too heavy. In the light of grand unification theories, attention has now been turned to the big bang itself as the only source of energies above 10^{16} GeV. It is very important to note that the GUT monopole would be produced at low velocity and would be accelerated only by the weak galactic magnetic and gravitational fields (Preskill 1982). Thus, the most likely velocity seen by a detector on earth would correspond to $\beta = 10^{-4}$ to 10^{-3}. This means that most searches already made with large scintillation or ionisation devices may not be valid since low-velocity monopoles do not excite (much less ionise) matter very efficiently. Clearly, a new approach must be taken to monopole searches—namely it is exceedingly important to use detectors in which the response to low-velocity monopoles is well understood.

Perhaps the most reliable monopole detector would be based on the induction method which is not sensitive to velocity. Such a method involving a superconducting loop and a SQUID detector was used by Cabrera (1982) in a search which reported one candidate event. This event was surprising in view of the small size of the detector and the Parker limit. The flux of magnetic monopoles is severely limited by demanding that the galactic magnetic field energy is not substantially depleted in a time t of order 10^8 years, i.e. the field generation time; (Parker 1970, Turner *et al* 1982). Thus,

$$nv \leqslant B/8\pi gt \approx 2 \times 10^{-4} \, \text{m}^{-2} \, \text{year}^{-1}$$

if $B = 3 \times 10^{-6}$ gauss. Cabrera *et al* (1983) have repeated their observations without success, even with a large detector.

In the next section we describe a development concept which could lead to large monopole detectors which work well at low velocities, and would be based on simple principles which offer monopole detectors of known response. In view of the enormous impact that the discovery of magnetic monopoles would make on particle physics and on our understanding of the very early universe, the development of detectors with these characteristics is very desirable.

11.7 Concept of a monopole detector using RIS

A theoretical study by Drell *et al* (1983) on monopole interaction in helium shows that in this simple atom a monopole will excite He(2^3S) exclusively and without ionisation. The work of these authors provides the basis for an ionisation detector which has the potential of being as reliable as the Cabrera induction experiment.

The yield of He(2^3S) excited by monopoles as a function of the velocity parameter β (which equals v/c), is plotted in figure 11.5 according to the theory of Drell *et al* (1983). At STP, more than 100 of the triplet states are produced per centimetre, even at the low values of $\beta = 10^{-4}$. Furthermore, the production increases rapidly as the velocity increases. The most remarkable feature of the monopole interaction in helium is that, while these triplet states are created in great abundance, little else happens in helium—no singlet states and no ionisation occur.

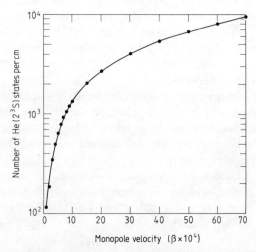

Figure 11.5 Calculated (Drell *et al* 1983) number of triplet metastable states created per centimetre of path length in He at STP by a magnetic monopole as a function of its velocity.

Here we are proposing to take explicit advantage of this unique monopole signature.

Helium has been studied in much detail and the fate of various kinds of excited states is known over a wide range of gas pressures. Even in admixtures of helium with other gases, much is known about the energy pathways following charged particle excitation (see Chapters 1 and 2). Therefore, it is possible to have a high degree of confidence in He(2^3S) as a monopole detector—a confidence which is not at all justified in other monopole detectors, except for the Cabrera (1982) detector. For example, some detectors are based on the ionisation of gas mixtures such as P-10 (90% Ar and 10% CH_4). Arguments are even made (Drell *et al* 1983) that since such detectors do not show monopoles, surely monopoles must be very slow because many metastable states are made in Ar, and these are quenched by ionising CH_4. Studies (Melton *et al* (1954), see also Chapter 1) with charged particles do show that long-lived states are created in Ar which can ionise CH_4. However, the states so involved are likely to be the resonance states (Hurst *et al* 1965) $3p^55s(^3P_1)$ at 14.09 eV and $3p^55s(^1P_1)$ at 14.26 eV which can ionise CH_4 with an ionisation potential 13.12 eV. (These high-lying states in Ar have a long lifetime due to the imprisonment of resonance radiation rather than their metastability.) The state which the monopole would excite in Ar, analogous to He(2^3S), would be $3p^54s(^3P_2)$ at 11.55 eV. If a monopole produced this $^3P_2$ level in Ar, it would excite, but not ionise, CH_4, and no signal would be observed in an ionisation detector.

The possibility that certain plastic scintillators respond to monopoles has been discussed (Ahlen and Tarle 1983) and has recently been used (Tarle *et al* 1984) to set the low limit of 4.1×10^{-13} cm^{-2} sr^{-1} s^{-1} for the monopole flux in the velocity range 6×10^{-4} c to 2.1×10^{-3} c. However, the meaning of these limits is unclear, since the treatment of a monopole interaction in a plastic scintillator utilises the highly schematic model of a degenerate electron gas recently employed (Echenique *et al* 1981) to calculate the stopping power of a slow-moving, electrically charged particle.

Compared to the above complex detectors, a monopole detector, based on excitation of He(2^3S), is much simpler to understand in detail. Monopole interactions producing He(2^3S) are understood and quantitative calculations have been made. Furthermore, it is possible to detect He(2^3S) by reliable and well known ionisation methods. Here we describe two methods for detecting He(2^3S)—namely a Penning ionisation method and a method based on RIS. Both of these are possible because much basic research has been done to understand not only the production of excited states in He by charged particles, but also the fate of the excited species produced (Bartell *et al* (1973), Hurst and Klots (1976), Payne *et al* (1975); see also Chapter 1).

Before discussing these ionisation detectors, it will be useful to describe the behaviour of the initial state $He(2^3S)$. In He at low pressure the lifetime of the $He(2^3S)$ species is governed by diffusion to the walls, but at pressures above 100 Torr it is dominated by the three-body process $He(2^3S) + He + He \rightarrow He_2(a\Sigma_\mu^+) + He$. The rate for this process is known (Phelps and Molner 1953, Phelps 1955) to be 0.26 $P^2(s^{-1})$ where P is in torr. This excited He dimer is highly metastable and diffuses slowly to the walls where it is de-excited over a period of time; thus, no detectable ionisation is seen. In practice, He will be contaminated with a few PPM of molecular gas, N_2, and the rate of destruction of $He(2^3S)$ is increased due to the Penning ionisation process $He(2^3S) + N_2 \rightarrow He + N_2^+ + e^-$. But these rates are also well known (Ueno *et al* 1980). For N_2, the cross section is given by $\sigma_M = 5.1 \times 10^{-16}\,cm^2$ and the rate constant $k_M = 6.8 \times 10^{-11}\,cm^3\,s^{-1}$. The effect on lifetime due to 10 PPM, the typical contamination level, is hardly observable at the higher He pressures; see figure 11.6. On the

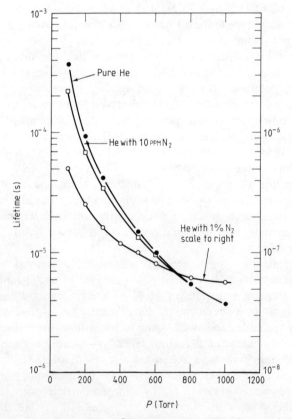

Figure 11.6 Lifetime of $He(2^3S)$ in pure He, with 10 PPM of N_2, and with 1% N_2 as a function of pressure.

other hand, if 1% of a molecular gas, such as N_2, is added to He at 1000 Torr, the He(2^3S) state is converted to ionisation by the Penning process in less than 10^{-7} s (see figure 11.6).

To take advantage of these facts, consider three ionisation chambers A, B and C stacked close together in that order, where A and C contain He + 1% N_2 and B contains pure He (see figure 11.7). Ionisation signals from detectors A and C would exhibit delayed coincidence (due to the finite velocity of the monopole), while chamber B would show no ionisation signal when a monopole penetrates all of the chambers. The data *Y–N–Y* suggest that some event could create a metastable species, but *not* ionisation. This would utilise the essence of the Drell *et al* (1983) calculation and would preserve the quantum state selectivity inherent in their results. On the other hand, use of He mixtures in all detectors does not preserve quantum state specificity—instead, timing information would be used to detect only slow particles which ionise He mixtures. With this Penning ionisation detector for He(2^3S), high pressures (e.g. 3000 Torr) and large plate separations (e.g. 3 cm) could be used to increase sensitivity. Thus, even at $\beta = 10^{-4}$, more than 1000 electrons would be produced in chambers A and C and none in chamber B. With modern preamplifiers, signals from A and C are easily detected. At $\beta = 10^{-4}$, a monopole would make pulses in A and C that are separated by about 3 μs, while other penetrating particles would make similar pulses in all chambers and in time coincidence.

We now consider the detection of He(2^3S), using the RIS method which retains all the quantum state specificity in the monopole interaction. Resonance ionisation spectroscopy (Hurst *et al* 1975, 1979) has been suggested (Inokuti, private communication) as a selective detector

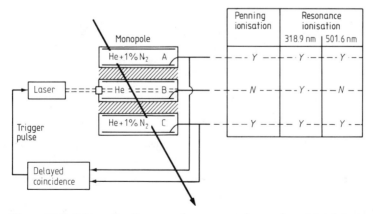

Figure 11.7 Schematic diagram of a proposed experiment to detect monopoles, using the property that they create triplet metastable states but not ionisation in He. Experimental options using Penning ionisation or resonance ionisation are shown.

of He(2^3S). In the work on He(2^1S) (Chapter 2), a pulsed laser was used to provide photons at 501.6 nm in sufficient quantities such that all He atoms in the 2^1S state which were located in the pulsed laser would be selectively ionised. Ionisation measurements then gave the absolute population of He(2^1S). Similarly, the 2^3S state can be measured by using a laser tuned to 388.9 nm, as is also illustrated in figure 11.8. However, a more interesting scheme, demanding less from the pulsed laser now tuned to 318.9 nm, is suggested for monopole detection and will be discussed in more detail. At a He pressure of 1000 Torr the lifetime of He(2^3S) is about $4\,\mu$s, which gives time to fire the laser tuned to 318.9 nm. Consider, then, the experimental logic of figure 11.7. When chambers A and C provide information that a particle may have a monopole, the laser is fired into the pure He chamber B to look specifically for He(2^3S). Therefore, if Y–N–Y is converted to Y–Y–Y when the laser fires, a monopole is almost surely detected.

The transition 2^3S $\rightarrow 4^3$P at 318.9 nm is highly allowed with an oscillator strength of 0.023. A very simple laser (for example, a small

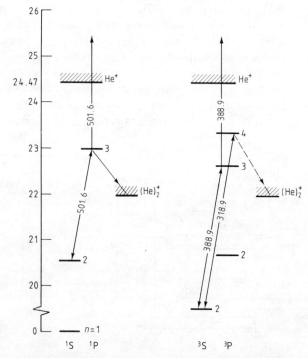

Figure 11.8 Alternative RIS schemes for the selective ionisation of the triplet state He(2^3S) compared with the RIS scheme previously used to study the singlet state of He(2^1S). Wavelengths are shown in nanometres.

nitrogen laser producing 4 mJ per pulse at 337 nm) can be used to pump a dye laser to produce 0.03 mJ of radiation at 318.9 nm. If the band width of this laser is 0.03 Å, the effective cross section for absorption in the 2^3S to 4^3P transition is 7.3×10^{-14} cm^2. With a fluence, ϕ, of 4.8×10^{13} photons per cm^2 per pulse, the transition rate for a laser pulse width of 4 ns is about 10^9 s^{-1}. As implied in figure 11.8, the 4^3P state can collide with a ground state He atom to make $(He)_2^+$, since the molecule, like all such noble gas molecular ions, is bound by a few eV (Mulliken 1970). For He (Liu 1971), the binding energy is 2.47 eV, putting the 4^3P state well above the threshold for this ionisation process. The magnitude of the cross section for this so-called Hornbeck–Molnar process for He(4^3P) is not available; however, the $n = 3$ states have been considered in detail (Wellenstein and Robertson 1972). For inst-ance, $\sigma = 4.5 \times 10^{-16}$ cm^2 for He(3^3D) and 20×10^{-16} cm^2 for 3^1D; for the higher lying He(4^3P) state, we estimate $\sigma \leqslant 10^{-15}$ cm^2. At a pressure of 1000 Torr, the rate of ionisation is 3×10^9 s^{-1}. Therefore, on application of the photon field (which drives the optical transition at a rate of about 10^9 s^{-1}), the He(2^3S) state produced by the passage of a monopole is converted to $(He)_2^+ + e^-$ at a high rate. Within the 4 ns nitrogen laser pulse, the process is essentially complete.

When looking for the slower monopoles (e.g. $\beta = 5 \times 10^{-4}$), using the RIS method, it is necessary to keep chambers A, B and C less than 10 cm apart so that the monopole traverses all detectors before the He(2^3S) state decays (3 μs at 1000 Torr). Furthermore, ionisation must be collected with high electric fields to avoid additional trigger delays due to low electron mobility (see Chapter 2). The observation of Y–Y–Y with a laser tuned to 318.9 nm is strong evidence that the metastable species produced by a particle which could not ionise He was, in fact, the triplet metastable He(2^3S). A laser tuned to 501.6 nm could be used but would add only the confirmation (Y–N–Y) that the metastable species was *not* the singlet metastable. In view of the first two columns in the table of figure 11.7, this is not important new information.

Implementation of a programme to search for primordial magnetic monopoles is not especially difficult, except for the fact that recent results—using the most reliable detector available (Cabrera *et al* 1983)—suggest that the flux is below 10^{-10} cm^{-2} sr^{-1} s^{-1}; therefore, any new detector should have a very large (greater than 10 m^2) area. Ideally, ionisation detectors should be position sensitive so that the pulsed laser beam can be directed to the desired location in detector B. Rotating mirrors or electro-optical methods can be used (Kramer and Boyer, private communication) to direct laser beams to any location at any desired time. Thus, we have proposed a He detector where the monopole interaction is understood, is quantum-state-selective for He(2^3S), and is sensitive to a monopole of any velocity $\beta > 10^{-4}$.

References

Ahlen S P and Tarle G 1983 *Phys. Rev.* D **27** 688
Albrecht A and Steinhardt P J 1982 *Phys. Rev. Lett.* **48** 1220
Bartell D M, Hurst G S and Wagner E B 1973 *Phys. Rev.* **7** 1068
Cabrera B 1982 *Phys. Rev. Lett.* **48** 1378
Cabrera B, Taber M, Gardner R and Bourg J 1983 *Phys. Rev. Lett.* **51** 1933
Deser S and Zumino B 1976 *Phys. Lett.* **62B** 335
Drell S D, Kroll N M, Mueller M T, Park S J and Ruderman M A 1983 *Phys. Rev. Lett.* **50** 644
Echenique P M, Nieminen R M and Ritchie R H 1981 *Solid State Commun.* **37** 779
Fowler W A 1984 *Rev. Mod. Phys.* **56** 149
Freedman D Z, van Nieuwenhuizen P and Ferrara S 1976 *Phys. Rev.* D **13** 3214
Georgi H and Glashow S L 1974 *Phys. Rev. Lett.* **32** 438
Giacomelli G 1984 *Jella Societa Italiana di Fisica* vol. **7** Series 3, No 12
Glashow S L 1961 *Nucl. Phys.* **22** 579
Guth A H 1981 *Phys. Rev.* D **23** 347
't Hooft G 1974 *Nucl. Phys.* B **79** 279
Hurst G S, Bortner T E and Glick R E 1965 *J. Chem. Phys.* **42** 713
Hurst G S and Klots C E 1976 in *Advances in Radiation Chemistry* vol. 5 ed M Burton and J L Magee (New York: Wiley) pp 1–96
Hurst G S, Payne M G, Kramer S D and Young J P 1979 *Rev. Mod. Phys.* **51** 767
Hurst G S Payne M G, Nayfeh M H, Judish J P, Chen C H, Wagner E B and Young J P 1975 *Phys. Rev. Lett.* **35** 82
Linde A D 1982 *Phys. Rev. Lett.* **108B** 389
——— 1984 *Rep. Prog. Phys.* **47** 925
Liu B 1971 *Phys. Rev. Lett.* **27** 1251
Melton C E, Hurst G S and Bortner T E 1954 *Phys. Rev.* **96** 643
Mulliken R S 1970 *J. Chem. Phys.* **52** 5170
Parker E N 1970 *Astrophys. J.* **160** 383
Payne M G, Klots C E and Hurst G S 1975 *J. Chem. Phys.* **63** 1422
Phelps A V 1955 *Phys. Rev.* **99** 1307
Phelps A V and Molner J P 1953 *Phys. Rev.* **89** 1202
Polyakov A M 1974 *JETP Lett.* **20** 194
Preskill J 1983 Monopoles in the Very Early Universe in *Proc. of Nuffield Workshop The Very Early Universe (Cambridge, England) 1982* ed G W Gibbons, S W Hawkins and S T C Siklos (Cambridge: Cambridge University Press)
Salam A 1968 *Elementary Particle Theory* ed N Svartholm (Stockholm: Almquist and Wiksell)

Tarle G, Ahlen S P and Liss T M 1984 *Phys. Rev. Lett.* **52** 90

Trefil J S 1983 *The Moment of Creation* (New York: Charles Scribner's Sons)

Turner M S, Parker E N and Bogdan T J 1982 *Phys. Rev.* D **26** 1296

Ueno T, Yokoyama A, Takao S and Hatano Y *Chem. Phys.* 1980 **45** 261

Weinberg S 1967 *Phys. Rev. Lett.* **19** 1264

—— 1972 *Gravitation and Cosmology* (New York: Wiley)

—— 1977 *The First Three Minutes* (New York: Basic Books)

Wellenstien H F and Robertson W W 1972 *J. Chem. Phys.* **56** 1077

Zeldovich Ya B and Novikov I D 1975 *Structure and Evolution of the Universe* (Moscow: Nauka) (Engl. Transl. 1983 *Relativistic Astrophysics* vol. II (Chicago: University of Chicago Press))

12

Search for other primordial particles

12.1 Introduction

In Chapter 11 we discussed the possibility of using RIS methods to make a more definitive search for magnetic monopoles. If sufficiently massive, as predicted by grand unification theories, monopoles could have been formed only in the very early universe. According to the inflationary model, electroweak interactions freeze out at about 10^{-35} s and quarks become distinct particles (see figure 11.3). In this chapter we will discuss the use of RIS (based on the SIRIS method described in Chapter 8) to search for free quarks, or fractional charge, and we will describe searches for superheavy hadrons as other possible relics of the early universe.

12.2 Quark composition of matter and quark confinement

The fundamental particles are now thought to be the leptons and the quarks. Baryons are combinations of three quarks, while mesons are built up by combining one quark with one antiquark. An impressive number of experiments in accelerator high-energy physics are consistent with a model in which quarks come in several types (flavours). Figure 12.1 is reproduced from a comprehensive tabulation of particle properties by Wohl *et al* (1984). Leptons and antileptons come in charges which are either zero or the same in magnitude as the electron charge, while quarks have $(-1/3)e$ or $(+2/3)e$. Since quark combinations make up the baryons, while quarks and antiquarks make up the mesons, quarks are components of all hadrons. Both the leptons and the quarks come in six flavours. However, quarks must be further characterised by

Quark type (flavour)	d	u	s	c	b	t
$\mathcal{Q}$ — electric charge	$-\dfrac{1}{3}$	$+\dfrac{2}{3}$	$-\dfrac{1}{3}$	$+\dfrac{2}{3}$	$-\dfrac{1}{3}$	$+\dfrac{2}{3}$
$\mathcal{I}_z$ — z component of isospin	$-\dfrac{1}{2}$	$+\dfrac{1}{2}$	0	0	0	0
$\mathcal{S}$ — strangeness	0	0	-1	0	0	0
$\mathcal{C}$ — charm	0	0	0	+1	0	0
$\mathcal{B}$ — bottomness	0	0	0	0	-1	0
$\mathcal{T}$ — topness	0	0	0	0	0	+1

Figure 12.1 Quantum numbers of quarks, based on Wohl *et al* (1984).

another variable called colour, or colour charge. See figure 12.2, based on an excellent *Scientific American* article by Georgi (1981).

The property of colour distinguishes quarks from leptons in a major way. The strong force is an interaction between colours and thus is missing for the leptons. Leptons appear as free particles, but quarks are not seen in isolation. (A possible exception will be discussed below.) Quark confinement is consistent with the elegant theory of quantum chromodynamics (QCD). In quantum electrodynamics (QED), photons carry the force between electrical charges; in QCD theories, gluons mediate the forces between quarks. Photons and gluons are massless

	Leptons		Quarks					
Third generation	ν_τ	0	t	+2/3	t	+2/3	t	+2/3
	τ^-	-1	b	-1/3	b	-1/3	b	-1/3
Second generation	ν_μ	0	c	+2/3	c	+2/3	c	+2/3
	μ^-	-1	s	-1/3	s	-1/3	s	-1/3
First generation	ν_e	0	u	+2/3	u	+2/3	u	+2/3
	e^-	-1	d	-1/3	d	-1/3	d	-1/3

Figure 12.2 Classification of leptons and quarks according to their flavour. Each quark with a given flavour also has three colours as illustrated in the last three panels. This illustration is a derivative of one used by Georgi (1981) where colours were shown in red, green and blue for greater visual impact.

particles, but gluons differ from photons in an essential way—they carry colour charges. This property of gluons has a major effect on the force law between quarks, in contrast with the inverse square law applicable to electrical charge. The virtual gluons, which represent the exchange between quarks (in a time domain consistent with the uncertainty principle), have the effect of spreading out the colour charge. These ideas lead to the concept of asymptotic freedom of the quarks at short distances and a force which does not fall off as rapidly as the inverse square at long distances. In fact, it is conjectured that an infinite amount of energy would be required to isolate quarks in a hadron.

This close connection between asymptotic freedom and quark confinement is important to quark searches, since asymptotic freedom is consistent with a number of high-energy experiments which probe the internal structure of hadrons. However, the important point is that the force law at large distances is not proven; and QCD—in particular, the SU(5) unification—though a beautiful theory with much internal consistency, does not prove quark confinement. Nevertheless, it should be stressed that the concept of colour charge arose from very basic considerations, as described by Glashow (1975). Greenberg's suggestion that each flavour of quark comes in three colours was made in order to solve the problem that quarks behave as fermions in accounting for the known spins of baryons and mesons, but behave as bosons in building up certain baryons such as the omega particle.

12.3 Other predictions of particle physics theories

Some salient features of the electromagnetic, the strong and weak interactions are shown in table 12.1. The weak interaction arises from the spin angular momentum of elementary particles. 'Handedness' of particles refers to the fact that only two alignments of spin with direction of motion are possible. Thus, a right-handed particle has a spin vector parallel to the velocity vector and for a left-handed particle it is antiparallel. The weak force is also associated with a charge. However, the weak charge is assigned on the basis of handedness—left-handed particles and right-handed antiparticles carry the weak charge, while right-handed particles and left-handed antiparticles are neutral. These considerations are important in neutrino physics since the handedness of a massless particle can never be reversed. Neutrino mass is, therefore, a crucial question in weak interaction theory. Electroweak unification involves the product of groups $SU(2) \times U(1)$; hence, it might be expected that the mediating W and Z particles would be massless. However, the weak charge is not always conserved, and the forces are observed to have very short ranges. The large mass is attributed to spontaneous symmetry breaking involving the quantum-mechanical vacuum.

The SU(5) group is the smallest symmetry group containing both U(3) and SU(2) × U(1) and is the basis of a grand unification theory. A new particle associated with this group is the massive (10^{15} GeV) X particle corresponding to a 10^{-29} cm unification scale. Thus, such a particle could only have been formed in the very early universe. Searches for these superheavy hadrons continue.

Table 12.1 Some salient features of the electromagnetic, strong and weak interactions, in the context of grand unification.

Force	Symmetry group	Comments
Electromagnetic	U(1)	In quantum electrodynamics the force is mediated by a massless particle called a virtual photon. Vacuum fluctuations lead to production of pairs of particles with identical features, except for the sign of charge; e.g. electrons have a charge of $-e$, while positrons have a charge of $+e$.
Strong	SU(3)	Force between quarks of electric charge $(+2/3)$ and $(-1/3)$ for the six flavours of quarks (up, down, charm, strange, top and bottom) is mediated by massless virtual particles called gluons. In quantum chromodynamic theories, each quark can also have three colours, and the gluons carry colour charge which can change quark colours. Thus, quarks carry electric charge and a colour charge.
Weak	SU(2)	Weak interactions arise from spin angular momentum of elementary particles associated with the weak charge. These interactions are mediated by W^+, W^-, and Z^0 particles having a large mass (order of 100 AMU). The W^+ an W^- particles transform the flavour of particles.
Unified	SU(5)	A new particle associated with the SU(5) group is called the X particle, which carries the colour charge, the weak charge and the electric charge $(0, +1, -1)$. Interactions mediated by the X particles violate baryon number conservation.

Supersymmetric theory (see Haber and Kane (1986)) is an extension of grand unification in an effort to further simplify nature. The basic idea of supersymmetry is the postulate that for every particle there is a superpartner with the same properties except for spin. In this way, particle spins that are multiples of 1/2 (fermions) and integer spin

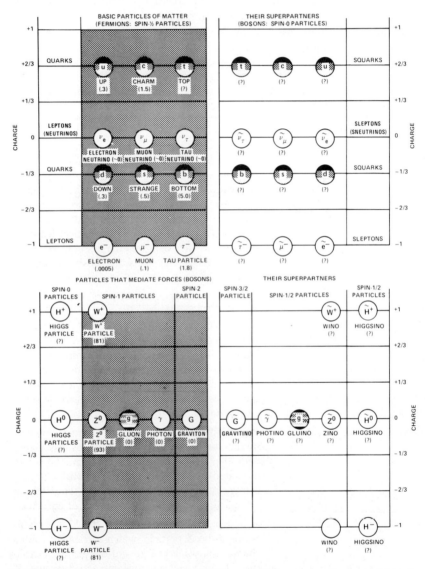

Figure 12.3 Classification of basic particles, their superpartners, particles that mediate forces and their superpartners, according to supersymmetric theories. (Reproduced by permission H E Haber and Gordon L Kane (1986).)

particles (bosons) can be incorporated into the same theory: see figure 12.3.

These intriguing and compact theories make predictions which, as yet, are not verified. For instance, grand unification predicts proton decay (baryon non-conservation) which is not observed after extensive searches. As Georgi points out, the most compelling evidence for grand unification is the observed baryon excess, consistent with the very existence of matter. Furthermore, the GUT monopoles have not been observed (with one possible exception—see Chapter 11), and X particles have not been seen. The prediction of quark confinement needs further investigation in spite of many searches (see below).

12.4 Searches for fractional charge

Given the importance of the subject, it is not surprising that a large number of searches have been made for free quarks—or, more generally, for fractional charge. These have included accelerator, cosmic-ray and stable matter experiments (see the review articles by Jones (1973), Kim (1973) and Jones (1977)). In accelerator experiments, it is necessary to state limits on quark production cross sections for a range of quark masses. Depending on the model used, one can only say that the cross section for quark production—by diffraction of hadrons or pair production—is probably less than 10^{-34} cm^2 for $m_Q \leqslant 20$ GeV. From cosmic-ray experiments it was concluded that there exists fewer than one quark in 10^{10} baryons, i.e. $n_Q/n_B < 10^{-10}$.

A large number of searches have been made by a number of groups for fractional charge in stable matter. Only a few of these are included in table 12.2. Nearly all investigators obtained 'negative' results, i.e. only an upper limit to N_Q/N_B was obtained. Searches at Stanford University by the Fairbank group use a superconducting magnetic levitation method (Larue *et al* 1977) and consistently find evidence for fractional charges on niobium spheres. Their results are summarised in figure 12.4, with a remarkable correlation about $(+1/3)e$ and $(-1/3)e$.

A recent search (Milner *et al* 1985) for fractional charge in niobium and tungsten, using the accelerator mass spectrometer (AMS) method (see Chapter 8), finds no evidence for fractional charge. A sputter source was used and the negatively charged particles were examined for fractional charge, using the tandem method involving charge exchange in a gas stripper. For the $(+1/3)e$ fractional charge, which would be seen as $(-2/3)e$, the concentration limit per host atom was estimated to be about 10^{-18} if the mass of the quark is around 2 AMU. On either side of this mass the experimental sensitivity decreased.

Table 12.2 Some representative fractional-charge searches in stable matter.

Reference	Method	Materials searched	Results (n_Q/n_B) and comments
Hillas and Cranshaw (1959)	Charge of gas sample	Ar,N_2	$< 10^{-22}$
Bennett (1966)	Solar spectrum	C,N,O	$< 10^{-10}$
Gallinaro and Morpurgo (1966)	Magnetic levitation	Graphite spheres	$< 5 \times 10^{-19}$
Chupka et al (1966)	Charge counter	Air	$< 10^{-30}$
		Sea-water	$< 3 \times 10^{-24}$
Stover et al (1967)	Magnetic levitation	Iron spheres	$< 4 \times 10^{-19}$
Rank (1968)	Millikan oil drop	Various oils	$< 10^{-20}$
Braginsky et al (1970)	Magnetic levitation	Iron spheres	$< 10^{-20}$
Elbert et al (1970)	Mass spectrometer	Tungsten	$< 5 \times 10^{-15}$
Morpurgo et al (1970)	Magnetic levitation	Graphite spheres	$< 5 \times 10^{-19}$
Garris and Ziock (1974)	Magnetic levitation	Iron spheres	$> 5 \times 10^{-12}$, residual forces not studied [†]
Larue et al (1977)	Magnetic levitation	Niobium spheres	$> 2 \times 10^{-20}$, measured residual forces [†]
Larue et al (1980)	Magnetic levitation	Niobium spheres	$> 2 \times 10^{-20}$ [†]
Marinelli and Morpurgo (1980)	Magnetic levitation	Steel spheres	$< 10^{-21}$
Milner et al (1985)	Accelerator mass spectrometer	Niobium and tungsten	See text

[†] Experiments with 'positive' results, showing possible existence of free quarks.

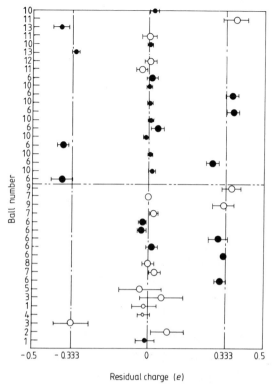

Residual charge (e)

Figure 12.4 Results of fractional charge searches at Stanford University using superconducting levitation experiments. Remarkable correlation is seen at $(-1/3)e$ and $(+1/3)e$. (Illustration based on data furnished by William Fairbank. See also Larue *et al* (1977, 1979).)

12.5 RIS searches for fractional charge

William Fairbank Jr has conducted a number of searches of fractional charge using RIS as a detector (Fairbank 1984, Fairbank *et al* 1984, Fairbank *et al* 1987). The general types of exotic atoms for which the group is searching are illustrated in figure 12.5. The exotic particle either forms a nucleus or is bound close to a nucleus by electric or strong forces. Thus the spectroscopic differences between exotic atoms and normal atoms are due to modified nuclear properties: effective charge, mass or volume (Fairbank *et al* 1984).

Spectroscopic features of the one-electron quark atom (called the 'H-quark' atom because it is hydrogen-like) are essentially given by the Bohr formula with $Z = 2/3$. Fine structure, hyperfine and reduced mass factors for $m > 100$ AMU are all less than the laser line width. The wavelengths of the first four transitions in the H-quark atom of large

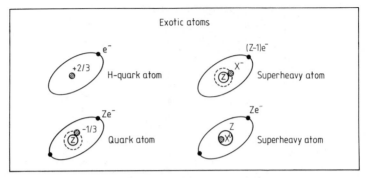

Figure 12.5 Searches are made for several types of exotic atoms, as illustrated, using RIS and other methods. (Courtesy of William Fairbank Jr.)

mass are illustrated in figure 12.6. For the Lyman α line at 273.3 nm, the ionisation step can be achieved with photons at 546.6 nm, a convenient wavelength for dye lasers. Note that the fundamental of the Nd:YAG laser at 1.06 μm (denoted '1R' in figure 12.6) is not energetic enough to ionise the $n = 2$ state. For this reason the second, third and

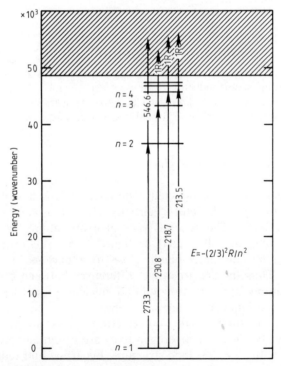

Figure 12.6 Energy levels of the H-quark atom with $m > 100$ AMU. All wavelengths listed in nm. For $m \sim 1/3$ AMU, the UV transitions are shifted about 0.4 nm to the red.

fourth transitions illustrated in figure 12.6 are preferable, since weak ultraviolet light can be used for the resonance step and strong infrared light for the ionisation step. This scheme is also attractive because there is insufficient ionisation of undesired atoms and molecules in non-resonance processes, therefore little SIRIS background.

For quark atoms with more than two electrons, the spectroscopy is difficult. Quantum-mechanical calculations are not available for the energy levels. However, one can obtain reasonable predictions of energy levels by using a fit to experimental data on the energy levels of the sequence of atoms and ions which are isoelectronic to the quark atom of interest. An example of such a fit for argon quark atoms is given in figure 12.7. Here one of the possible two-photon resonances (248.55 nm) is shown. Note that the wavelength uncertainty is less than 0.1 nm. In general, the results of these fits are good when an interpolation rather than an extrapolation can be done (Fairbank 1984). For example, with $-1/3$ quark atoms it is quite advantageous to have data on the negative-ion binding energy, as for Cl^- in figure 12.7. In cases like $NaQ^{-1/3}$, where the negative ion of the sequence is unbound, the wavelength uncertainties are of the order of 10 nm.

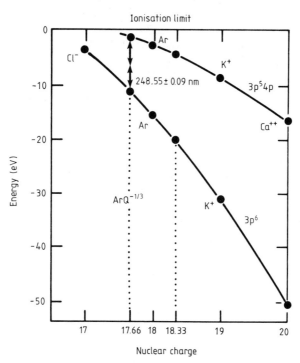

Figure 12.7 The experimental data for the isoelectronic sequence of atoms and ions with 18 electrons is used to determine the ArQ energy levels.

The experimental apparatus developed for the exotic atom searches (Fairbank *et al* 1987) is illustrated in figure 12.8 and is based on the SIRIS method described in Chapter 8. The salient features of the method include a pulsed ion beam for vaporising the solid sample, a laser for resonance ionisation of the atoms of interest, energy analysis of the created ions and time-of-flight mass analysis. For each laser shot, a time-to-pulse-height converter (TPHC) is triggered by the laser light after a variable delay. If an ion arrives at the detector within the specified time interval (e.g. 40 or 80 μs in heavy atom searches), a voltage pulse with amplitude proportional to the time of arrival is generated by the TPHC. The pulses are digitised and stored in a multichannel array in a computer according to arrival time. Times can be converted to masses through a square-root dependence.

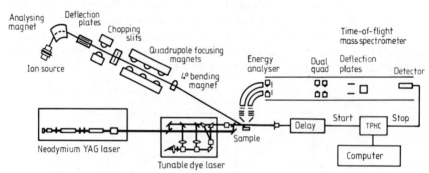

Figure 12.8 Schematic diagram of the SIRIS apparatus in the configuration used for exotic atom searches.

The response of the system can be predicted from diagnostic tests with normal atoms. For this reason, the system's mass resolution for the TOF apparatus, as illustrated for molybdenum in figure 12.9, was determined. The mass resolution was improved substantially by proper energy-spread compensation and through the use of focusing in the flight tube. Each peak in figure 12.9 is about 20 ns wide. This corresponds to a mass resolution greater than 500 at 100 AMU.

Some results on quark searches using the methods described above, are shown in figure 12.10. The interesting peaks at 254 and 270 AMU are broad, consistent with molecular origin, and were attributed to UO and UO_2 from prior experiments in which U was analysed in the SIRIS apparatus at Atom Sciences Inc. No evidence, therefore, was found for hydrogen-like quark atoms in niobium at a concentration of about 10^{-10} over the mass range from 200 to 4500 AMU. Similar conclusions were

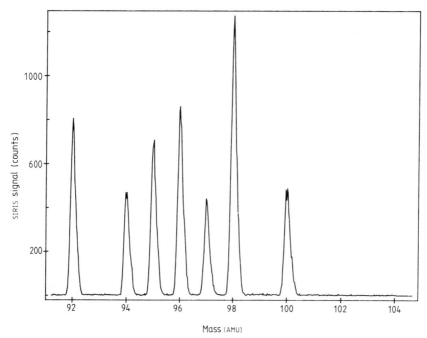

Figure 12.9 Time-of-flight spectrum for molybdenum isotopes, using the SIRIS method.

made from searches in tungsten (Fairbank *et al* 1987): see figure 12.11. These limits are less sensitive by several orders of magnitude than are the concentration limits derived from the AMS method. Further work is in progress to improve these limits, using the SIRIS method.

12.6 Previous searches for stable, heavy, elementary particles

A number of theories in the field of elementary particles attempt to extend physics above the region of mass or energy currently available with accelerators. It is not known if the discovery of the W and Z particles just below 100 GeV marks the beginning of a new mass range which is richly populated with new particles, or whether there is only a 'desert'.

Cahn and Glashow (1981) have pointed out a special effect which occurs with the normally unstable ^{8}Be nucleus. The added coulomb binding of an X^- particle is expected to make this important nucleus stable. It may also be true that the addition of an X^0 particle could similarly stabilise ^{8}Be (e.g. the extra neutron in ^{9}Be does just that).

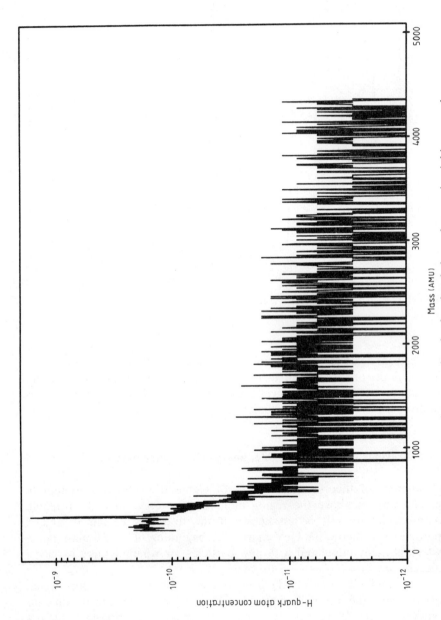

Figure 12.10 Sample data from searches for fractional charged atoms in niobium metal.

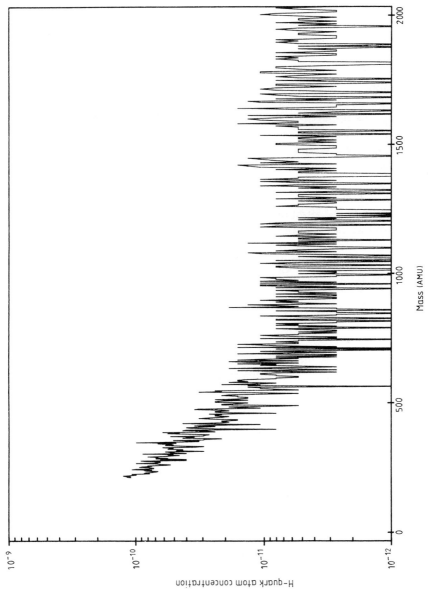

Figure 12.11 Results of searches for heavy quark atoms with $Z = 2/3$ in tungsten metal.

Both these possibilities might have major consequences for the cosmological fate of heavy X^- and X^0 particles.

In the past two decades several independent searches for stable, heavy, elementary particles in exotic atoms (see table 12.3) have been reported in the literature (Kudavadz *et al* 1965, 1966, Alvager and Naumann 1967, Muller *et al* 1977, Middleton *et al* 1979, Fairbank Jr *et al* 1985, Smith and Bennett 1979, Smith *et al* 1982, Dick *et al* 1984). For comparison, the present and anticipated future state of affairs in the RIS experiment is also listed in table 12.3. The reported heavy-atom concentration limit varies considerably beween experiments, due primarily to the different degrees with which enrichment has been used.

There are only two experiments which probe the interesting mass range above the W and Z particles, which mediate the weak interaction: see table 12.1. These are Smith's experiments (Smith *et al* 1982) with enriched heavy water and the photon burst experiments on sodium by Dick *et al* (1984). The Smith *et al* experiments place limits of 10^{-28} to 10^{-29} on the concentration of heavy hydrogen of mass up to 1200 AMU in 'natural water'. The photon burst experiment of Dick *et al* sets a limit of 5×10^{-12} for heavy particles up to mass 100 000 AMU attached to sodium nuclei. Smith *et al* also quote a limit on very massive hydrogen atoms based on density measurements of the enriched heavy water.

12.7 RIS search for heavy elementary particles

Basically, the SIRIS method described above for the quark searches can also be used to search for superheavy elementary particles (Fairbank 1985 and Fairbank *et al* 1984, 1987). In the lithium atom there is a large isotope shift estimated to be about 5 GHz between masses six and seven. If a superheavy lithium atom existed at about 100 AMU, the isotope shift is $+30$ GHz compared to that of ^{7}Li. Above 100 AMU, further isotope shifts are within a typical laser band width—which is a convenient property for searching above 100 AMU. In the RIS experiments to date, 247.5 nm dye laser light was used which would excite heavy lithium atoms to the 6P state, followed by 1.06 μm light to the ionisation continuum.

Some recent results (Fairbank *et al* 1987) for searching for superheavy lithium atoms are shown in figure 12.12. Since the average background in the mass range 350 to 1350 AMU was low, it was possible to set a concentration limit below 5×10^{-12}. Much lower concentration limits are possible using the RIS method, thus the work is being extended. As suggested in table 12.3, a 'photon burst' detector could be substituted for the present particle detector, allowing the TOF unit to extend the detectable particle mass from 100 to possibly 100 000 AMU.

Table 12.3 Summary of searches for stable heavy atoms. The cosmological factors are estimated factors by which the heavy/normal isotope ratio for an element might be enhanced relative to the overall heavy particle/baryon ratio in the universe.

Experiment[†]	Method	Element	Experimental sensitivity	Enrichment factor	Concentration limit, n_X/n_B	Mass range probed (AMU)	Cosmological factor X^{+1}	X^0	X^{-1}
1	Mass spectrometer	H	2×10^{-7}	7×10^3	3×10^{-11}	1–12	1	0	0.1
2	Mass spectrometer	H	2×10^{-14}	6×10^3	3×10^{-18}	6–16	1	0	0.1
3	Cyclotron	H	7×10^{-15}	3×10^4	2×10^{-19}	2–8	1	0	0.1
4	Accelerator mass spectrometer	O	2×10^{-16}	5×10^2	3×10^{-19}	20–54	1	> 1	10^{-4}
5	Accelerator mass spectrometer	H	2×10^{-17}	6×10^{11}	3×10^{-29}	12–1200	1	0	0.1
6	Density	H,O	6×10^{-3}	6×10^{11}	1×10^{-14}	> 1000	1	> 1	0.1
7	Photon burst	Na	5×10^{-12}	—	5×10^{-12}	100–100000	0	1	0.1
8	SIRIS	Li	4×10^{-13}	—	6×10^{-13}	420–1000 (?)	0	1	10^7 (?)
Proposed	SIRIS	Li,Be,B	1×10^{-15}	1×10^6	1×10^{-21}	100–1000 (?)	0	10^7 (?)	$> 10^5$
	SIRIS with photon burst	Be	1×10^{-14}	1×10^6	1×10^{-20}	100–100000 (?)	0	10^7 (?)	$> 10^5$

† 1 Kudavadz et al (1965); 2 Alvager and Naumann (1967); 3 Muller et al (1977); 4 Middleton et al (1979); 5 Smith and Bennett (1979); Smith et al (1982); 6 Dick et al (1984); 8 Fairbank et al (1985).

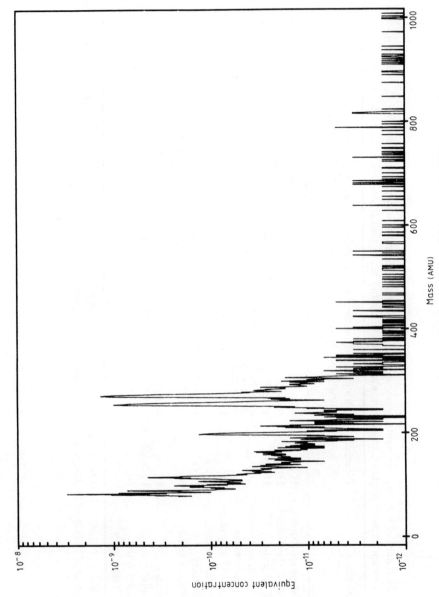

Figure 12.12 Results of a search for superheavy Li isotopes in lithium metal.

References

Alvager T and Naumann R 1967 *Phys. Lett.* B **24** 647

Bennett Jr W R 1966 *Phys. Rev. Lett.* **17** 1196

Braginsky V B, Kornienko L S and Poloskov S S *Phys. Lett.* 1970 **33**B 613

Cahn R N and Glashow S L 1981 *Science* **213** 607

Chupka W A, Schiffer J P and Stevens C M 1966 *Phys. Rev. Lett.* **17** 60

Dick W J, Greenless G W and Kaufman S L 1984 *Phys. Rev. Lett.* **53** 421

Elbert J W, Herb R G, Nielson K E, Petrilak M and Weinberg A 1970 *Nucl. Phys.* B**20** 217

Fairbank Jr W M in *Near Zero: New Frontiers in Physics* ed C W F Everett (San Francisco: Freeman) To be published in 1988

Fairbank Jr W M, Hurst G S, Parks J E and Paice C 1984 in *Resonance Ionization Spectroscopy 1984* ed G S Hurst and M G Payne (Inst. Phys. Conf. Ser. 71) pp 287–96

Fairbank Jr W M, Perger W F, Riis E, Hurst G S and Parks J E 1985 in *Laser Spectroscopy VII* ed T W Hansch and Y R Shen (Berlin: Springer) pp 53–4

Fairbank Jr W M, Riis E, LaBelle R D, Parks J E, Spaar M T and Hurst G S 1987 in *Resonance Ionization Spectroscopy 1986* ed G S Hurst and C Grey Morgan (Inst. Phys. Conf. Ser. 84) pp 275–80

Gallinaro G and Morpurgo G 1966 *Phys. Lett.* **23** 609

Garris E D and Ziock K O H 1974 *Nucl. Instrum. Methods* **117** 467

Georgi H 1981 *Sci. Amer.* (April) **244** 48–63

Glashow S L 1975 *Sci. Amer.* (October) **233** 38–50

Haber H E and Kane G L 1986 *Sci. Amer.* **254** (6) 42–50

Hillas A M and Cranshaw T E 1959 *Nature* **184** 892

Jones L W 1973 *Phys. Today* **26** (5) 30

—— 1977 *Rev. Mod. Phys.* **49** 717

Kim Y S 1973 *Contemp. Phys.* **14** 2897

Kukavadz G, Memelova L and Suvorov L 1965 *Zh. Eksp. Teor. Fiz.* **48** 389 (Engl. Transl. 1966 *Sov. Phys.–JETP* **22** 272)

Larue G S, Fairbank W M and Hebard A F 1977 *Phys. Rev. Lett.* **38** 1011

Larue G S, Fairbank W M and Phillips J D 1979 *Phys. Rev. Lett.* **42** 142

Marinelli M and Morpurgo G 1980 *Phys. Lett.* **94**B 427, 423

Middleton R, Zurmuhle R W, Klein J and Kollarits R V 1979 *Phys. Rev. Lett.* **43** 429

Milner R G, Cooper B H, Chang K H, Wilson K, Labrenz J and McKeown R D 1985 *Phys. Rev. Lett.* **54** 1472

Morpurgo G, Gallinaro G and Palmieri G 1970 *Nucl. Instrum. Methods* **79** 95

Muller R A, Alvarez L W, Holley W R and Stephenson E J 1977 *Science* **196** 521

Rank D M 1968 *Phys. Rev.* **176** 1635

Smith P F and Bennett J R J 1979 *Nucl. Phys.* B **149** 525

Smith P F, Bennett J R J, Homer G J, Lewin J D, Walford H E and Smith W A 1982 *Nucl. Phys.* B **206** 333

Stover R W, Moran T I and Trishka J W 1967 *Phys. Rev.* **164** 1599

Wohl C G, Cahn R N, Rittenberg A, Trippe T G and Yost G P 1984 *Rev. Mod. Phys.* **56** No 2, Part 11, S2–S73

13

Stellar evolution and the solar neutrino mystery

13.1 Introduction

Throughout the history of science, the origins of stars, of our solar system and of the universe have been topics of expansive speculations and tentative theories. In spite of the fact that observations of stars have inspired much of this intellectual activity, we do not understand the more interesting features of our unique star—the Sun. Even though the Sun's size, its composition, its dynamics and its total energy production are known, our knowledge of the interior of the sun may not be adequate for predicting its neutrino production. In a classic experiment, Raymond Davis Jr and his colleagues showed that the neutrino flux was less than 1/3 that expected from standard solar models. Either these models are inadequate or there is some deep mystery concerning neutrino physics.

This chapter briefly reviews the current theories of stellar evolution and stellar models, especially as they relate to solar neutrino production. The chlorine experiment and plans for new solar neutrino experiments are discussed. One of these involves the $^{81}Br(\nu,e^-)^{81}Kr$ reaction, a natural sequel to the $^{37}Cl(\nu,e^-)^{37}Ar$ detector—the only experiment ever performed to measure the neutrino production of the sun. Since the Br experiment was made possible by RIS, we will give more attention to it than to other proposals for additional solar neutrino experiments.

13.2 Stellar evolution and stellar structure

Many ideas have been put forth in attempts to 'explain' the origin of the solar system. Interesting historical summaries of some theories (Reeves

1978) and some 'myths' (Alfven 1978) are found in a convenient source (Dermott 1978). Modern theories tend to agree with the 1755 Kant philosophy further developed by Laplace in 1796. The supposition was made that the sun and the planets were created nearly simultaneously, on the cosmic time-scale, from the same cloud of interstellar material called a 'protosolar nebula'. At some stage this protosolar nebula was a rapidly rotating mass of gas which flattened into a disc. In the colder regions of the disc, condensation of the less volatile materials created the planets around a hot central portion which became our Sun. Other models do not accept this cogenesis of the Sun with the rest of the solar system, but our purpose here is not a critical discussion of solar evolution.

According to plausible theory (Reeves 1978), our entire galaxy was formed about 15 billion years ago (see the time-line of Chapter 11) from a huge gaseous mass (10^{11} solar masses!) which contained only primordial hydrogen and helium. A first generation of massive stars was formed, after a few billion years, which ejected the products of nucleosynthesis into space. At about the same time as the formation of these heavier atoms the large spherical galaxy collapsed into a flattened shape with extended spiral arms. Churning of clouds, exchanged from various spiral atoms, continued to make heavier elements by nucleosynthesis and after about 10 million years of agitation a particle cloud gave birth to a large number of stars, one of which was our Sun. During collapse, the large cloud fragmented into smaller masses. These protostellar nebulae were flattened under the influence of combined gravitational, rotational and magnetic forces. Around the rotational axis, our Sun was formed in the hot interior, while the planets were formed by condensation around dust particles already present. Thus, the particular cogenesis theory of Laplace is left essentially intact, with modern astrophysics providing splendid detail.

The solar neutrino mystery motivates new interest in the interior of stars, especially the Sun. Modern astrophysics appears to lay such a firm foundation to the understanding of the solar interior that a discrepancy between predicted and observed flux of more than a factor of three is highly significant. The removal of this discrepancy will surely tell us something new about stars—or about neutrino physics.

The physical basis for the structure of a star is succinctly described in the first pages of Chandrasekhar's paper (1984) on his Nobel† lecture. In this simple theory the equation of hydrostatic equilibrium of a star is

$$dP/dr = - (GM(r)/r^2)\, \rho$$

where P is the total pressure, G is the gravitational constant, $M(r)$ is

† S Chandrasekhar and William A Fowler shared the Nobel Prize in physics in 1983 for their contributions to the development of modern astrophysics.

the mass inside the radius r and ρ is the density. Combining the equation of hydrostatic equilibrium with the ideal gas law, and with Stefan's law for the radiation pressure, gives a lower limit to the mass of a star, i.e.

$$M \geqslant (6/\pi)^{1/2} [(k^4/\mu H) (e/a) (1 - \beta_c)/\beta_c^4]^{1/2} (1/G^{3/2}).$$

In this equation, $1 - \beta_c$ is the fraction of the total pressure due to radiation, k is Boltzman's constant, H is the mass of the hydrogen atom, a is Stefan's radiation constant and μ is the mean molecular weight (close to unity in stellar atmospheres). Remarkably, in this derivation the only mathematical assumption made is a theorem which asserts that the actual pressure at the centre of a star must be intermediate between those at the centres of two configurations of uniform density—one of density equal to the mean density and the other of density equal to the central density. From this last equation, Chandrasekhar shows that

$$\mu^2 M = 5.48 (1 - \beta_*)^{1/2}\beta_*^{-2} M_S$$

where $1 - \beta_*$ is uniquely determined by the mass M of a star in terms of the mass M_S of the Sun. This simple equation, based on no special assumptions, except for hydrostatic equilibrium, is a model-independent theory of the physical structure of stars. It is noted that the maximum fraction of pressure, $1 - \beta_*$, due to radiation at the centre of the Sun is 0.03 but becomes 0.90 for the very heavy stars where $\mu^2 M/M_S = 520$. Eddington (1926) first called attention to the importance of radiation pressure in stars. When the radiation pressure can be neglected, the mean temperature of the star is given by

$$\bar{T} > 3.84 \times 10^6 \, \mu(M/M_S) \, (R_S/R).$$

where R is the radius of any star and R_S is the radius of the Sun. Thus, mean temperatures of a few million degrees can be derived from these elementary considerations. Central core temperatures are much higher, e.g. about 15 million degrees for the Sun.

13.3 Energy production in the sun

Eddington (1919) discusses the question of energy production by the Sun and the stars. If gravitational attractions were the only source, giant stars could live only a few thousand years and even the dwarfs could live only 10 million years. This contradicted age determination by geological methods. The recently discovered radioactivity could also be ruled out as a new source. Thus, Eddington followed up the 'radical' suggestion of Russell (1919) that some unknown internal source produces large quantities of energy per unit mass to account for the observed radiation from the Sun and the stars. Further, this new source must be under control to account for the long-term stability of stars, but must eventually be exhausted to allow stars to evolve to the dwarf stage. The essence of Eddington's suggestion was that the energy equivalence of the mass of the Sun $(1.7 \times 10^{54}$ ergs$)$ could support the current radiation rate $(1.2 \times 10^{41}$ ergs yr$^{-1})$ for 15 billion years, even if only 1/1000 of the mass is burned. Eddington speculated that the Sun produces energy by burning hydrogen atoms, but had no details of how this could happen.

Bethe (1939) showed that the stars produce energy by fusing H atoms into He atoms. Two reaction sequences were shown to be responsible: (a) the P–P chain in which two protons react to make D and (b) the C–N–O cycle in which carbon and nitrogen serve as catalysts to fuse four atoms of H into one atom of He according to

$$^{12}C + H \rightarrow {}^{13}N + \gamma, \; {}^{13}N \rightarrow {}^{13}C + e^+ + \nu$$

$$^{13}C + H \rightarrow {}^{14}N + \gamma$$

$$^{14}N + H \rightarrow {}^{15}O + \gamma, \; {}^{15}O \rightarrow {}^{15}N + e^+ + \nu$$

$$^{15}N + H \rightarrow {}^{12}C + {}^4He.$$

The relative importance of the two mechanisms depends on the temperature of the interior of the star. Bethe concluded that the two sources are about equally probable in the Sun, with a central temperature of 16 million degrees. However, it is now believed that the P–P chain is the Sun's primary energy source; only in somewhat hotter stars does the C–N–O cycle dominate. These mechanisms for energy production, in terms of the best nuclear information of the time, led to a lifetime estimate of 12 billion years for the Sun and satisfied another of Russell's requirements on the new energy source—namely that when its hydrogen is almost exhausted a light star can contract into a dense white dwarf. In the dwarf stage (characterised as a degenerate electron gas), the star can have a nearly infinite lifetime, owing to its low energy production.

Fowler (1984) credits Fred Hoyle (1964) with the 'grand concept of nucleosynethesis in stars'. In 1954 Fowler suggested that more than 90% of the solar luminosity is due to P–P burning. This large shift from the C–N–O cycle to the P–P chain was due to improved knowledge in the cross section for the reaction

$$^1H + {}^1H \rightarrow {}^2H + e^+ + \nu$$

and recognition of the role of

$$^3He + {}^3He \rightarrow {}^4He + 2P.$$

For more information on the history of our knowledge on solar power, see Kavanagh (1982).

13.4 Solar models and neutrino production

In this section the P–P chain is discussed in context with solar models which predict the energy spectrum and the flux of neutrinos emitted by the Sun. It is believed that the Sun and its internal energy source are understood well enough to make an accurate prediction of solar neutrino production. However, a careful experiment has been carried out (see below) and the result is a neutrino flux that is significantly lower than predicted. Because of this problem, the calculations by Bahcall and associates, as well as experimental refinements by Davis and associates, have continued but have not resolved the problem. The origin of the discrepancy is still unknown; it may be due to a flaw in the standard astronomical model, or it could be due to a lack of knowledge in neutrino physics. Recent reviews of a wide variety of possible ways to resolve the solar neutrino problem are given in Weneser and Friedlander (1987).

In a brief discussion of solar models, we follow Bahcall (1978, 1979). A more recent review (Bahcall *et al* 1982) gives a critical evaluation of uncertainties in predicting capture rates in solar neutrino detectors, using standard solar models. The standard theory of main-sequence stars (Schwarzschild 1958) assumes local hydrostatic equilibrium (see §13.2), energy transport by radiation and convection, and energy production by hydrogen burning. An equation of state is used, together with the radiative opacity (which depends on the detailed composition of the Sun) and nuclear energy cross sections for the various reactions. Models based on this standard theory, with reasonable assumptions of the initial composition, are referred to as standard solar models. Examples of non-standard models involve unusual assumptions of initial composition, black holes in the Sun, fractional charges, etc.

To the uninitiated, it seems improbable to understand the solar interior well enough to calculate neutrino production. However, with only the assumption of hydrogen burning to make He and with the measured luminosity, L_S, it is simple (Bahcall 1979) to estimate the total flux of neutrons on the Earth. Thus, at the Sun-to-Earth distance, 1 AU, the flux is

$$F = (2L_S/25\text{MeV}) \, 4\pi \, (1\text{AU})^2 \approx 10^{11} \, \text{cm}^{-2}\text{s}^{-1}$$

since the P–P chain, amounting to $4P \rightarrow \alpha + 2e^+ + 2\nu$, releases 25 MeV of energy and an average of two neutrinos. This calculation is, of course, independent of a solar model. Further, as Schwarzschild (1958) points out, a solar model can be based only on a solar mass and a distribution of chemical composition throughout the star. We noted in §13.2 the relationship of mean temperature and the mass of a star. However, to do a careful calculation of the flux of neutrinos due to various sources requires considerable effort. We will not describe the method of calculation; instead, the input data will be listed and the results given.

For our purpose, the Sun can be represented as a large spherical object (see figure 13.1) with a hot gas compressed by gravity to a density of about 150 g cm^{-3} at the interior. The most important assumption about composition is that when the Sun becomes a main-sequence star (at $t = 0$) its composition is the primordial mixture of H and He. Also, as H is burned at the core to make He, there is no mixing. Thus the He fraction (by mass) is given by $f(t,R) = 0.25$ at $t = 0$ for all R, and it increases appreciably only near the core. Other input data are listed in table 13.1.

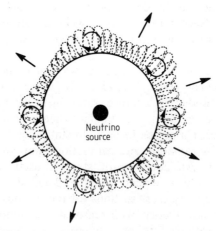

Figure 13.1 Model of the Sun, containing a hot core where neutrino production can occur.

Table 13.1 Some input data on the Sun applicable to the standard solar model according to Bahcall *et al* (1982).

Parameter	Value
Luminosity, L_S	3.86×10^{33} erg s^{-1}
Mass, M_S	1.99×10^{33} g
Radius, R_S	6.96×10^{10} cm
Age	4.55×10^9 yr
Central density	156 g cm^{-3}
Central temperature	15.5×10^6 K
Central hydrogen abundance, by mass	0.355
Effective surface temperature	5.78×10^3 K
Primordial helium abundance, by mass	0.25 ± 0.01
Primordial ratio of heavy elements to hydrogen mass	0.0228

The hot core where neutrino production can occur is only a small fraction of the volume of the Sun, as illustrated in figure 13.1. Composition uncertainties are not too important in determining neutrino production in the core, however the small percentage of heavy elements does affect the mean solar opacity. This, in turn, would affect the use of luminosity in estimating the central temperature.

The results of incorporating nuclear reaction cross sections, the solar constant, elemental abundance, mean opacity, equation of state and solar age into the standard solar model are shown in table 13.2 for the P–P neutrino sources and in table 13.3 for the C–N–O sources. Based on the currently accepted solar model of Bahcall, the fraction of energy produced by the P–P chain is 0.985 and only 0.015 for the C–N–O cycle. Figure 13.2 shows the neutrino fluxes that should be observed at the Earth, and figure 13.3 shows the energy spectra of the neutrino sources.

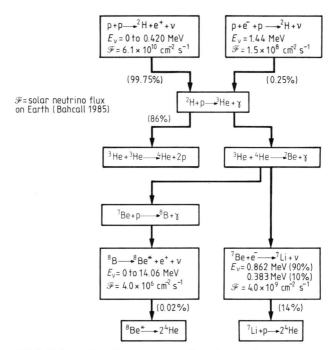

Figure 13.2 Values for the neutrino flux for various sources of production are shown, as calculated by John Bahcall (1985).

13.5 The $^{37}Cl(\nu,e^-)^{37}Ar$ solar neutrino experiment

The only solar neutrino flux measurement to date was made in the landmark experiment by Ray Davis Jr and his associates, using the

Table 13.2 The proton–proton chain.

Reaction		Branching ratio (%)†	Energy (MeV)	Neutrino energy (MeV)
	$p + p \rightarrow d + e^+ + \nu$	99.75	1.442	0.0–0.42 spectrum
	or			
	$p + p + e^- \rightarrow d + \nu$	0.25	1.442	1.44 line
PPI	$d + p \rightarrow {}^3He + \gamma$	100	5.493	
	${}^3He + {}^3He \rightarrow 2p + {}^4He$	86	12.859	
	or			
	${}^3He + {}^4He \rightarrow {}^7Be + \gamma$	14	1.587	
PPII	${}^7Be + e^- \rightarrow {}^7Li + \nu$	99.985	0.862	0.86(90%), 0.38(10%) lines
	${}^7Li + p \rightarrow 2\,{}^4He + \gamma$		17.347	
	or			
	${}^7Be + p \rightarrow {}^8B + \gamma$	0.015	0.135	
PPIII	${}^8B \rightarrow {}^8Be^* + e^+ + \nu$		15.079	0.0–14.1 spectrum
	${}^8Be^* \rightarrow 2\,{}^4He$		2.995	

† The relative branching ratios are given for a standard solar model.

Table 13.3 The carbon–nitrogen–oxygen cycle.

Reaction	Energy (MeV)	Neutrino energy (MeV)
$p + {}^{12}C \rightarrow {}^{13}N + \gamma$	1.94	
${}^{13}N \rightarrow {}^{13}C + e^+ + \nu$	1.20	0.0–1.20 spectrum
$p + {}^{13}C \rightarrow {}^{14}N + \gamma$	7.54	
$p + {}^{14}N \rightarrow {}^{15}O + \gamma$	7.29	
${}^{15}O \rightarrow {}^{15}N + e^+ + \nu$	1.73	0.0–1.73 spectrum
$p + {}^{15}N \rightarrow {}^{12}C + {}^{4}He$	4.96	

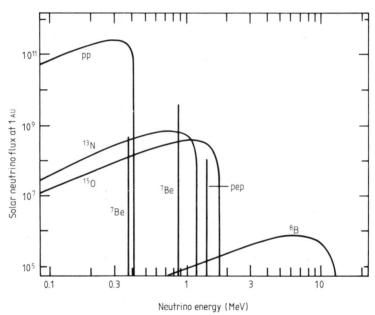

Figure 13.3 Energy spectra and neutrino flux from the Sun, stated at 1 AU. For the line sources flux is plotted as $cm^{-2}s^{-1}$ and for the continuum sources the units are $cm^{-2}s^{-1} MeV^{-1}$.

reaction ${}^{37}Cl(\nu,e^-){}^{37}Ar$. For a very interesting history of this classic experiment, see the account of Bahcall and Davis (1982). Neutrino capture in ${}^{37}Cl$ proceeds according to

$$\nu_e + {}^{37}Cl \rightarrow {}^{37}Ar + e^-$$

which is the inverse of radioactive decay by electron capture, i.e.

$$^{37}Ar + e^- \rightarrow {}^{37}Cl + \nu_e$$

with a half-life of 35 days. Such a detection method was independently proposed by Pontecorvo (1946) and was implemented when Davis and his collaborators constructed an experiment in the Homestake Gold

Mine in South Dakota. A tank containing 380 000 l (615 tons) of tetrachloroethylene (C_2Cl_4) is situated underground to take advantage of about 1500 m of rock as a shield against cosmic-rays (primarily muons) which could also produce ^{37}Ar. After an appropriate integration time, e.g. six weeks, the ^{37}Ar atoms which have not decayed are removed from the tank by purging with He gas. These atoms are then decay counted, using a small proportional counter.

Cross sections for neutrino capture are very small but must be known before converting ^{37}Ar activity to neutrino flux. In the case of ^{37}Cl, the cross section for neutrino capture can be calculated (Bahcall 1978) directly from experimental measurements. Table 13.4 lists the calculated values of the flux on Earth, F, and the capture cross section, σ, for each neutrino source in the Sun. The product $F\sigma$ is a capture rate; the solar neutrino unit, denoted SNU, is defined as one capture per second in 10^{36} target atoms. For the Cl detector, the predicted rate is 5.8 SNU with 4.3 SNU coming from the ^{8}B decay neutrino. Thus, the Cl solar neutrino experiment should detect primarily the energetic component of the ^{8}B neutrino which is a relatively small (5×10^{-5} compared to the P–P neutrino) component of the total neutrino spectrum.

This difficult experiment has been done, refined, and repeated over the last two decades; for recent reviews, see Cleveland *et al* (1984). Table 13.5 shows some results of typical runs of the Cl experiment, where it is seen that the total rate of ^{37}Ar production is just 0.38 atoms per day. After background correction, the value of 0.30 ± 0.038 atoms per day corresponds to 1.6 ± 0.4 SNU. Hence, the solar neutrino problem—the measured flux is a factor of 3.6 smaller than the value calculated from the standard model (see table 13.4). These low values persisted in a series of experiments from 1971 until 1983 (see figure 13.4).

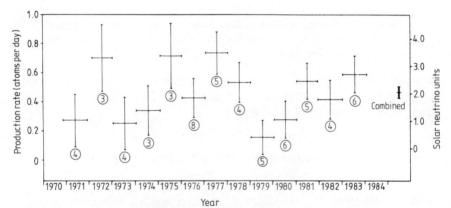

Figure 13.4 Experimental results from the chlorine solar experiment: yearly average production rates are shown over a thirteen year period.

Table 13.4 Solar neutrino fluxes and cross sections for the $\nu + {}^{37}\text{Cl} \rightarrow {}^{37}\text{Ar} + e^-$ detector

Neutrino sources and energies (MeV)	Flux on Earth F (cm^{-2} s^{-1})	Cross section σ (cm^2)	Capture rate in ^{37}Cl $F\sigma \times 10^{36}$ s^{-1} (SNU)
$\text{H} + \text{H} \rightarrow \text{D} + e^+ + \nu$ (0–0.42)	6.1×10^{10}	0	0
$\text{H} + \text{H} + e^- \rightarrow \text{D} + \nu$ (1.44)	1.5×10^8	1.72×10^{-45}	0.26
^{7}Be decay (0.86)	3.4×10^9	2.9×10^{-46}	0.99
^{8}B decay (0–14)	3.2×10^6	1.35×10^{-42}	4.32
^{15}O decay (0–1.74)	1.8×10^8	7.8×10^{-46}	0.14
^{13}N decay (0–1.19)	2.6×10^8	2.1×10^{-46}	0.05
			Total: 5.8

Table 13.5 Summary of results.

Run number	Production Rate (^{37}Ar per day)	
	Most likely value	68% Confidence range
$18 \rightarrow 39$	0.38	0.31–0.46
$40 \rightarrow 47$	0.39	0.27–0.50
$18 \rightarrow 47$	0.38	0.33–0.45

Average ^{37}Ar production rate $(18{\rightarrow}47) = 0.38 \pm 0.07$
Cosmic-ray background (muons and v_μ) $= 0.08 \pm 0.03$

Rate above known backgrounds $= 0.30 \pm 0.08$

Possible solar neutrino rate $= 5.24 \times (0.30 \pm 0.08) = 1.6 \pm 0.4$ SNU

13.6 The ^{81}Br$(v,e^-)^{81}$Kr solar neutrino experiment

The large discrepancy between predictions of the standard model and experimental results from the Cl experiment has set the stage for a number of interesting speculations. In very general terms, the problem must be in the standard model or in neutrino physics. In the standard model it is possible that some astrophysics or nuclear physics facts are missing, or that some uncertainties come into the transport calculations. In the area of neutrino physics, perhaps all types of neutrinos have rest mass. A difference in mass amongst v_e, v_μ, and v_τ could lead to oscillations (vacuum oscillations) between neutrino types. It is also possible that a new type of neutrino interaction with matter (matter oscillations) is responsible for the decreased Cl flux. An excellent view of the many mechanisms proposed to explain the low Cl flux is Weneser and Friedlander (1987). These mechanisms fall in several categories: solar physics, neutrino decay over long distances, neutrino spin flip and various oscillation theories. As pointed out by Weneser and Friedlander, the Br experiment is most useful in the study of the solar interior itself. For instance, a lower core temperature would decrease the ^{8}B flux by a large amount, the ^{7}Be by a intermediate amount and the P–P flux only a small amount. Thus, a Br experiment, sensitive to the ^{7}Be flux, would help to establish or rule out the interior of the sun as the site of the neutrino problem.

It is not surprising that a number of new experiments have been seriously considered and proposed (Friedlander and Weneser 1987) to try to resolve the solar neutrino mystery. Other radiochemical experiments, following the original Cl experiment, are the Ga and the Br experiments. With Ga, low-energy neutrinos could be measured since the interaction $^{71}Ga(\nu,e^-)^{71}Ge$ has a threshold at 233 keV. The inverse decay, by electron capture, occurs with a half-life of 11.4 days; thus, detection of ^{71}Ge decay is a measure of the neutrino flux provided cross sections are well known. This experiment was first developed at Brookhaven National Laboratory with theoretical support by Bahcall. Currently, an experiment is planned in West Germany (Kirsten 1984, Hampel 1985) and in the USSR (Barbabanov *et al* 1985).

The Br experiment would utilise the reaction $^{81}Br(\nu,e^-)^{81}Kr$ which has a threshold at 470 keV and would measure the neutrinos of intermediate energy, primarily the ^7Be source in the Sun. Since ^{81}Kr has a half-life of 2.1×10^5 years, a solar neutrino experiment using this reaction cannot be done by decay counting. Since it appears that RIS is the only feasible way to count small numbers of ^{81}Kr atoms, we will discuss this experiment (Hurst *et al* 1984) in more detail. Scott (1976) first suggested the use of Br as a geophysical experiment—here we are discussing a Davis-type radiochemical solar neutrino detector.

The calculation of the neutrino-induced ^{81}Kr production rate from ^{81}Br requires the ^{81}Br cross section for neutrino capture. Branching ratio measurements by Bennett *et al* (1980) imply that the $ft_{1/2}$ value for neutrino capture from the 3/2 ground state of ^{81}Br to the $1/2^-$ (190 keV) excited state of ^{81}Kr is $(7.6^{+2.2}_{-1.7}) \times 10^4$ s (see figure 13.5). On the basis of this value, Bahcall (1981) and Haxton (1981) calculated the cross sections for neutrino capture given in table 13.6. Two new determinations of the branching ratio suggest that the cross section for the ^7Be source may have been over-estimated. Thus, Davids *et al* (1987) suggest a reduction factor of 1.66, while Lowry *et al* (1987) suggest a factor of 2.5.

The calculations of Bahcall include only the transition from the ground state of ^{81}Br to the first excited state of ^{81}Kr. Haxton's calculation uses a nuclear shell model to estimate the magnitude of the neutrino capture transitions to many of the excited states of ^{81}Kr. A statistical model calculation by Itoh and Kohyama (1981), considering all states in ^{81}Kr below the particle emission threshold, yields a cross section for capture of ^8B neutrinos of 7.4×10^{-43} cm^2, in substantial agreement with Haxton. Uncertainty about neutrino capture to the higher excited states, especially the $5/2^-$ level at 457 keV in ^{81}Kr, has been emphasised by Bahcall (1981). An estimate of the cross section for this $5/2^-$ level by Liu and Gabbard (1983), based on $^{81}Br(^3He,t)^{81}Kr$ reaction data, suggests that its contribution to the total capture rate may be nearly half that of the $1/2^-$ state. Similarly, in the proposed ^{71}Ga experiment there is a 5af08/2$^-$ excited state at an energy of 175 keV. Orihara *et al* (1983) how that neutrino capture to this level may be substantial. Charge exchange measurements, using (p,n) reactions at

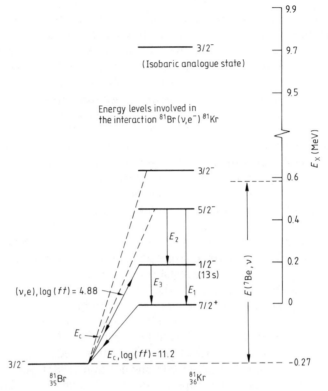

Figure 13.5 Some energy levels in ^{81}Br and ^{81}Kr relevant to a bromine solar neutrino experiment. The energy of the ^{7}Be neutrino is shown and is above the threshold for both the $1/2^-$ and $5/2^-$ level in ^{81}Kr.

intermediate energies, are in progress to reduce uncertainties in the contribution due to these higher excited states. For instance some recent (p,n) studies on ^{81}Br have been made at the Indiana University Cyclotron Facility (IUCF) (Krofcheck *et al* 1987). In this work, there is tentative evidence for considerable GT strengths in the excitation energy range 3 to 7 MeV.

Combining the cross sections in table 13.6 with the fluxes of the standard and Cl-consistent solar models yields capture rates for the Br detector. Approximately 65% of the total signal in both of these models is due to the ^{7}Be neutrinos. However, the new (p,n) experiments suggest considerable contribution of the ^{8}B neutrino source—about equal to the ^{7}Be contribution, based on the Cl-consistent solar model. The Ga experiment, in contrast, is dominated by the P–P neutrinos if excited states are neglected, but becomes increasingly sensitive to the ^{7}Be neutrinos as the effect of excited states increases. Results from a Br experiment may thus be essential to interpret a Ga experiment. A

Table 13.6 Calcuated ^{81}Br neutrino capture rates for the major reactions. (One SNU (solar neutrino unit) equals 10^{-36} captures per target atom per second.)

Source	Energy (MeV)	Neutrino flux (10^6 cm^{-2} s^{-1})		^{81}Br cross section (10^{-46} cm^2)		^{81}Br capture rate (SNU)	
		Standard model	Consistent model	Bahcall (1981)	Haxton (1981)	Standard model	Consistent model
P–P	(0–0.42)	61000	64000	0	0	0	0
pep	(1.44)	150	150	78	85	1.3	1.3
^{7}Be	(0.862)	4300	1800	25	27	11.8	4.9
^{8}Be	(0–14)	5.6	1.1	1700	5400	3.0	0.6
^{13}N	(0–1.20)	500	160	19	20	1.0	0.3
^{16}O	(0–1.73)	400	130	41	44	1.7	0.6
	Total rate					18.8	7.7

combination of Ga, Br and Cl experiments may be required to make additional progress on the solar neutrino problem.

The Cl-consistent model predicts a capture rate for the Br experiment of 8 SNU, and the standard model, assuming that neutrino oscillations are responsible for the low result of the Cl experiment, predicts a result in the range 4.5 to 6.0 SNU. With a detector size comparable to that of the present Cl experiment, the rate of production of ^{81}Kr is about two atoms per day for the Br compounds $CHBr_3$, CH_2, Br_2, $C_2H_2Br_4$, and $C_2H_2Br_2$. Each run of six months to a year will then contain several hundred atoms. Extraction of ^{81}Kr from a Br-containing compound can be performed by using a He purge system like that used for extracting ^{37}Ar from C_2Cl_4. The entire Kr extraction process using the 380 m^3 tank of C_2Cl_4 at Homestake has been demonstrated (see figure 13.6).

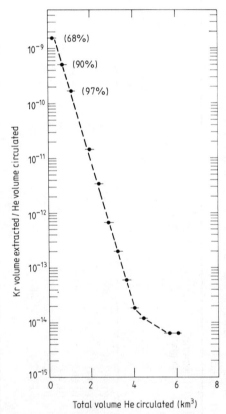

Figure 13.6 Extraction of Kr from the C_2Cl_4 tank at Homestake. An initial volume of 1 cm^3 of Kr was added to the 380 m^3 tank and the extracted volume of Kr was measured for fifteen solar neutrino runs. The horizontal bar indicates the He flow of each run. Accumulated per cent of Kr recovered is indicated for the first three runs (unpublished data from B T Cleveland and R Davis Jr.)

Background effects have to be considered for any proposed solar neutrino experiment (Rowley *et al* 1980). These arise from the pentrating cosmic-ray muons, from α decay in the target itself and from neutrons generated by fission decay or (α,n) reactions in surrounding rock. Cosmic-ray muons can create protons by the photonuclear process and the reaction $^{81}Br(p,n)^{81}Kr$ leads to a background. At the depth of the Homestake mine $(410 \text{ kg cm}^{-2}$ or 4100 hg cm^{-2}, where hg = hectogram) this background is reduced to about 0.07 atoms of ^{81}Kr per day, with the assumption of a target of 380 m^3 for the Br-rich organic solution. Apha particles from the decay of U or Th in the target would initiate $^{81}Br(\alpha,p)^{81}Rb$ followed by $^{81}Br(p,n)^{81}Kr$. Furthermore, the α process $^{78}Se(\alpha,n)^{81}Kr$ leads to background if ^{78}Se is an impurity. The total α-induced background is about 0.03 atoms of ^{81}Kr per day, assuming impurity levels to be the same as in the Cl solution. Similarly, $^{81}Br(n,p)^{81}Se$ followed by $^{81}Br(p,n)^{81}Kr$ is a neutron-induced background. And $^{84}Sr(n,\alpha)^{81}Kr$ leads to ^{81}Kr if ^{84}Sr is an impurity (unlikely). These neutron-induced reactions would produce about 0.1 atoms of ^{81}Kr per day in the target; however, the neutron flux can be easily reduced by a water shield around the tank. Thus, we are left with a total background rate of about 0.1 atoms per day, considerably less than the expected rate of about 2.0 per day due to solar neutrinos. The reaction $^{79}Br(p,n)^{79}Kr$ could provide a monitor of (p,n) associated backgrounds. More frequent recovery of Kr atoms, followed by decay counting of ^{79}Kr (electron capture, $T_{1/2} = 35$ h) could confirm that the (p,n) background is negligible.

Any Kr leaks will contain the atmospheric abundance of ^{81}Kr, namely 1.6×10^7 atoms of ^{81}Kr per cubic centimetre of Kr (Loosli and Oeschger 1969, Barabanov *et al* 1973). Measurements made of Kr extraction from the 380 m^3 C_2Cl_4 tank give an upper limit of 10^{-6} cm^3; thus atmospheric ^{81}Kr will not be a serious source of background. Excessive ^{82}Kr could interfere with the RIS detection of ^{81}Kr; thus, one step of isotopic enrichment could be necessary to reduce the number of ^{82}Kr atoms due to air contamination before doing the RIS counting.

A method for counting a small number of ^{81}Kr atoms was proposed some time ago (Hurst *et al* 1980, 1983), and it was shown recently (Chen *et al* 1984) that fewer than 1000 atoms of ^{81}Kr can be counted without waiting for radioactive decay (see Chapter 10). The method utilises a resonance ionisation process to selectively ionise Kr atoms which are then mass selected with a quadrupole mass filter (*A* selection). An atom buncher (see Chapter 10) reduces the time required to ionise the Kr atoms, using the RIS scheme described elsewhere (Kramer *et al* 1983). After *Z* and *A* selection, these ions are accelerated to about 10 keV and implanted in a Si target. Assume that a sample of 500 atoms of ^{81}Kr and not more than 10^8 atoms of ^{82}Kr were recovered from the neutrino tank and introduced into the static detector system. After nearly all of the ^{82}Kr atoms are implanted (requiring about one hour), there will also be about 2×10^4 atoms of ^{82}Kr in the target, as a result of limited abundance sensitivity of the mass filter. The residual gas-phase atoms, essentially 10^8 atoms of ^{81}Kr, are then pumped out before the atoms in the Si target are removed by laser annealing. During a second cycle the 500 atoms of ^{81}Kr are implanted along with about 40 atoms of ^{82}Kr. If desired, a further isotopic enrichment could be done, but in any case the final implantation will utilise a Cu–Be target which emits enough electrons per pulse to ensure nearly absolute atom counting.

In figure 13.7 we show recent data on the direct counting of approximately 1000 atoms of ^{81}Kr that had been enriched at the National Bureau of Standards to simulate a solar neutrino experiment. In the experiment, all the lasers (buncher and RIS lasers) were pulsed at a rate of 10 Hz and individual counts due to ^{81}Kr were recorded and then plotted in groups of 2500 laser shots. It is seen that the free-atom concentration of ^{81} Kr decays with about a one hour half-life as the ^{81}Kr ions are implanted in a target of Cu–Be. A background signal associated with non-resonant laser ionisation is observed. Calibrations based on the

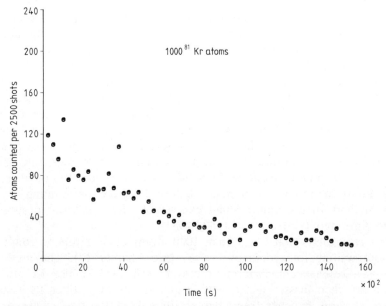

Figure 13.7 Demonstration that less than 1000 atoms of ^{81}Kr can be detected by RIS. Atoms are counted individually and then grouped into 2500 laser shots to show exponential decay of the free atoms as they are implanted into a target. When the laser is operated at 10 Hz, the free-atom sample of ^{81}Kr appears to have about a one hour half-life compared to the 2×10^5 yr radioactive decay of ^{81}Kr.

decay counting of ^{81}Kr and our calibrations based solely on knowledge of the detector are in good agreement. The estimated detection limit is about 300 atoms of ^{81}Kr. However, laser improvements to increase vacuum ultraviolet generation and to reduce backgrounds should make it possible to count less than 100 atoms in the near future. The data of figure 13.7 can be regarded as a simulation of a typical neutrino run; thus, we believe that all the steps of a Br solar neutrino experiment are feasible. The salient features of the proposed ^{81}Br$(v,e^-)^{81}$Kr solar neutrino experiment are shown in table 13.7.

Table 13.7 Summary of proposed bromine solar neutrino experiment.

Reaction:	^{81}Br$(v,e^{-1})^{81}$Kr, primarily ^{7}Be
Facilities:	Davis radiochemical, like Cl except that atom counting requires RIS method
Compound:	380 m^3 (1000 tons) CH$_2$Br$_2$
Signal levels (Atoms ^{81}Kr per day):	
Consistent model	2
Standard solar model	5
Noise/signal examples (%):	
Sudbury (6000 hg cm^{-2})	0.3
Homestake (4000 hg cm^{-2})	6
Gran Sasso (3800 hg cm^{-2})	8

References

Alfven H 1978 *The Origin of the Solar System* ed S F Dermott NATO Advanced Study Institute (Chichester: Wiley)

Bahcall J N 1978 *Rev. Mod. Phys.* **50** 881

—— 1979 *Space Science Rev.* **24** 227–51

—— 1981 *Phys. Rev.* C **24** 2216

—— 1985 in *Solar Neutrinos and Neutrino Astronomy* ed M L Cherry, W A Fowler and K Lande (Am. Inst. Phys. Conf. Proc.) **126** 60

Bahcall J N and Davis R Jr 1982 in *Essays in Nuclear Astrophysics* ed C A Barnes, D D Clayton and D N Schram (Cambridge: Cambridge University Press) pp 243–85

Bahcall J N, Huebner W F, Lubow S H, Parker P D and Ulrich R K 1982 *Rev. Mod. Phys.* **54** 767–99

Barabanov I R, Gavrin V N, Golubev A A and Pomansky A A 1973 *Bull. Acad. Sci. USSR, Phys. Ser.* **37** 45

Barabanov I R *et al* 1985 in *Solar Neutrinos and Neutrino Astronomy* (AIP Conf. Proc. 126) ed M L Cherry, K Lande and W A Fowler p 175

Bennett C L, Lowry M M, Naumann R A, Loeser F and Moore W H 1980 *Phys. Rev.* C **22** 2245

Bethe H A 1939 *Phys. Rev.* **55** 434–56

Chandrasekhar S 1984 *Rev. Mod. Phys.* **56** 137–47; *Science* **226** 497–505

Chen C H, Kramer S D, Allman S L and Hurst G S 1984 *Appl. Phys. Lett.* **44** 640

Cleveland B, Davis R Jr and Rowley J K 1984 in *Resonance Ionization Spectroscopy 1984* ed G S Hurst and M G Payne (Inst. Phys. Conf. Ser. 71) pp 241–50

Davids C N, Wang T F, Ahmad I, Holtzmann R and Janssens R V F 1987 *Phys. Rev.* C **35** 1114–18

Dermott S F 1978 (ed) *The Origin of the Solar System* NATO Advanced Study Institute (Chichester: Wiley)

Eddington A S 1919 *Observatory* **42** 371–7

—— 1926 *The Internal Constitution of the Stars* (Camrbidge: Cambridge University Press)

Fowler W A 1984 *Rev. Mod. Phys.* **56** 149

Friedlander G and Weneser J 1987 *Science* **235** 760–5

Hampel W 1985 in *Proc. Conf. on Solar Neutrinos and Neutrino Astronomy* ed M L Cherry, W A Fowler and K Lande (New York: American Institute of Physics) pp 162

Haxton W C 1981 *Nucl. Phys.* A**367** 517

Hoyle F 1964 *Mon. Not. R. Astron. Soc.* **106** 343

Hurst G S, Chen C H, Kramer S D, Payne M G and Willis R D 1983 in *Science Underground* ed M M Nieto, W C Haxton, C M Hoffman, E W Kolb, V D Sandberg and J W Toevs (AIP Conf. Proc. 96) pp 96–104

Hurst G S, Chen C H, Kramer S D, Cleveland B T, Davis R Jr, Rowley R K, Gabbard F and Schima F J 1984 *Phys. Rev. Lett.* **53** 1116

Hurst G S, Payne M G, Kramer S D and Chen C H 1980 *Phys. Today* **33** (9) 24

Itoh N and Kohyama Y 1981 *Astrophys. J.* **246** 989

Kavanagh R W 1982 in *Essays in Nuclear Astrophysics* ed C A Barnes, D D Clayton and D N Schramm (Cambridge: Cambridge University Press) pp 159–70

Kirsten T 1984 in *Resonance Ionization Spectroscopy 1984* ed G S Hurst and M G Payne (Inst. Phys. Conf. Ser. 71) pp 251–61

Krofcheck D *et al* 1987 *Phys. Lett.* B **189** 299–303

Kramer S D, Chen C H, Payne M G, Hurst G S and Lehmann B E 1983 *Appl. Optics* **22** 3271

Liu K F and Gabbard F 1983 *Phys. Rev.* C **27** 93

Loosli H H and Oeschger G 1969 *Earth Planet. Sci. Lett.* **7** 67

Lowry M M, Kouzis R T, Loeser F, McDonald A B and Naumann R A 1987 *Phys. Rev.* C **35** 1950

Orihara H, Zifiratos C D, Nishihara S, Furukawa K, Kabasawa M, Maeda K and Ohnuma H 1983 *Phys. Rev. Lett.* **51** 1328

Pontecorvo B 1946 *Vhslk Tibrt yoty Trpoty* PD-205

Reeves H 1978 (ed) *The Origin of the Solar System* NATO Advanced Study Institute (Chichester: Wiley)

Reeves H and Meyer J P 1978 *Astrophys. J.* **226** 613

Rowley J K, Cleveland B T, Davis R Jr, Hampel W and Kirsten T 1980 *Geochim. Cosmochim. Acta. Suppl.* **13** 45

Russell H N 1919 August Publication of the Astronomical Society of the Pacific

Schwarzschild M 1958 *Structure and Evolution of the Stars* (Princeton: Princeton University Press)

Scott R D 1976 *Nature* **264** 729

Weneser J and Friedlander G 1987 *Science* **235** 755–9

14

Earth and planetary sciences

14.1 Introduction

In this final chapter we examine studies of the solar system, the planetary system, the Earth and the environmental system for possible RIS applications. Of course, we cannot do justice to these enormous fields; thus, we choose some representative examples where methods of sensitive analyses can be used either to determine the composition of a material or to date objects or events.

The standard methods for sensitive analyses for these topics are (a) nuclear decay methods for dating samples and (b) neutron activation analyses and mass spectrometers for composition and age determinations. More recently, the accelerator-based mass spectrometers have emerged as a powerful method for more sensitive analyses. We are just beginning to see the use of RIS for dating and for sensitive analyses in these fields.

14.2 Origin of meteorites and atmospheric xenon

Analyses of isotopic anomalies found in meteorites give information on the solar system, extending back in time to the proto-solar nebula (Begemann 1980). An example of how isotopic anomalies can give information on the origin of materials will be discussed. Oxygen has three stable isotopes with masses of 16, 17 and 18 AMU and mean abundances of 99.756%, 0.039% and 0.205%, respectively. In stable isotope work, experimental abundance data are usually expressed in terms of standard mean ocean-water (SMOW) ratios as follows:

$$\delta(^iO) = [(^iO/^{16}O)_{\text{sample}}/(^iO/^{16}O)_{\text{SMOW}} - 1] \times 1000.$$

Thus, the δ value, expressing an isotopic anomaly, represents a small variation in the ratio $^{17}O/^{16}O$ (or $^{18}O/^{16}O$) in a sample compared with the standard. These small differences in concentrations of stable isotopes may be due to spontaneous transmutation of radioactive nuclides into stable ones (radiogenic). Or, they may be due to the interaction of particles (such as protons, neutrons, α-particles, etc) with matter, producing spallogenic effects. Spallogenic effects are common in extra-terrestrial matter, but occur in the Earth as well. Finally, isotopic anomalies can be brought about by slow chemical differentiation in which a linear dependence on mass difference is found. The physical–chemical effect would be twice as large with ^{18}O compared with ^{16}O. Thus, the δ values depend on the time and the place in the universe where the material was created. The importance of this point to studies of the early solar system is illustrated in figure 14.1 for the oxygen example (Clayton *et al* 1976). When δ ^{17}O is plotted against δ ^{18}O for various classes of meteorites, it is found that all meteorites of a class fall on a straight line of slope 1/2. Any change occurring due to chemical effects can only move a point on the straight line but not off it.

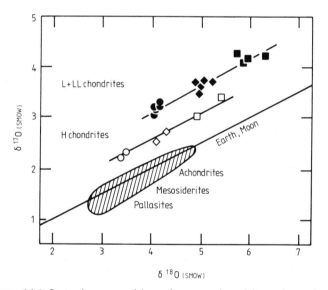

Figure 14.1 Isotopic composition of oxygen found in various classes of meteorites. The L (low-iron) and LL (low-iron, low-metal) chondrites fall on a different line than the H (high-iron) chondrites. Lunar and Earth samples and other meteorites form still another linear array. Begemann (1980) regards the fact that not all samples fall on the same line as unambiguous evidence for a non-homogeneous isotopic composition of the pre-solar nebula. (Data from Clayton *et al* (1976) and reproduced with the permission of F Begemann and Robert N Clayton.)

Therefore, the existence of several lines shows that the samples have various sources and implies that the isotopic composition of the pre-solar nebula is not homogeneous. This discovery had great significance for the understanding of the early universe, since it called into question the classical picture that the pre-solar nebula was a hot and well-mixed cloud of isotopically uniform composition. Earlier studies (Clayton *et al* 1973) had discovered that certain inclusions from carbonaceous chondrites contained oxygen with plots similar to those of figure 14.1. This was preliminary evidence of a non-homogeneous pre-solar nebula, but the later work of 1976 in which the correct slope was found is regarded as unambiguous proof (Begemann 1980). According to an illustration (figure 14.2) by Schramm (1978), the model for the formation of the solar system explicitly involves the ejection of grains from a supernova into a proto-solar nebula which triggers the condensation of the solar system.

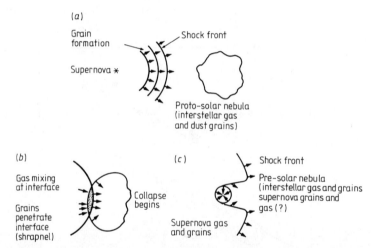

Figure 14.2 Model of the formation of the solar system according to Schramm (1978). In (*a*) gas and grains form a supernova mix with the dust and gas in the proto-solar nebula, triggering condensation, (*b*) which propagates in a shock wave as in (*c*). (Figure reproduced by permission from an article by David N Schramm (1978) in *Protostars and Planets* ed T Gehrels (Tucson: University of Arizona Press).)

These discoveries of irregularities in the isotopic abundances imply that the proto-solar nebula was not homogeneous, and this runs against the basic assumption of solar cosmology (that the pre-solar nebula is a hot gas of uniform chemical and isotopic composition). These questions are not fully resolved and the analysis of small inclusions in meteorites is a matter of renewed interest. Some of the grains are submicron in size and require considerable sensitivity and good spatial resolution for their analysis. Microprobe techniques such as SIMS, SIRIS and laser microprobes should be of real value in answering these profound questions concerning the solar system. Thus, RIS (e.g. as used in SIRIS) should increase both the sensitivity and the selectivity of the measurements of material composition. For the analyses of inclusions, the elements oxygen, magnesium, silicon, calcium, titanium, strontium, barium, neodymium, samarium, tellurium, mercury and uranium are of special interest (Begemann 1980). Extinct nuclides include plutonium-244, iodine-129, palladium-107, aluminium-26, and sodium-22.

Before leaving this subject, we wish to discuss the importance of some of the noble gases. Begemann (1980) states that 'xenon, although a relative newcomer in meteorite research, has turned out to be perhaps the most prolific single element'. Xenon has nine stable isotopes, and in the Earth's atmosphere, the isotopic abundance varies widely (see table 14.1). Use of a rare gas has the advantage that its memory is reduced by many orders of magnitude when the meteorite is formed, and thus any effects on xenon or its isotopes that occur after the system closes are more easily detected. On the measurement side, xenon can easily be removed from a sample by heating generally or by laser or ion-beam microprobing. The elegant mass spectrometry methods of Reynolds (1950) have been used to measure down to about 20 000 atoms of xenon. Figure 14.3 is a plot of two meteoritic sources of xenon, compared to the isotopic distribution of xenon in the terrestrial atmosphere. It is generally concluded that xenon atoms found in meteorites

Table 14.1 Abundance of xenon isotopes in the Earth's atmosphere. This common abundance is not reproduced in the Earth's interior or elsewhere in the universe.

Xenon isotope	Abundance (%)
124	0.10
126	0.090
128	1.91
129	26.4
130	4.1
131	21.2
132	26.9
134	10.4
136	8.9

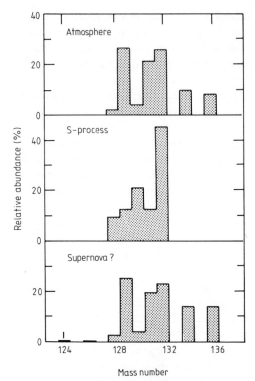

Mass number

Figure 14.3 Isotopic composition of xenon in the terrestrial atmosphere, compared with two anomalous compositions, made in the s-process in stars and in a supernova (Begemann 1980). (Figure reproduced with permission of F Begemann.)

come from at least two sources. In the atmosphere a considerable portion of the xenon is due to radiogenic, spallogenic and fission decay (fissiogenic) processes. In stars, it is known that the isotopes in the high-mass region are made by successive neutron capture. There is a rapid capture where decay is not important (called the r-process), and a slow process (s-process) where radioactive decay of intermediate steps followed with neutron capture is the pathway to the heavier nuclides. Thus, there is evidence in the data of figure 14.3 that some of the xenon is made by the s-process, while another major component originates in some other way, perhaps in a supernova. Clearly, much more data is needed to unravel the complex pathways of meteorite formation. But observation of the relative abundance of the nine stable isotopes of xenon can give strong clues.

Sensitive analysis of xenon in meteorites, combined with microprobes to sample small inclusions, is a key to learning the origin of the materials in a sample. An RIS system could play a useful role in this regard. It has already been shown (see Chapter 10) that less than 1000 atoms of ^{81}Kr can be counted using Maxwell's demon (Hurst *et al* 1985). Thonnard *et al* (1984) are making progress in improving the method. At Sheffield University (England), Granville Turner (1987) is planning to use RIS in a time-of-flight mass spectrometer designed to improve the already superb sensitivity for xenon detection.

14.3 Age of the solar system

Information on the ages of planets comes from the analyses of materials taken from meteorites, the Earth and the Moon. Here, we wish to give a few examples of how age determinations are made, following the lucid article by T Kirsten (1978).

Many kinds of phenomena involving irreversible processes can be observed and, when sufficiently characterised, can be used as 'clocks'. These include radioactive decay, chemical composition change or transport, and natural cycles. However, we will be concerned primarily with the nuclear methods involving radioactive decay. The basic idea of a clock based on radioactivity is, of course, very simple. The first use of the method was made by Rutherford (1906) when he showed that the lower limit for the age of a uranium mineral could be determined by measuring the helium content of the mineral. Uranium (and its radium in equilibrium) emits α-particles, which collect as helium in a non-porous mineral. Thus, the 'age' can be determined if the half-life for radioactive decay is known. A mineral's 'age' is determined by a clock which was reset to $t = 0$ at the 'time of closure' or the time of formation of the mineral. Using these ideas, Rutherford estimated the age of several uranium minerals to be more than 500 million years. Rutherford's method has become the most useful clock for the geological sciences.

To review how the radiometric method is currently used to date samples, we follow the discussion of Kirsten (1978). In the modern setting, dating methods are applied to obtain isotopic anomalies in meteoritic, lunar and terrestrial materials in an effort to learn the history of the solar system. These studies are made to determine how solar matter is related to its original sources and to determine the duration and time sequence of events occurring in the formation of the solar system. As the Rutherford example illustrates, chemical fractionation—to some degree—must occur during the singular event, resetting the clock. If the daughter elements in a sample are due in part to a radiogenic contribution, ^iD_r, and in part to an initial component, $^iD_0$, present at closing, then the total number of atoms of the element present is given by $^iD = {}^iD_r + {}^iD_0$. Using a stable element of amount ^jD as a reference, it can be shown that

$$^{i}D/^{i}D = (^{k}P/^{i}D)(e^{\lambda t} - 1) + \left[\frac{^{i}D_0}{^{i}D}\right]$$

where ^{k}P is the number of atoms of a parent of isotope k which decays to the daughter atom ^{i}D at the rate λ. The technique, then, for dating an unknown source is to plot $^{i}D/^{i}D$ against $^{k}P/^{i}D$ to obtain an 'isochron' whose slope is $(e^{\lambda t} - 1)$ containing the age of a sample. For example, if several samples are taken from a meteorite, the ratio $^{k}P/^{i}D$ can vary with location if different degrees of chemical fractionation occurred; yet the data should fall on a straight line if the samples are truly of the same origin (cogenic). The slope of an isochron gives a unique age independent of the degree of fractionation. In figure 14.4 an illustration is given of an age determination of a meteorite using the β decay of ^{87}Rb to ^{87}Sr (half-life = 4.88×10^{10} years) with stable ^{86}Sr as a reference isotope. Isotopes are available for geological dating covering the half-life range of 10^4 to 5×10^{10} years (see table 14.2 (Kirsten 1978)).

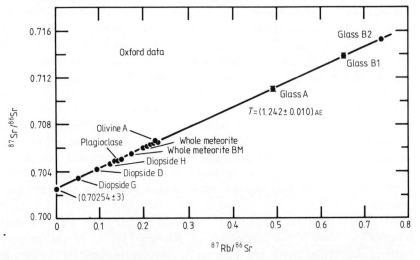

Figure 14.4 An internal isochron using Rb–Sr in the Nakhla meteorite. The slope of the isochron, together with the half-life for β^- decay of ^{87}Rb to ^{87}Sr (see table 14.2), gives the 'age' of the sample—in this illustration, 1.24×10^9 years. (Figure reproduced with permission from N Gale (Gale *et al* 1975).)

Radiometric methods have been used to determine the age of planets, the duration of nucleosynthesis, the mean age of the elements and the age of the galaxy in the time relationship shown in figure 14.5.

Cosmic-ray interactions with interplanetary objects can complicate age determinations of meteorites striking the Earth, since high-energy pro-

Table 14.2 Half-lives of isotopes with cosmochronological significance. (Reproduced with the permission of Professor T Kirsten and John Wiley and Sons Ltd. See Kirsten (1978).)

Nuclide	Isotopic abundance (%)	Decay type	Decay product	Half-life (years)
Primordial				
^{87}Rb	27.83	β^-	^{87}Sr	4.99×10^{10}
				4.88×10^{10}
^{232}Th	100	α	^{208}Pb	1.40×10^{10}
^{238}U	99.28	α	^{206}Pb	4.50×10^{9}
				4.47×10^{9}
		Spontaneous fission	$^{131-136}$Xe† tracks	8.2×10^{15}
^{235}U	0.72	α	^{207}Pb	7.13×10^{8}
				7.04×10^{8}
^{40}K	0.0117	(β^-)	$(^{40}$Ca$)$	1.25×10^{9}
		K-capture	^{40}Ar	
^{147}Sm	15.0	α	^{143}Nd	1.06×10^{11}
^{187}Re	62.6	β^-	^{187}Os	$\sim 5 \times 10^{10}$
Extinct				
^{129}I	—	β^-	^{129}Xe	1.7×10^{7}
^{244}Pu	—	(α), spontaneous fission	$(^{232}$Th$)$ $^{131-136}$Xe† tracks	8.2×10^{7}
^{26}Al	—	β^+	^{26}Mg	7.4×10^{5}
^{146}Sm	—	α	^{142}Nd	1.03×10^{8}
^{205}Pb	—	K-capture	^{205}Tl	2×10^{7}
^{248}Cm	—	(α), spontaneous fission	$(^{244}$Pu$)$ $^{131-136}$Xe†	3.7×10^{5}
^{250}Cm	—	Spontaneous fission	$^{131-136}$Xe	1.1×10^{4}

†The isotopic compositions of fission Xe from these nuclides are distinct from each other.

tons can penetrate to about one metre in a solid. However, the spallation products produced can also be useful in studying the cosmic-ray age of a material. For instance, if large bodies such as planets, asteroids, comets and meteorites collide and break up into objects less than one metre in diameter, cosmic-ray exposure ages can be determined to give valuable information on the history of the objects during the last 1 to 100 million years. According to Kirsten, the commonly used radio isotopes are Al ($T_{1/2} = 0.74$ million years), ^{36}Cl ($T_{1/2} = 0.31$ million years), ^{3}H ($T_{1/2} = 12.3$ years), ^{39}Ar ($T_{1/2} = 269$ years), ^{22}Na

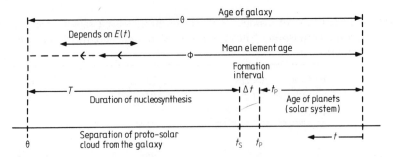

Figure 14.5 Time definitions used by Kirsten (1978) to illustrate mean element age and its dependence on the rate of production, $E(t)$. The diagram is a compact illustration of some of the questions being addressed in the field of cosmochronology.

($T_{1/2} = 2.6$ years), ^{40}K ($T_{1/2} = 1.3$ billion years), and ^{81}Kr ($T_{1/2} = 0.21$ million years). Low-level counting techniques are used for all of these except ^{40}K and ^{81}Kr, which require mass spectrometers. Obviously, RIS could be used to great advantage on some of these. See Chapter 8 for RIMS and SIRIS methods, and Chapter 10 for ^{81}Kr detection.

14.4 Principles of environmental dating

Dating methods play key roles in developing an understanding of the environment (Oeschger 1982). Both radioactive and chemical methods have been used; however, the use of the latter is far more uncertain because of the temperature dependence of chemical reaction rates. Environmental systems are complex due to the variety of subsystems which interact with each other (see the general model in figure 14.6). Because of these complexities, it is useful to use several isotopes, all produced by cosmic-ray interactions, but representing three types of behaviour in the environment. It is useful to distinguish (a) the noble gases, (b) radio-isotopes which became incorporated in molecular gases, and (c) radio-isotopes which become attached to aerosol particles. The six most important isotopes used to untangle the complexities of environmental research are ^{39}Ar and ^{81}Kr for category (a), ^{14}C and ^{3}H for category (b), and ^{10}Be and ^{36}Cl for category (c) (see table 14.3).

Use of cosmic-ray-produced isotopes to study the environment depends on knowledge of the rate of production of the isotopes over long spans of time. The most important example of the complexity of production rates is that of ^{14}C. The ratio ^{14}C/C shows evidence of small cosmic-ray variations (tree ring data), and fluctuations in global CO_2

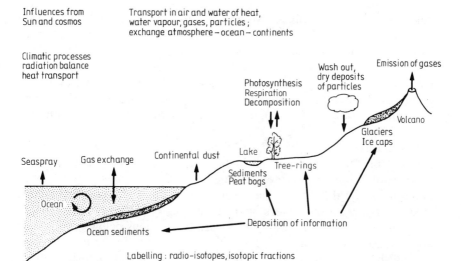

Labelling: radio-isotopes, isotopic fractions

Figure 14.6 Schematic model of the environmental system. (Reprinted with permission from Oeschger (1982). Copyright 1982, American Chemical Society.)

Table 14.3 Cosmic-ray-produced isotopes of key importance in environmental research.

Radio-isotope	Half-life	Application (Role)
^{39}Ar	269 a	Noble gas free atoms in the
^{81}Kr	2.1×10^5 a	atmosphere, absorbed in water, trapped in ice caps and other solids
^{14}C	5730 a	Become incorporated in molecular
^{3}H	12.33 a	gases, then into organic materials
^{10}Be	1.6×10^6 a	Attach to aerosol particles and are
^{36}Cl	3.0×10^5 a	removed from the atmosphere by precipitation

further complicate matters. Finally, man-made ^{14}C leads to changes in the ratio ^{14}C/C that are larger than fluctuations due to natural causes. In spite of these complications (perhaps extreme for ^{14}C), radio-isotopes yield valuable information on the complex environmental cycles. Age information can be obtained from two sources. In one of these, the decay of a long-lived radio-isotope created in the original nucleosynthesis into a daughter atom can be used to give the date at which the system closed, as discussed in §14.3. For example, the accumulation of ^{40}Ar from decay of ^{40}K($T_{1/2} = 1.3 \times 10^9$ years) could reveal the time of impact of a meteorite on the Moon. But, for environmental research on the Earth the use of radioactive elements created by the interaction of cosmic-rays with the Earth's atmosphere is most important (see table 14.3). These give information on mixing and circulation in the atmosphere and the oceans and on global cycles. Histories of environmental processes are stored in glaciers, ice caps, tree rings, peat bogs and sediments (Oeschger 1982), and these histories can be read by counting radio-isotopes.

Noble gases play a special role in environmental research, primarily because of their chemical inertness. See table 14.4 for the useful isotopes of argon and krypton and their specific activities in the Earth's atmosphere. Of these, ^{37}Ar has been measured in the atmosphere, while ^{39}Ar levels have been determined in samples from the ocean, ground-water and ice. For more information, see the sections below on polar ice and ground-water dating. An illustration of the use of ^{39}Ar to determine the age of ice samples of Station Crete in Greenland (Loosli 1979) is shown in figure 14.7. These measurements required *in situ* melting of about three tons of ice in bore holes, followed by argon separation from the air trapped in the samples, and finally very low-level decay counting at the University of Bern, Switzerland, One of the major attractions of RIS for these applications is the reduction of sample size (see below).

14.5 Age of ground-water and polar ice

The RIS technique has provided the basis for a new method of dating ground-water and polar ice (Lehmann *et al* 1985), using the ^{81}Kr isotope produced by cosmic rays in the Earth's atmosphere. It appears that ground-water or polar ice samples as old as 1 000 000 years can be analysed with the new method. In this section we will discuss some details of the method and give results of a demonstration in which about 1000 atoms of ^{81}Kr were counted after recovery from a few litres of water.

A new long-lived krypton activity was dicovered by Reynolds (1950) after intense neutron irradiation of a bromine target. Following analysis by mass spectrometry and decay counting, Reynolds concluded that the radioactive noble gas isotope ^{81}Kr had been produced by n-capture from ^{80}Kr and that its half-life was 210 000 ($\pm$50 000) years. A remeasurement of the half-life by Eastwood and co-workers (1964) yielded 213 000 (within +16 000 −26 000) years, in excellent agreement with Reynolds. Cosmic-ray-produced ^{81}Kr was first detected by Marti (1967) in a meteorite with high concentrations of strontium, yttrium and zirconium from which ^{81}Kr was produced by spallation. Krypton-81

Table 14.4 Cosmic-ray-produced noble gas radio-isotopes; $T_{1/2} > 1$ month. (The unit 'dpm' denotes 'disintegrations per minute.')(Reproduced with permission of H Oeschger (1978) and Nuclear and Chemical Dating Techniques. Copyright 1978 American Chemical Society.)

Isotope	$T_{1/2}$	Specific activity	Comments
^{37}Ar	35.1 days	~0.003 dpm l^{-1}Ar	Additional production by underground nuclear reaction [^{40}Ca$(n, \alpha)^{37}$Ar] up to 0.2 dpm l^{-1} Ar
^{39}Ar	269 years	~0.1 dpm l^{-1}Ar	Anthropogenic contribution less than 5%
^{81}Kr	2.1×10^5 years	0.1 dpm l^{-1}Kr	
^{85}Kr	10.6 years	Cosmic-ray-produced?	Cosmic-ray-produced component not yet identified
		Anthropogenic ~3 × 10^4 dpm l^{-1}Kr	Fission product

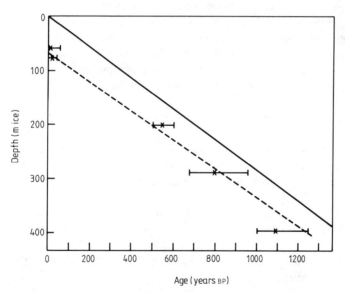

Figure 14.7 Ages of ^{39}Ar samples against depth for a bore hole at Station Crete in Central Greenland, compared with δ^{18}O ages (solid line). (Reprinted with permission from Oeschger (1982). Copyright 1982, American Chemical Society.)

radiation ages of meteorites (Eugster *et al* 1967) and lunar material (Eberhardt *et al* 1970) were subsequently determined with highly sensitive mass spectrometers.

In the Earth's atmosphere, ^{81}Kr is produced by cosmic-rays in p- , n- , or γ-induced spallation reactions from the stable isotopes ^{82}Kr, ^{83}Kr, ^{84}Kr, ^{86}Kr and, by neutron capture, in ^{80}Kr. The atmospheric specific activity is low, measured by Loosli and Oeschger (1967) to be 0.1 ($\pm 10\%$) dpm l^{-1} krypton. This measured value is in general agreement with an estimated global production rate given by Oeschger *et al* (1970) for a constant cosmic-ray flux. A recent re-measurement of the ^{81}Kr atmospheric activity by Kuzminov and Pomansky (1983) yielded a value of 0.076 (± 0.004) dpm l^{-1} krypton. They discussed the nuclear reactions that produce ^{81}Kr in the atmosphere in detail and calculated a theoretical value for the production rate of 0.060 (± 0.013) dpm l^{-1} krypton, which also led them to conclude that the present atmospheric ^{81}Kr activity is in agreement with the assumption of constant average ^{81}Kr production over the last 100 000 years. An average value of 0.088 dpm l^{-1} krypton corresponds to a Kr/^{81}Kr ratio in modern air of 1.9×10^{12}, where Kr represents all isotopes of krypton.

It has long been recognised that ^{81}Kr could be used for dating ground-water or polar ice core samples in the range 50 000 to 1 000 000 years. A ^{81}Kr-based technique would considerably extend the range that is accessible to ^{14}C dating and is expected to have definite advantages over other dating methods because of (a) the inert chemical character of krypton, (b) the fact that the atmosphere is the main reservoir with a concentration that has probably been constant for a long time, and (c) the expectation that underground production should be small, (Davis and Bentley 1981).

With a solubility of krypton in ground-water of 9.2×10^{-5} cm^3 of krypton per litre of water (10° C) and a Kr/^{81}Kr ratio of 1.9×10^{12}, we expect to find only 1300 atoms of ^{81}Kr in 1 litre of modern water. Because of this very low concentration, it has been impossible to use this isotope in geophysical studies. Even the best low-level, decay-counting techniques would require hundreds of tons of water. Furthermore, contamination with as little as 0.1% of modern air would add enough ^{85}Kr activity to completely mask the ^{81}Kr signal (Lehmann and Loosli 1984).

Obviously, it would be very desirable to have a technique for counting ^{81}Kr atoms directly rather than having to wait for their decay. The recently developed accelerator-based atom-counting systems have successfully been used for several cosmic-ray-produced radio-isotopes such as ^{14}C, ^{10}Be and ^{36}Cl in geophysical studies (Suter *et al* 1984, Beer *et al* 1984, Finkel *et al* 1980). They cannot be used, however, for ^{81}Kr analyses because krypton does not easily form negative ions for use in a tandem accelerator. Cyclotron machines operating with Kr^+ ions could, in principle, be used for noble gas work but, again, the current estimates for sample size are in the range of several hundred thousand litres of water.

To show the use of the Maxwell demon (Chapter 10) for ground-water analysis, Lehmann *et al* (1985) extracted krypton from a ground-water sample by bubbling helium gas through the water and trapping the extracted air in a charcoal trap cooled by liquid nitrogen. Noble gases were then separated and purified, using getter techniques and gas chromatography. From one litre of water, they expected more than 10^{15} atoms of krypton and only 1300 or less atoms of ^{81}Kr. Such a krypton gas sample could not be introduced immediately to the ^{81}Kr counter because the $^{82}Kr/^{81}Kr$ ratio of about 2×10^{11} is too large to be resolved by the relatively simple mass filter in the detector system (see Chapter 10).

In most cases the level of neighbouring isotopes (^{82}Kr, ^{80}Kr) must first be reduced by isotope enrichment before RIS analysis. The number of spurious counts at mass m due to neighbouring isotopes of mass ($m \pm 1$) leaking though the mass discriminator represents a counting error. For example, to count 1000 atoms of ^{81}Kr with an acceptable counting error of 10% and with a mass filter abundance sensitivity of 10^5, the number of ^{82}Kr atoms must be reduced to 10^7. To achieve this level of enrichment, the atom bank is useful where atoms of a selected isotope can be deposited and withdrawn after unwanted species have been pumped out of the system. Ions of ^{81}Kr are implanted at 10 kV into a target and are subsequently recovered either by laser evaporation or laser annealing. This permits several enrichment cycles. With a quadrupole device, in the first enrichment cycle ions were implanted into aluminised kapton foil and recovered by evaporating the aluminium coating with a pulse of second harmonic light (532 nm) of a Nd:YAG laser. In the second enrichment cycle, ions were implanted into high-impurity silicon and recovered by annealing the silicon surface by scanning with a focused beam of second harmonic Nd:YAG pulses. In each enrichment cycle the $^{82}Kr/^{81}Kr$ ratio is reduced by at least three orders of magnitude.

Lehmann *et al* (1985) used a small fraction of gas that was extracted from about 10 000 l of water for ^{39}Ar dating from a sandstone aquifer near Zurich, Switzerland (AQUI). The first cycle of isotope enrichment was performed in a quadrupole system using its conventional electron-impact ion source. Since the throughput and the abundance sensitivity of such a system deteriorate at higher pressures, the 3 l volume was filled only to 6×10^{-6} Torr. Atoms of ^{81}Kr were implanted into an aluminised foil for one hour, then the rest of the gas was pumped out of the system. More sample was introduced and these steps were repeated 10 times to collect a total of approximately 1500 atoms of ^{81}Kr, a number that was calculated based on pressure and ion current measurements, assuming a modern ^{81}Kr level. The total amount of sample processed was 2×10^{-4} cm^3 of krypton of which 55% was actually used and the rest was pumped out of the system. A second enrichment step with the quadrupole took one hour. This time, ^{81}Kr was implanted into a silicon target which was next introduced to the ^{81}Kr detector, where krypton atoms were released by laser annealing.

Figure 14.8 shows the mass spectrum after annealing, taken on a sensitivity scale that does not reveal the small number of atoms at mass 81. As expected, mass 82 is the dominant isotope and the number of ^{82}Kr atoms agrees with an estimated enrichment factor of approximately $(2000)^2$ in two cycles. Figure 14.9 displays the mass 81 region with greater sensitivity. It was originally planned to run a third cycle of enrichment in the ^{81}Kr detector itself. However, due to the very good abundance sensitivity of the quadrupole system when operated with the laser/buncher ion source, Lehmann *et al* (1985) were able to detect ^{81}Kr

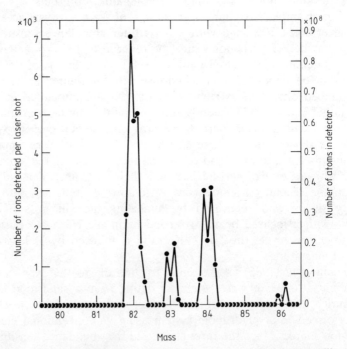

Figure 14.8 Mass spectrum of krypton atoms released from a silicon target by laser annealing. Data taken with an RIS ionisation source in a quadrupole mass spectrometer.

atoms without another cycle of enrichment. It is very easy to check if the signal at mass 81 is indeed produced by krypton atoms, since, with a slight detuning of 0.3 to 0.4 nm of the yellow light (558.1 nm, the second resonant step in the RIS scheme), the signal decreases to the background level which was approximately 5 counts per 200 laser pulses. Calibration of the number of atoms of ^{81}Kr was based on an ionisation probability per pulse of 8×10^{-5} which was determined using an NBS ^{81}Kr standard gas. The signal at mass 81.0 represent 1200 ($\pm$300) atoms of ^{81}Kr.

Mass 81 was then implanted for one hour into a silicon target. As can be seen in figure 14.10, ^{81}Kr atoms were indeed thereby removed from the system. The ^{82}Kr level remained unchanged. The observed decrease of the ^{81}Kr signal after one hour of implantation is in agreement with a value for the ionisation probability corresponding to a one *e*-fold counting time of 35 minutes at a pulse repetition rate of 6 Hz.

Thus, it was demonstrated for the first time that ^{81}Kr atoms originating from a ground-water sample of only a few litres can be detected. The complete chain of sample processing—including sampling and degassing of water, separation and purification of noble gases, two

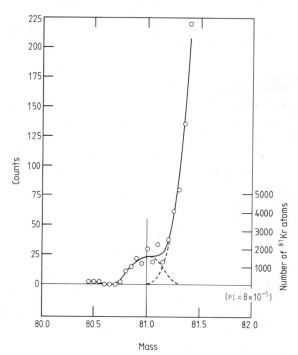

Figure 14.9 Counts per 200 laser pulses for the same sample as in figure 14.8, amplified in the 81 mass region. (PI denotes 'probability of ionisation'.)

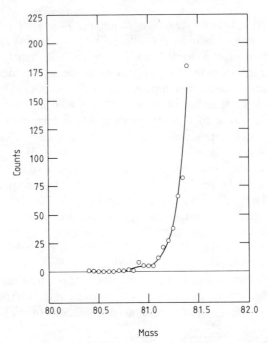

Figure 14.10 Counts per 200 laser pulses after implanting ^{81}Kr from a sample, as in figure 14.9, for one hour.

cycles of isotope enrichment and the final detection of ^{81}Kr atoms—was successfully completed. The fact that 1200 ($\pm$300) atoms of ^{81}Kr were counted from an initial calculated level of 1500 atoms proves that losses in the two isotope enrichment cycles, where ions are implanted into and recovered from different targets, can be kept reasonably small. Since these losses were not well known and since the overall accuracy was not very high in this first demonstration, it was too early to assign any 'age' to the ^{81}Kr determination.

Improved methods of sample processing, isotopic enrichment and atom counting have been made at Atom Sciences Inc. (Thonnard *et al* 1984). The potential of this new isotope for dating polar ice core and ground-water samples in the range 50 000 to 1 000 000 years is under investigation. Deep polar ice cores from the Greenland and Antarctic ice shields contain an invaluable record of past climatic conditions, probably extending several hundred thousand years into the past. Establishing a chronology for these ice cores is clearly of great scientific importance, but a reliable dating technique for the deepest parts of such cores, where the ice is older than about 10 000 years, does not exist (Patterson and Waddington 1984). Since 1 kg of modern ice contains roughly the same amount of krypton as 1 l of modern ground-water, the sample processing and ^{81}Kr analysis for ice is analogous to the one outlined for ground-water.

Dating of very old ground-water is especially important in projects for safe disposal of chemical and radioactive waste in geological formations. Whereas certain ground-waters are known to be very old, e.g. in the Great Artesian Basin in Australia (Calf and Habermehl 1983) or in other aquifers in the USA, Canada, Africa and Europe (Davis and Bentley 1980, Rudolph *et al* 1983), absolute dating of such ground-waters is not easy. Recently, considerable progress has been made using the tandem accelerator mass spectrometer for the analysis of ^{36}Cl (Bentley *et al* 1982, Phillips *et al* 1983, 1984). Based on the progress of Lehmann *et al* (1987) and Thonnard *et al* (1987), we believe that RIS is a method of real promise for ground-water dating.

14.6 Ocean water circulation

Similar applications of RIS have been considered for circulation studies in the oceans. A very suitable isotope for these studies would be ^{37}Ar with a half-life of 270 years. Surface water would have a concentration of ^{39}Ar in equilibrium with cosmic-ray production in the atmosphere, or about 6000 atoms per litre of top-water. Decay counting requires very large samples of water over long counting times; thus, the method is used only infrequently. In a collaboration with H Craig and R D Willis of the Scripps Institute of Oceanography an attempt was made to develop RIS for these measurements. However, this application depends on the future development of the RISTRON (see Chapter 10) because of the excessive amount of ^{40}Ar which must be rejected by the mass spectrometer. At present, oceanic studies are conducted with sensitive mass spectrometers which trace primordial ^{3}He and the more common ^{4}He in ocean water (Craig and Lupton 1981, Lupton and Craig 1981). These discoveries of natural vents in the ocean are important for both geophysical interest and oceanic circulation studies.

14.7 Concluding remarks

In this book we have described in detail a new measurement principle which was originated at the Oak Ridge National Laboratory in the mid-1970s. The theoretical understanding of this physical principle (RIS) was developed at a satisfactory level which was useful in guiding a number of experiments designed to illustrate the basic features of RIS as a sensitive measurement method. Furthermore, two fundamentally different measurement technologies (for gas analyses and for solids analyses) are still evolving. In spite of their youth, these RIS methods have been called upon for some demanding applications. Some of these have succeeded and some have failed, but most are active and show promise for the future. It is our belief, as well as our fervent hope, that RIS will mature into methods which can be called forth to solve some of our most demanding problems in the analyses of small populations of atoms.

References

Beer J, Andree M, Oeschger H, Siegenthaler U, Bonani G, Hofmann H, Morenzoni E, Nessi M, Suter M, Woelfli W, Finkel R and Langway C 1984 *Nucl. Instrum. Methods* **233**(2) 380

Begemann F 1980 *Rep. Prog. Phys.* **43** 1309–56

Bentley H W, Phillips F M, Davis S N, Gifford S, Elmore D, Tubbs L E and Gove E 1982 *Nature* **300**(5894) 737

Calf G E and Habermehl M A 1983 in *Isotope Hydrology* (Vienna: International Atomic Energy Agency) p 397

Clayton R N, Grossman L and Mayeda T K 1973 *Science* **182** 485–8

Clayton R N, Onuma N and Mayeda T K 1976 *Earth Planet. Sci. Lett.* **30** 10–18

Craig H and Lupton J E 1981 in *The Sea vol 7: The Oceanic Lithosphere* ed C Emiliana (New York: Wiley) 391–428

Davis S N and Bentley H W 1980 in *Nuclear and Chemical Dating Techniques* ed L A Currie (Am. Chem. Soc. Symp. Ser. 176) p 187

—— 1981 Possible RIS applications to problems of tracing and dating old ground water: paper presented at *1st Symp. on Resonance Ionization Spectroscopy and Its Applications (Gatlinburg, Tennessee) (June 1981)* unpublished

Eastwood T A, Brown F and Crocker I H 1964 *Nucl. Phys.* **58** 328

Eberhardt P, Geiss J, Graf H, Groegler N, Kraehenbuehl U, Schwaller H, Schwarzmueller J and Stettler A 1970 *Science* **167** 558

Eugster O, Eberhardt P and Geiss J 1967 *Earth Planet. Sci. Lett.* **2** 77

Finkel R C, Nishiizumi K, Elmore D, Ferraro R D and Gove H E 1980 *Geophys. Res. Lett.* **7**(11) 983

Gale N, Arden J and Hutchison R 1975 *Earth Planet, Sci. Lett.* **26** 195–206

Hurst G S, Payne M G, Kramer S D, Chen C H, Phillips R C, Allman S L, Alton G D, Dabbs J W T, Willis R D and Lehmann B E 1985 *Rep. Prog. Phys.* **48** 1333–70

Kirsten T 1978 in *Origin of the Solar System* ed S F Dermott (Chichester/New York: Wiley) pp 267–346

Kuzminov V V and Pomansky A A 1983 in *Proc. 18th Int. Cosmic Ray Conference (Bangalore, India)* vol. 2 p 357

Lehmann B E and Loosli H H 1984 in *Resonance Ionization Spectroscopy 1984* ed G S Hurst and M G Payne (Inst. Phys. Conf. Ser. 71) pp 219–26

Lehmann B E, Oeschger H, Loosli H H, Hurst G S, Allman S L, Chen C H, Kramer S D, Payne M G, Phillips R C, Willis R D and Thonnard N 1985 *J. Geophys. Res.* **90**(B13) 11 547–551

Lehmann B E, Rauber D F, Thonnard N and Willis R D 1987 in *Resonance Ionization Spectroscopy 1986* ed G S Hurst and C Grey Morgan (Inst. Phys. Conf. Ser. 84) pp 81–4

Loosli H H 1979 *Eine Altersbestimmungsmethode mit Ar-39 Habilitationsschrift* (Bern, Switzerland: Universität Bern)

Loosli H H and Oeschger H 1967 *Earth Planet Sci. Lett.* **7** 67

Lupton J E and Craig H 1981 *Science* **214** 13–18

Marti K 1967 *Phys. Rev. Lett.* **18** 264

Oeschger H, Houtermans J, Loosli H and Wahlen M 1970 in *Proc. 12th Nobel Symp. (Uppsala, Sweden)* (New York: Wiley) p 471

Oeschger H 1982 in *Nuclear and Chemical Dating Techniques* ed L A Currie (Am. Chem. Soc. Symp. Ser. 176) pp 5–42

Patterson W S B and Waddington E D 1984 *Rev. Geophys. and Space Phys.* **22**(2) 123

Phillips F M, Goff F, Vuataz F, Bentley H W, Elmore D and Gove H E 1984 *Geophys. Res. Lett.* **11**(12) 1227

Phillips F M, Smith G I, Bentley H W, Elmore D and Gove H E 1983 *Science* **222** 925

Reynolds J H 1950 *Phys. Rev. Lett.* **79** 886

Reynolds J H, Lumpkin G R and Jeffrey P M 1980 *Z. Naturf.* **35a** 257–66

Rudolph J, Rath H K and Sontag C 1983 in *Isotope Hydrology* (Vienna: International Atomic Energy Agency) p 467

Rutherford E 1906 in *Radioactive Transformations* (New Haven: Yale University Press) pp 187–93 (Reprinted in *Geochronology: Radiometric Dating of Rocks and Minerals* ed C T Harper (Stroudsburg, Pennsylvania: Dowden, Hutchinson and Ross) pp 15–21)

Schramm D N 1978 *Protostars and Planets* ed T Gehrels (Tucson, Arizona: The University of Arizona Press) pp 384–398

Suter M, Balzer R, Bonani G, Hofmann H, Morenzoni E, Nessi M, Woelfli W, Andree M, Beer J and Oeschger H 1984 *Nucl. Instrum. Methods* **233**(2) 117

Thonnard N, Payne M G, Wright M C and Schmitt H W 1984 in *Resonance Ionization Spectroscopy 1984* ed G S Hurst and M G Payne (Inst. Phys. Conf. Ser. 71) pp 227–34

Thonnard N, Willis R D, Wright M C and Davis W A 1987 in

Resonance Ionization Spectroscopy 1986 ed G S Hurst and C Grey Morgan (Inst. Phys. Conf. Ser. 84) pp 81–4

Turner G 1987 in *Resonance Ionization Spectroscopy 1986* ed G S Hurst and C Grey Morgan (Inst. Phys. Conf. Ser. 84) pp 51–8

Index